PERGAMON INTERNATIONAL L
of Science, Technology, Engineering
The 1000-volume original paperback
industrial training and the enjoyment
Publisher: Robert Maxwell, M.C.

G000043311

WORKED EXAMPLES

IN ELECTRICAL MACHINES

AND DRIVES

THE PERGAMON TEXTBOOK
INSPECTION COPY SERVICE

An inspection copy of any book published in the Pergamon International Library will gladly be sent to academic staff without obligation for their consideration for course adoption or recommendation. Copies may be retained for a period of 60 days from receipt and returned if not suitable. When a particular title is adopted or recommended for adoption for class use and the recommendation results in a sale of 12 or more copies, the inspection copy may be retained with our compliments. The Publishers will be pleased to receive suggestions for revised editions and new titles to be published in this important International Library.

APPLIED ELECTRICITY AND ELECTRONICS

General Editor: P. HAMMOND

Other titles of interest in the
PERGAMON INTERNATIONAL LIBRARY

WORKED EXAMPLES
IN ELECTRICAL MACHINES
AND DRIVES

John Hindmarsh, B.Sc.(Eng.), C.Eng., M.I.E.E.

Senior Lecturer at the University of Manchester Institute of Science and Technology

PERGAMON PRESS

OXFORD · NEW YORK · TORONTO · SYDNEY · PARIS · FRANKFURT

U.K.	Pergamon Press Ltd., Headington Hill Hall, Oxford OX3 0BW, England
U.S.A.	Pergamon Press Inc., Maxwell House, Fairview Park, Elmsford, New York 10523, U.S.A.
CANADA	Pergamon Press Canada Ltd., Suite 104, 150 Consumers Rd., Willowdale, Ontario M2J 1P9, Canada
AUSTRALIA	Pergamon Press (Aust.) Pty. Ltd., P.O. Box 544, Potts Point, N.S.W. 2011, Australia
FRANCE	Pergamon Press SARL, 24 rue des Ecoles, 75240 Paris, Cedex 05, France
FEDERAL REPUBLIC OF GERMANY	Pergamon Press GmbH, 6242 Kronberg-Taunus, Hammerweg 6, Federal Republic of Germany

First edition 1982

British Library Cataloguing in Publication Data

Hindmarsh, J.
Worked examples in electrical machines and drives. –
(Applied electricity and electronics). – (Pergamon international library)

    1. Electric motors
    I. Title
    621.46'2   TK2511   80-42239

    ISBN 0-08-026131-0 Hardcover
    ISBN 0-08-026130-2 Flexicover

Printed in Great Britain by A. Wheaton & Co. Ltd., Exeter

CONTENTS

N.B. Instead of an Index, the Example Numbers are given below with an indication of the topics covered.

CONTENTS

EDITOR'S PREFACE

THIS is a companion volume to the author's textbook *Electrical Machines and Their Applications*, a well-loved book now in its third edition. The success of that book is due to the unusual combination in the author of great teaching skill and long first-hand experience of the design, manufacture and application of electrical machines.

Although much has changed in electrical technology in the last few years, the role of rotating machines and transformers is as important as it ever was. It is by their means that electrical energy is generated and then reconverted to mechanical energy in homes and factories. Of course, these machines are continually being improved and modified, but their fundamental principles remain the same. Hence no electrical engineering course is complete without a study of the principles of electrical machines and drives.

But this is not an easy subject. The interaction of electrical and mechanical energy can be understood by students only when they have had practice at solving numerical problems. In his new book the author provides such problems, mostly with their solutions, graded in difficulty and interspersed with advice, all against a background of sound engineering practice. The reader who has worked through these examples will be able to face with confidence many problems about the behaviour of machines and the choice of drives. Not every electrical engineer needs to be a machine specialist, but he needs to be able to co-operate with such specialists and this book will enable him to do so.

I am very happy to commend the book both to students and to teachers, who will find it a great help in strengthening their lectures and practical classes.

P. HAMMOND

University of Southampton

AUTHOR'S PREFACE

DISCUSSION of the summary and objective of this book is deferred to the first section of Chapter 1 lest this preface, like many others, goes unread. However, there are some matters which need to be covered here, especially those which concern the author's debt to others. Every author likes to believe that he has created something original or shed new light on an old topic. But, inevitably, much of the work must have been derived from his experiences as a student, from his own teachers, from books read, from his own students and from his colleagues. This last is particularly true in the present case. A major influence has been the author's long association with Dr. N. N. Hancock, whose deep perception of the subject and ever-sympathetic ear when difficulties of understanding arose have been a source of constant sustenance. To Dr. A. C. Williamson, with his remarkable facility for cutting clean through the theoretical fog to grasp the essential nature of tricky machines problems, especially those associated with power-electronic circuits, I am deeply indebted. Much time was spent by him in kindly checking and correcting formative ideas for the material on constant-current and variable-frequency drives. Sections 4.3, 5.5, 7.3 and 7.4 are heavily reliant on his contributions. Dr. B. J. Chalmers' experience, with saturated a.c. machines particularly, was very important to the clarification of this section of the work. I am grateful, too, to Dr. M. Lockwood for his suggestions on simplifying simulation problems.

With regard to the examples themselves, an attempt has been made to cover thoroughly the basic machine types, but the subject is very wide. Very small and special machines have been omitted, quite apart from study of the economic and environmental factors which influence the decision in choosing an electrical drive, though some brief comments are made as appropriate. This selective treatment seemed to be the best way of meeting the many requests in response to which this book was written. Many of the examples are taken, or modified, from examination papers set at the University of Manchester Institute of Science and Technology (UMIST), and permission to publish these is gratefully acknowledged. Other examples, especially those in the Appendix, are drawn from a variety of sources. The author cannot deny that some of them may have originated in form from other books read over the years since first meeting the topic as a student, and from discussions and contact with present and past colleagues.

Finally, the author would like to record his thanks to the Consulting Editor, Professor Percy Hammond, for his encouragement, for reading the text and making his usual perceptive comments and suggestions to get the balance right. To the Managing Editor, Mr. Jim Gilgunn-Jones, and his colleagues at Pergamon Press, who have been so patient in spite of delays and last-minute changes, I tender my grateful appreciation.

J.H.

August 1981

LIST OF SYMBOLS

THE following list comprises those symbols which are used fairly frequently throughout the text. Other symbols which are confined to certain sections of the book and those which are in general use are not included, e.g. the circuit symbols like R for resistance and the use of A, B and C for 3-phase quantities. Some symbols are used for more than one quantity as indicated in the list. With few exceptions, the symbols conform to those recommended by the British Standards Institution BS 1991.

Instantaneous values are given small letters, e.g. e, i, for e.m.f. and current respectively.

R.M.S. and steady d.c. values are given capital letters, e.g. E, I.

Maximum values are written thus: $\hat{E}$, $\hat{I}$.

Bold face type is used for phasor and vector quantities and for matrices, e.g. **E**, **I**. In general, the symbol E (e) is used for induced e.m.f.s due to mutual flux and the symbol V (v) is used for terminal voltages.

At Ampere turns.

B Flux density, in teslas (T) (webers/metre^2).

d Symbol for direct-axis quantities.

d Armature diameter, in metres.

e Base of natural logarithms.

E_f Induced e.m.f. due to field m.m.f. F_f.

f Frequency, in hertz (Hz) (cycles per second).

F Magnetomotive force (m.m.f.) in ampere turns. Peak m.m.f. per pole per phase.

F'_a Effective d.c. armature-winding magnetising m.m.f. per pole.

F_a Peak armature-winding m.m.f. per pole.

F_f Peak field-winding m.m.f. per pole.

    (Note that the suffices a and f are also used with the

symbols for currents, fluxes and resistances of armature and field respectively.)

F_r Peak resultant m.m.f. per pole.

$I_{f.l.}$ Full-load current.

I_0 Current in magnetising branch.

I_m Reactive or magnetising component of I_0.

I_p Power component of I_0.

J Polar moment of inertia (rotational inertia), in kg m^2.

k   Coefficient. A constant.

k_f Generated volts per field ampere or per unit of m.m.f.

k_{fs} Saturated value of k_f.

k_ϕ Flux factor; generated volts per radian/sec or torque per ampere.

l Conductor length. Magnetic path length.

l (or l_1, l_2, etc. Leakage inductance.

L General inductance symbol; e.g. L_{11} = self-inductance of coil 1; L_{12}, L_{13}, etc., for mutual inductances.

m Number of phases.

M Alternative mutual-inductance symbol for two coils.

n Rev/sec.

n_s Rev/sec synchronous = f/p.

N Number of turns. Rev/min.

N_s Rev/min synchronous = $60f/p$.

p   Operator d/dt.

p Number of pole pairs.

p.u.   Suffix for per-unit quantities.

P Power.

$P_{control}$ Power at control terminals.

P_{elec} Power (total) at electrical terminals (P_e = per phase).

P_{gap} Air-gap power (total) (P_g = per phase).

P_m Mechanical power converted (per phase) ($m.P_m = \omega_m.T_e$).

P_{mech} Power at mechanical terminals ($\omega_m.T_{coupling} = P_{coupling}$).

q   Symbol for quadrature-axis quantities.

R_m Magnetising resistance, representing iron losses.

s Fractional slip $= (n_s - n)/n_s$.

S *Per-unit* relative motion n/n_s $(= 1 - s)$.

T_{coupling} Torque at mechanical shaft coupling.

T_{loss} Sum of all machine internal loss torques.

T_e Torque developed electromagnetically, in newton metres.

T_m Torque arising mechanically $= T_e$ in steady state.

v Velocity, in metres per second.

V Voltage measured at the terminals of a circuit or machine.

x (or x_1, x_2, x_{al}, etc.) Leakage reactance.

X General reactance symbol.

X_m Magnetising reactance.

X_{ms} Saturated value of X_m. X_m Unsaturated value of X_m.

X_s Synchronous reactance $= X_m + x_{\text{al}}$.

z_s Number of series-connected conductors per phase or per parallel path of a winding.

Z_s Synchronous impedance.

α General angle. Slot angle. Impedance angle $\tan^{-1} R/X$.

δ Load angle.

δ_{fa} (or δ_T) Torque angle.

η Efficiency.

Λ Magnetic permeance, webers/ampere-turn.

μ_0 Magnetic constant $= 4\pi/10^7$.

μ_r Relative permeability.

μ Absolute permeability $= B/H = \mu_0\mu_r$.

φ Power-factor angle. N.B. This must be distinguished from the symbol for flux ϕ below.

ϕ Instantaneous value of flux. Flux per pole, in webers.

ϕ_m Mutual flux, in webers, due to resultant m.m.f.

Φ Flux time-vector.

θ Shaft angular position. Temperature rise. General variable.

τ Time constant.

ω Angular velocity of rotating time-vectors $= 2\pi f$ radians/sec.

ω_m Mechanical angular rotational velocity $= 2\pi n$ radians/sec.

ω_s Synchronous angular velocity $= 2\pi n_s = 2\pi f/p$ radians/sec.

Note: SI units (Système International d'Unités) are used in the text unless specifically stated otherwise.

CHAPTER 1

INTRODUCTION AND REVIEW OF BASIC THEORY

1.1 AIM OF THE BOOK

On entering the world of electrical machines, the student meets many conceptual difficulties not experienced for example in the early studies of digital systems, with their simple and precise 2-state operation. More assistance is required to permit the new-comer to gain confidence in dealing with non-linear, 3-dimensional, rotating electromagnetic devices. The purpose of this book is to provide this aid to understanding by showing how, with a limited number of equations derived from basic considerations of power flow and elementary circuit and electromagnetic theory, the elec-tromechanical performance can be explained and predicted with reasonable accuracy.

Such an aim, which will permit the calculation of power-input/output characteristics almost close enough in engineering terms to those of the device itself, can be achieved by representing the machine as a simple electrical circuit—the equivalent-circuit model. This concept is explained in many books, for example in the author's companion volume *Electrical Machines and Their Ap-plications*. Though more detailed theoretical treatment is given there, the present text may be regarded as a suitable revision handbook. It might also be considered as a textbook on electrical drives, taught through worked examples, for a reader already familiar with basic machine theory.

Perhaps it is appropriate to point out that complete and exact analysis of machine performance is so complex as to be virtually impossible. The additional accuracy achieved by attempts to approach such methods is primarily of interest to the specialist designer who must ensure that his product will meet the user's needs without breakdown and he must judge when the analytical complication is justified. For the user, and for the engineering student who is not yet a specialist, the simpler methods are adequate for general understanding and provide a lead-in if necessary for later specialisation.

There are many features of all machine types which are common, the obvious example being the mechanical shaft equations. But apart from these and the fundamental electromagnetic laws, the input/output relationships and modes of operation have many similarities. These are brought together where possible and also in this first chapter, some elementary mechanical, magnetic and circuit theory is discussed briefly, as a reminder of the basic knowledge required. Students should beware of underestimating the vital importance of this material, since experience shows that it is these very points, improperly understood, which hold back progress in coming to feel at ease with machines problems.

However familiar one may become with theory, as a student, the true test of an engineer is his ability to make things work. First steps to this goal of confidence are reached when a student is prepared to commit himself to selecting equations and inserting values in the algebraic expressions, producing answers to a specific problem. Hence the importance of practice with numerical examples. Understanding grows in proportion to one's ability to realise that the equations developed really can be used in a systematic fashion to solve such problems, since they describe the physical behaviour in mathematical terms. Appreciation of this last statement is the key to successful problem-solving.

The chapters are planned to sequence the examples at increasing levels of difficulty. Much theoretical support is given, in that the equations are discussed either at the beginning of each chapter, or as the need arises. Solution programmes indicate the kind of problems which can be formulated for the three basic types of

2

rotating machine: d.c., induction, and synchronous. Readers are encouraged to adopt an ordered approach to the solution; for example it is a good idea to incorporate the question data on a diagram. One of the difficulties of machines problems often lies in the amount of data given. By putting the values on a simple diagram assimilation is easier and it helps to avoid mistakes of interpretation, especially when working with 3-phase circuits. In following this recommended pattern, it is hoped that the text will help to remove the mystery with which some students feel the machines area is shrouded.

The emphasis is on machine terminal-characteristics, rather than on the internal electromagnetic design. In other words, the electrical-drives aspect is uppermost since this is the area in which most engineering students need to have some good knowledge. It is worth noting that about 60–70% of all electrical power is consumed by motors driving mechanical shafts and virtually all this power is produced by generators driven through mechanical shafts, so that the subject is of considerable importance to engineers. The problems and solutions are discussed where appropriate, to draw out the engineering implications. Electromechanical transients are not neglected and opportunity is also taken to consider the effects introduced by the impact of power-electronic control. In general, the usual methods of analysis are still effective in predicting machine performance. Full account of the influence of this important environment, in which harmonics proliferate, is somewhat beyond the scope of this book but some indication is given of the means used to deal with the machines problems which arise. Detailed study of machine/semi-conductor systems requires a knowledge of mathematical and computer simulation procedures. A few simple examples are considered at the end of the book to introduce this topic. Finally, in the Appendix, some tutorial examples are given along with the answers. Some of the worked examples in the text have been taken from Appendix E of *Electrical Machines and Their Applications*, but many of these remain as further exercises for the determined student.

1.2   FOUNDATION THEORY

Excitation Calculations

Virtually all machines have iron in the magnetic circuit to enhance the flux value and/or to reduce the excitation requirements. The price to pay for these advantages is reflected in iron loss and non linearity. Figure 1.1a shows a typical iron magnetisation-characteristic. The economic operating point is beyond the linear region and well clear of full saturation, at about $B = 1$ tesla, though certain short parts of the magnetic circuit, like armature teeth, may exceed this by 50% or more. Under transient conditions too, this limit can be exceeded. The equation governing the excitation requirements follows from:

$$B = \mu_0\mu_r H = \mu H = \mu IN/l.$$

Multiplying by area A:

$$B \times A = \mu\frac{IN}{l} \times A = IN \times \frac{\mu A}{l}.$$

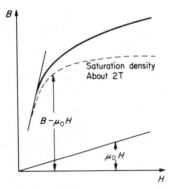

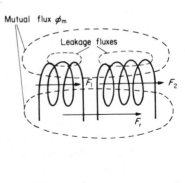

(a) Typical iron magnetisation curve   (b) Combination of two coil m.m.f.s

FIG. 1.1. Magnetic excitation.

In words:

Flux = Magnetomotive force × Permeance (or 1/Reluctance)

$$\phi = F \, (= IN) \quad \times \quad \Lambda \, (= \mu A / l)$$

The m.m.f. is shown in ampere turns (At) but is effectively the current enclosing the magnetic circuit.

The calculation of excitation m.m.f. (F) is often required for a given flux and magnetic geometry to determine the design of the coils. Frequently there are two (or more) such coils so that the resultant excitation F_r is the combination of F_1 and F_2 which produces ϕ_m, see Fig. 1.1b. The two m.m.f.s may be produced on opposite sides of a machine air gap; F_1 say, due to several stator coils, while F_2 similarly may be due to several rotor coils. Often, sinusoidal distribution of m.m.f. is assumed and the coils can be designed to approach this closely. "Vector" techniques can then be used to combine these two "sinusoidal quantities" giving $\mathbf{F}_1 + \mathbf{F}_2 = \mathbf{F}_r$ and ϕ_m, the mutual flux = function (F_r). It is often convenient to take the positive magnetising senses of $\mathbf{F}_1$ and $\mathbf{F}_2$ to be in the same direction, though in practice, the one is usually magnetising in the opposite sense to the other and would then be negative with respect to this.

Electromagnetic Theory

The most important equations for present purposes are:

$$e = N \, d\phi/dt; \quad e = Blv; \quad \text{and } Force = Bli;$$

most practical machines having the directions of B, v and i at right angles to one another.

For a fixed magnetic geometry:

$$e = N \frac{d\phi}{di} \frac{di}{dt} = L \frac{di}{dt}$$

5

where:

$$L = N\frac{d\phi}{di} = N\frac{iN\Lambda}{i} = N^2\Lambda$$

and will fall with the onset of saturation, so the inductance L is flux/current dependent. For a sinusoidally varying current

$$i = \hat{I} \sin 2\pi ft = \hat{I} \sin \omega t,$$

then:
$$e = L \times \omega\hat{I} \sin(\omega t + 90°)$$

and in r.m.s. and complex-number expressions:

$$E = j\omega LI = jXI = V,$$

and I lags V by 90°, see Fig. 1.2. The use of the back e.m.f. expression $(+L\,di/dt)$ instead of the forward e.m.f. expression $(-L\,di/dt)$ is seen to be preferable, since the current I comes out directly as lagging V by 90° for the inductive circuit, instead of having to deal with the concept of two identical but phase-opposed voltages.

For the general case with varying geometry, $e = d(Li)/dt$
$= L\,di/dt$ (transformer voltage) $+ i\,dL/dt$ (motional voltage).

Circuit Theory Conventions

Figure 1.3a shows a representation of a machine with its instantaneous e.m.f. and resistive and inductive voltage-drops. The voltage arrowheads are the assumed + ve ends. The directions of

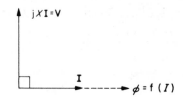

FIG. 1.2. Induced voltage (back e.m.f.).

6

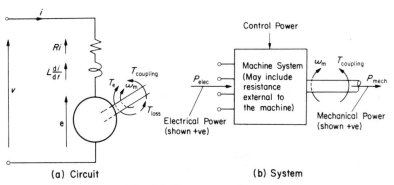

(a) Circuit (b) System

FIG. 1.3. Motor conventions.

the arrows for the instantaneous terminal voltage v and for e may be assigned arbitrarily but Ri and $L\,di/dt$ must oppose i, since the voltage arrowheads must be positive for $+$ve i and $+$ve di/dt respectively. The direction of i may also be assigned arbitrarily but the decision has consequences when related to the v and/or e arrows. As shown, and with all quantities assumed to be $+$ve, then the machine is a power sink; i.e., in a MOTORING mode; the vi and ei products are both positive. For GENERATING, when the machine becomes a power source, ei will then be negative, e or i reversed.

The above is called the MOTORING convention and it is often convenient in electrical-drives studies to use this throughout and let a negative ei product indicate a generating condition. Alternatively, a GENERATING convention could be used, as sometimes preferred in power-systems studies. By reversing the i arrow say, ei would then be positive for generating and the circuit equation would have a sign reversed. It would be a good check to complete the following short exercise to see if the above statements are properly understood.

Write down the MOTOR equation;	with MOTOR conventions:	$V = E \quad RI$
Write down the GENERATOR equation;	with MOTOR conventions:	$V = E \quad RI$

7

Write down the GENERATOR equation;	with GENERATOR conventions:	$V = E$ RI
Write down the MOTOR equation;	with GENERATOR conventions:	$V = E$ RI

The mechanical equation can be expressed as a simple extension of the above. The motor (as a mechanical power source) produces (generates) an electromagnetic torque T_e, and in equilibrium at steady speed, this is balanced by the total mechanical torque T_m, part of which is due to the internal mechanical resistance T_{loss} and the remainder is the load torque at the coupling "terminals", $T_{coupling}$.

So: $T_e = T_m = T_{coupling} + T_{loss}$ (cf. electrical source, $E = V + RI$).

This is also a MOTORING convention. For a generator, with rotation unchanged, both T_e and $T_{coupling}$ would be negative using this convention.

To illustrate how these conventions affect the machine considered as a system, with electrical-power terminals and mechanical-power "terminals"—excluding for the moment the control-power terminals, consider Fig. 1.3b. In general, either or both terminal powers can be negative and here, a motoring convention is being considered. The three practicable conditions are:

Electrical power positive;	mechanical power positive;	MOTORING	(A)
Electrical power negative;	mechanical power negative;	GENERATING	(B)
Electrical power positive;	mechanical power negative;	BRAKING	(C)

In the last mode, it will be noticed that both mechanical and electrical "terminals" are accepting power into the machine system. All the power is in fact being dissipated within this system, which may include resistance external to the machine itself. The mechanical power is usually coming from energy stored in the moving parts, and since this cannot be released without a fall of

8

speed, the action is one of braking. The machine is generating; not feeding power into the electrical supply, but assisting this to provide the power dissipated.

To understand how the mechanical "terminals" respond to these three modes, assume that T_{loss} is 1 unit and T_e is 10 units. Let the speed be positive and remembering that power is (torque × speed), use the mechanical balance equation to find:

$$T_{coupling} = T_e - T_{loss}$$

Mode A; Motoring $T_{coupling} = 10 - 1 \quad = +9. \quad \omega_m T_{coupling} +ve.$

Mode B; Generating $T_{coupling} = -10 - 1 = -11. \quad \omega_m T_{coupling} -ve.$
[T_e will be −ve for +ve ω_m]

Mode C; Braking (i) $T_{coupling} = -10 - 1 = -11. \quad \omega_m T_{coupling} -ve.$
[ω_m+ve. ∴$T_{loss} = +1$
 T_e will be −ve]

Mode C; Braking (ii) $T_{coupling} = +10 - (-1)$
[ω_m − ve. ∴ $T_{loss} = -1$ $= +11. \quad \omega_m T_{coupling} -ve.$
 T_e will be +ve]

Note that if rotation reverses, T_{loss} will reverse because it always opposes rotation. In mode C, the sign of T_e is opposite to that of ω_m because the machine itself is generating so for either rotation, the mechanical "terminal" power is negative.

Sinusoidal A.C. Theory

Most a.c. sources are of nominally constant r.m.s. voltage so the voltage phasor is taken as the reference phasor. It need not be horizontal and can be drawn in any angular position. A lagging power factor cos φ means *current* lagging the voltage as shown on Fig. 1.4a. The instantaneous power vi, which pulsates at double frequency, is also shown and has a mean value of VI cos φ. If φ were to be greater than 90°, the power flow would have reversed since I cos φ would be negative as seen on the phasor diagram for a current I'. Note that the phasor diagrams have been drawn at a time $\omega t = \pi/2$ for a voltage expressed as $v = \hat{V} \sin \omega t$.

For the reverse power-flow condition, if the opposite convention had been chosen (with v or i reversed), then VI' cos φ would

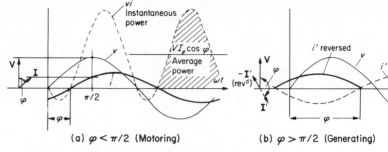

(a) $\varphi < \pi/2$ (Motoring)   (b) $\varphi > \pi/2$ (Generating)

FIG. 1.4. Power flow in single-phase a.c. circuit.

have been positive. This is shown on Fig. 1.4b where it will be noted that the current is at a leading power factor. Taking Fig. 1.4a as a motoring condition, it shows power being *absorbed* at lagging power factor whereas Fig. 1.4b shows power being *delivered* at a leading power factor.

Phasor Diagram including Machine E.M.F.; Motoring Condition

The equation, allowing for inductive impedance, is:

$$\mathbf{V} = \mathbf{E} + R\mathbf{I} + jX\mathbf{I},$$

and is shown as a phasor diagram on Fig. 1.5 for two different values of E. Note that on a.c., the e.m.f. may be greater than the terminal voltage V and yet the machine may still operate as a motor. The power factor is affected but the power flow is determined by the *phase* of $\mathbf{E}$ with respect to $\mathbf{V}$. Frequently, the current is the unknown and this is found by rearranging the equation as:

$$\mathbf{I} = \frac{\mathbf{V} - \mathbf{E}}{R + jX} = \frac{(\mathbf{V} - \mathbf{E})(R - jX)}{R^2 - X^2} = \frac{|\mathbf{V} - \mathbf{E}|}{Z}\left[\frac{R}{Z} - \frac{jX}{Z}\right] = I(\cos\varphi - j\sin\varphi)$$

N.B. φ will be taken as $-$ve for lagging power factor.

The appropriate exercise to check that these phasor diagrams are understood is to draw the corresponding diagrams for a generator using (a) motor conventions and (b) generator conventions.

10

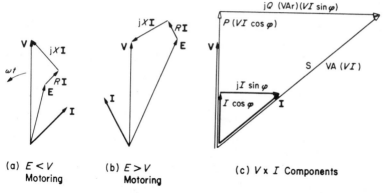

FIG. 1.5. Phasor diagrams.

Meaning of V × I Components

Multiplying the I, $I \cos \varphi$ and $I \sin \varphi$ current phasors by V gives:

VI (S voltamperes, VA)

$VI \cos \varphi$ (P watts) and

$VI \sin \varphi$ (Q voltamperes reactive, V Ar)

and a "power phasor diagram" can be drawn as shown on Fig. 1.5c.

Power devices are frequently very large and the units kVA, kW and kVAr, ($\times 10^3$), and MVA, MW and MVAr, ($\times 10^6$), are in common use. The largest single-unit steam-turbine generators for power stations are now over 1000 MW = 1 GW, (10^9 W).

3-phase Circuit Theory

For many reasons, including efficiency of generation and transmission, quite apart from the ease of producing a rotating field as in any polyphase system, the 3-phase system has become virtually

11

universal though there are occasions when other m-phase systems are used. For low powers of course, as in the domestic situation for example, single-phase supplies are satisfactory. It is only necessary for present purposes to consider balanced 3-phase circuits, i.e. where the phase voltages and also the phase currents are mutually displaced by 120 electrical degrees ($2\pi/3$ radians). Electrical angles are given by $\omega t = 2\pi f t$ radians.

On the assumption of balanced conditions, the power in a 3-phase system can be considered as available in three equal power "packages", each handling 1/3 of the total power, i.e.

$$\frac{\text{Total power}}{3} = V_{\text{phase}} I_{\text{phase}} \cos \varphi$$

where φ is the same for each phase.

There are two symmetrical ways of connecting the three phases as shown on Fig. 1.6:

in STAR (or wye);
for which it is obvious that the current through the line terminals is the same as the current in the phase itself, or:

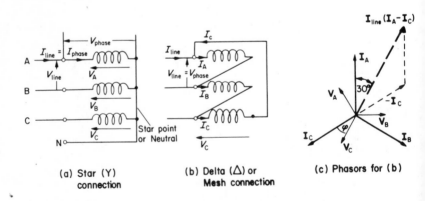

(a) Star (Y) connection

(b) Delta (Δ) or Mesh connection

(c) Phasors for (b)

FIG. 1.6. 3-phase circuits.

in DELTA (or mesh);

for which it is obvious that the voltage across the line terminals is the same as the voltage across the phase itself.

For the delta case: $I_{\text{line}} = I_A - I_C$ and $I_B - I_A$ and $I_C - I_B$.

For the star case: $V_{\text{line}} = V_A - V_B$ and $V_B - V_C$ and $V_C - V_A$;

assumed positive senses of phase currents and voltages being indicated.

The 120° displacement means that the magnitude of the line quantities in these two cases is equal to $\sqrt{3}$ times the magnitude of the phase quantities and there is a ± 30° displacement between line and phase phasors; ± depending on which phasors are differenced.

Hence, for star *and* delta circuits:

$$\text{Total power} = 3 \times \frac{V_{\text{line}} I_{\text{line}}}{\sqrt{3}} \times \cos \varphi$$
$$= \sqrt{3} \times V_{\text{line}} I_{\text{line}} \times \cos \varphi$$
$$(\text{or Power} = \text{Voltamperes} \times \cos \varphi)$$

which can be solved for any one unknown. Frequently this is the current, from the known power and voltage ratings. Sometimes, for parameter measurements, φ is required for dividing currents, voltages or impedances into resistive and reactive components. The total voltamperes for a 3-phase system are thus given by $\sqrt{3}\, VI$ where V and I are here, line values, or alternatively, three times the phase VI product. A.C. devices are rated on a VA (kVA or MVA) basis, since they must be big enough magnetically to deal with full voltage, whatever the current, and big enough in terms of the electrically-sensitive parameters to deal with the current-carrying capacity specified in the rating, whatever the voltage. This means for example, that at zero power-factor, at full voltage and current, the temperature rise will be as high as or even higher than at unity power factor (u.p.f.), where real power is being converted.

3-phase circuits will be analysed by reducing everything to phase values: *Power*/3, V_{line} or $V_{\text{line}}/\sqrt{3}$, I_{line} or $I_{\text{line}}/\sqrt{3}$, depending on the circuit connection. The problem can then be dealt with as a single-phase circuit but the total power is three times the phase power. The examples in Chapter 2 are especially valuable for revising this topic.

Torque Components

T_e, the electromagnetic torque, will have different expressions for different machine types. It is basically due to the sum of all the tangential electromagnetic forces between the currents in rotor and stator conductors. If the windings are so distributed that the m.m.f. space waves are sinusoidal in shape and of magnitudes F_{stator} and F_{rotor}, the axes being displaced by the torque angle δ_T, then T_e is proportional to the products of these m.m.f.s and the sine of the torque angle. Because of the sinusoidal distribution, the two m.m.f. space waves can be combined vectorially to give a resultant m.m.f. wave of magnitude F_r, which produces the resultant mutual (air-gap) flux ϕ_m. An alternative expression, invoking the sine rule, gives T_e as proportional to the product of F_r with either F_{stator} or F_{rotor} and the different angle between them. This alternative is used for a.c. machines (cf. Fig. 5.2) and since the angle is a function of load, it is called the load angle δ. For d.c. machines, the torque angle is fixed by the brush position (usually at maximum angle 90°) and so T_e can be expressed as $K \times \phi \times I_a$, where $K \times \phi$ can be combined as one coefficient k_ϕ which will be shown in Chapter 3 to be directly proportional to flux. The expression shows that k_ϕ is equal to the torque per ampere. It is also equal to the generated e.m.f. per radian/second.

T_{loss} is due to internal machine friction, windage and iron-loss torques.

$T_{coupling}$ is the terminal torque, supplying the load in the case of a motor. The load torque may have an active component due to gravity or stored energy in the load system. This may oppose or assist the rotation. The passive components of the load torque, like friction, can only oppose rotation and will therefore reverse with

14

rotation. The loss torques should be small and since they are mostly similar in nature to the passive load torques, it is convenient to combine them. At the balance point, where the speed is steady therefore, we have:

$$T_e = T_{loss} + T_{coupling} = T_m.$$

T_m is not a simple function of speed but is sometimes expressed in the form:

$$T_m = f(\omega_m) = k_1 + k_2\omega_m + k_3\omega_m^2$$

where k_1 is the idealised "Coulomb" friction.

$\quad k_2\omega_m$ is the viscous friction, proportional to speed and corresponding to "streamline" flow. It occurs when the torque is due to eddy currents.

$\quad k_3\omega_m^2$ is the torque due to "turbulent" flow; as an approximation. It occurs with fan- and propellor-type loads, e.g. windage losses.

Regulation; Speed/Torque Curves; 4-quadrant Diagram

The important characteristic of a power device is the way it reacts to the application of load. For a generator, the natural tendency is for the terminal voltage to fall as load current is taken. This fall is called the regulation and can be controlled by various means. The corresponding characteristic for a motor is the way in which speed changes as load torque is applied. With the d.c. motor as an example, the speed is nearly proportional to terminal voltage and the torque is proportional to current I_a, so the speed/torque axes follow the voltage/current axes for the generator. Figure 1.7 shows the natural characteristics for the various machine types. The d.c. machine can easily be given a variety of curve shapes and two distinct forms are shown, for shunt and series motors. The synchronous machine runs at constant speed and as load increases the speed does not fall; the load angle

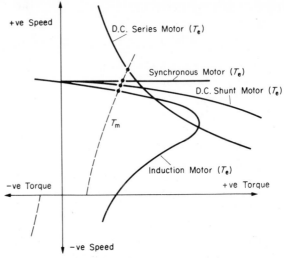

FIG. 1.7. Speed/torque characteristics.

increases to a maximum whereupon the speed will collapse to zero. The induction machine, like the d.c. machine, reacts to torque by a decrease of speed until it too reaches a maximum and stalls. The d.c. machine has a higher maximum though it rarely reaches it without damage.

Also shown on Fig. 1.7 is a typical load characteristic $T_m = f(\omega_m)$. Where this intersects the motor $\omega_m = f(T_e)$ characteristic, we have the balancing (steady-state) speed. There is not a universal practice in the assignment of axes and sometimes the torque axis is drawn vertically following the mechanical characteristic where T_m is the dependent variable. The usual practice for d.c. machines will be retained for all machine types in this text.

It will be noted that the axes have been continued into the negative regions, giving a 4-quadrant diagram with all combinations of positive and negative speeds and torques. Electromagnetic machines operate in all four regions as will be illustrated in later chapters.

16

1.3 EQUIVALENT CIRCUITS

These circuits represent a physical system by an electrical circuit. The simplest example is that for a battery, since over a limited range, the terminal voltage falls in proportion to the current taken. The battery behaves as if it consisted of a constant e.m.f. E, behind a resistance k equal to the slope of the "regulation" curve of V against I, see Fig. 1.8a.

The d.c. machine can be represented by the same equivalent circuit with the modification that the e.m.f. is controllable, being a function of speed and flux ($E = k_\phi \omega_m$); Fig. 1.8b. An a.c. machine can also be represented this way, with the further modification that inductance must be included. Normally, the inductive reactance is appreciably larger than the resistance. The reactance may be considered in components corresponding to the leakage fluxes (which are relatively small and proportional to current due to the large air path reluctance), and the mutual flux (non-linear with excitation and confined largely to a path having its reluctance sensitive to iron saturation), see Fig. 1.1b.

The equivalent-circuit parameters are often measured by conducting open-circuit and short-circuit tests. On open circuit for example, the current I is zero and the measured terminal voltage V is then equal to E. On short circuit, if this is possible without

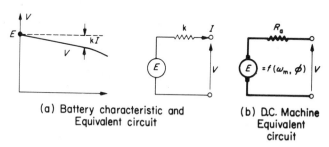

(a) Battery characteristic and Equivalent circuit

(b) D.C. Machine Equivalent circuit

FIG. 1.8. Equivalent circuits.

17

damage, i.e. if E is controllable, then the e.m.f. in the circuit is equal to the impedance drop since $V = 0$, so the impedance is obtained on dividing E by the current.

A full consideration of the induced voltages in the machine windings leads to circuit equations which can apply either to the machine or to another circuit which has the same equations. Starting with the 2-coil transformer, Fig. 1.9a, we arrive at the circuit shown in which R_1 and x_1 are the primary resistance and leakage reactance respectively. X_m is the magnetising reactance and represents the effect of the mutual flux common to both primary and secondary windings. $R_2' + jx_2'$ is the "referred" secondary leakage impedance, which is the actual value multiplied by the (turns ratio, $N_1/N_2)^2$. This is equivalent to replacing the secondary having N_2 turns with another secondary having the same number of turns as the primary, N_1. This would increase the voltage by N_1/N_2 and reduce the current by N_2/N_1. Hence the impedance (voltage/current) would be increased by $(N_1/N_2)^2$. Since it is not possible to tell from measurements on the primary side, how many turns there are on the secondary, this replacement by a 1/1 ratio is convenient, expressing secondary voltages and currents in primary terms. The ideal transformer at the end of the circuit converts these referred values back to actual values. Note that the positive directions of I_1 and I_2 have been taken in the same sense magnetically because this is convenient when developing the equations. Generally, however, the positive sense of I_2 is taken in the opposite direction to I_1 and the magnetising branch in the middle carries $I_1 - I_2' = I_0$ as usually designated.

For rotating machines, the above treatment can be adapted and extended by considering the stator m.m.f. as being produced by one specially distributed coil. Similarly the rotor m.m.f. is treated as due to one coil. The difference from the transformer is that the rotor coils move with respect to the stator coils, though their m.m.f.s are always in synchronism for the steady-state condition. The fluxes follow the same general pattern in that there is a common mutual flux, crossing the air gap and linking both stator

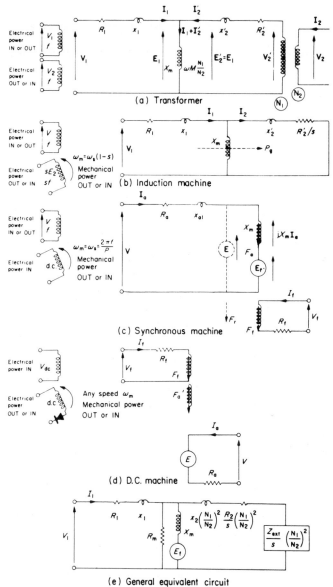

FIG. 1.9. Machine equivalent circuits.

19

and rotor windings, and leakage fluxes associated with each winding individually.

The way in which the equivalent circuit is modified from the transformer depends on the machine type. For a.c. machines, the m.m.f. of the stator (usually) produces a rotating field at synchronous speed $\omega_s = 2\pi n_s$ rad/s, where $n_s = f/p$ rev/s. The induction machine runs at a speed $\omega_m = \omega_s(1-s)$ where the slip s expresses the relative movement of the rotor with respect to the synchronous-speed m.m.f. wave. The rotor e.m.f. is reduced to $s E_2$ where E_2 is the e.m.f. at standstill with stator and rotor windings stationary as in a transformer. The rotor current $I_2 = s E_2/(R_2 + jsx_2) = E_2/(R_2/s + jx_2)$, so that the only difference from the transformer equivalent circuit is the replacement of R_2' by R_2'/s (Fig. 1.9b) and all parameters are *per-phase* values.

For the synchronous machine, $s = 0$ since $\omega_m = \omega_s$ and the right-hand side of the equivalent circuit carries no induced current on steady state since $R_2'/s = \infty$. A d.c. current has to be provided in the "secondary" winding which now becomes the field; Fig. 1.9c. The effect on the "primary" winding is now expressed as $E_f = f(\omega_s, I_f)$ instead of through $I_2'X_m$ as in the transformer and induction machines. The resultant m.m.f. F_r produces the mutual (air-gap) flux ϕ_m and e.m.f. E.

For the d.c. machine, both terminal currents are d.c. so the reactive elements may be omitted. The effect of the armature m.m.f. F_a on the field m.m.f. is more complex than for the other machines and is represented by its net magnetising action F_a', which is usually negative. Figure 1.9d shows the equivalent circuit.

This rather rapid review of equivalent-circuit development is obviously deficient in many details but is dealt with fully in reference 1. Figure 1.9e shows a general equivalent circuit which is applicable to all machine types discussed, with appropriate modifications. For the transformer, E_f is omitted and the value of s is unity. For the induction machine, s takes on any value. For the synchronous machine, $s = 0$ and the right-hand side of the equivalent circuit is omitted and E_f is inserted. For the d.c.

machine, the reactances are omitted for steady-state operation. It will also be noted that there is an additional element, R_m. The power dissipated here (E^2/R_m) represents the iron loss (per phase). When the circuit represents an a.c.-excited device like a transformer or an induction motor, this power is provided by the electrical supply. The value of R_m is relatively high and does not normally affect the calculations of currents very significantly.

1.4 POWER-FLOW DIAGRAM

Figure 1.10 is an extension of Fig. 1.3b showing more details of the power distribution within the machine. The expressions for the various power components sometimes differ as between the different machine types but the general pattern is the same. The power flow for motoring operation is from left to right, the electrical terminal power P_{elec} and the mechanical terminal power P_{mech} being both positive. For generating operation, these are both negative, power flowing from right to left. For braking, P_{mech} is negative

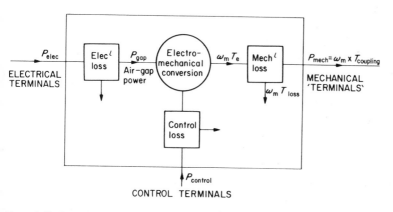

FIG. 1.10. Power-flow distribution between machine terminals (motoring convention).

21

and for reverse-current braking power flow is inwards from both ends. Electromechanical power conversion takes place through the air gap and the power P_{gap} is less than P_{elec} for motoring by the amount "Electrical loss". The power converted to mechanical power is always (speed × electromagnetic torque) = $\omega_m T_e$, where $\omega_m = \omega_s$ for the synchronous machine. For the induction machine the speed is $\omega_m = \omega_s(1 - s)$ so that there is a power sP_{gap} converted not to mechanical power but to electrical power in the secondary circuits. Continuing along the motoring power-flow path, the remaining elements are the same for all machine types. $\omega_m T_e$ is reduced by the mechanical loss $\omega_m T_{\text{loss}}$ to $\omega_m T_{\text{coupling}}$ which is the output motoring power at the mechanical terminals. There is a further set of terminals for the control power, P_{control}. For the d.c. and synchronous machines, this is absorbed entirely by the field Cu loss $I_f^2 R_F$. For the induction

TABLE 1.1

	D.C. motor	3-ph induction motor	3-ph synchronous motor
P_{elec}	VI_a	$\sqrt{3}V_L I_L \cos \varphi_1$ $= 3V_1 I_1 \cos \varphi_1$	$\sqrt{3}V_L I_L \cos \varphi$ $= 3VI_a \cos \varphi$
"Electrical loss"	$I_a^2 R_a + \text{brush}$	$3I_1^2 R_1 + \text{Fe loss}$	$3I_a^2 R_a + \text{Fe loss}$
Air-gap power P_{gap}	EI_a $= \omega_m T_e$	$3 E_1 I_2' \cos \varphi_2$ $= 3I_2^2 R_2/s = \omega_s T_e$	$3E_f I_a \cos(\varphi - \delta)$ $= \omega_s T_e \simeq 3VI_a \cos \varphi$
Control loss	$I_f^2 R_F$	$3I_2^2 R_2 = sP_{\text{gap}}$ if s.c.	$I_f^2 R_F$
P_{control}	$V_f I_f I_f^2 R_F$	$3V_3 I_2' \cos \varphi_2$ $= 0$ if s.c.	$V_f I_f = I_f^2 R_F$
P_{mech}	$\omega_m T_{\text{coupling}}$	$\omega_m T_{\text{coupling}}$	$\omega_s T_{\text{coupling}}$

Note. The Fe loss for d.c. and synchronous machines mostly manifests itself as a torque loss, part of T_{loss}. Figure 1.10 is useful for explaining the concepts of efficiency, control and a method of measuring the losses, by setting the power to zero at two sets of terminals and measuring the input at the other set.

machine, the control loss is the secondary Cu loss, $3I_2^2R_2$ and if the secondary terminals are short circuited, this is provided by the "transformer-converted" power, sP_{gap} and $P_{control}$ is zero. Sometimes however, for slip-power recovery schemes, control power is exerted from an external voltage source V_3 and this power may be inwards (for super-synchronous speeds) or outwards from the machine (for sub-synchronous speeds).

In Table 1.1 the power components for the various machine types are listed, using the symbols adopted in the text.

CHAPTER 2

TRANSFORMERS

ALTHOUGH the transformer is not an electromechanical converter like the other devices to be covered in this text, it forms the basis from which all the other equivalent circuits are derived. The theory is relatively simple, built up from Faraday's Law of Electromagnetic Induction. Only steady-state operation will be dealt with here but it is very important to the understanding of the remaining chapters; for example, in coming to grips with the referrring process by means of which two coupled windings of different voltage and current ratings can be replaced by a simple series/parallel circuit. There is also much vital practice to be obtained in the analysis and manipulation of 3-phase circuits. Multiple windings and the combination of winding m.m.f.s, together with basic work in a.c. circuit theory and use of complex numbers, are all illustrated by the various examples.

2.1 SOLUTION OF EQUATIONS

In this chapter, since some of the groundwork has already been covered in Chapter 1, equations will mostly be discussed as the need arises. The first example requires the important e.m.f. equation, which applies, with some slight modifications, to all a.c. machines. It relates the r.m.s.-induced e.m.f. E to the maximum flux $\hat{\phi}$ in webers, frequency f and number of turns N:

From the law of induction, the instantaneous e.m.f. $= N \, d\phi/dt$ and for a sinusoidal variation of flux, expressed as $\phi = \hat{\phi} \sin 2\pi ft$, it is readily shown by differentiation and substitution

that:
$$E = 4.44 \times \hat{\phi} \times f \times N \text{ volts} \qquad (2.1)$$

Note especially that E is r.m.s. e.m.f. and flux is the maximum value.

EXAMPLE 2.1

A transformer core has a square cross-section of 20 mm side. The primary winding is to be designed for 230 V, the secondary winding for 110 V and a further centre-tapped, 6/0/6-V winding is to be provided. If the flux density $\hat{B}$ is not to exceed 1 tesla, find a suitable number of turns for each winding, for a frequency of 50 Hz. Neglect all transformer imperfections.

The low-voltage winding is always designed first because voltage ratios can rarely be obtained exactly and since there are the fewest turns on the low-voltage winding and the actual number of turns must always be integral, the adjustment is also the coarsest.

The maximum flux must not exceed $\hat{\phi} = \hat{B} \times A = 1 \times (20 \times 10^{-3})^2$.

From the e.m.f. equation $6 = 4.44 \times 400 \times 10^{-6} \times 50 \times N_3$ from which $N_3 = 67.57$ and the nearest integral number is 68 to avoid the specified maximum flux density being exceeded. It will now be slightly lower than $\hat{B} = 1$.

For the secondary winding: $\dfrac{N_2}{N_3} = \dfrac{110}{6}$, so $N_2 = \dfrac{110 \times 68}{6} = 1246.7$ say <u>1247 turns</u>.

For the primary winding: $\dfrac{N_1}{N_3} = \dfrac{230}{6}$, so $N_1 = \dfrac{230 \times 68}{6} = 2606.7$ say <u>2607 turns</u>.

The tertiary winding requires <u>2 × 68 turns</u>.

Note 1   On core-type transformers, the windings are divided into two sections, one on each limb. In this case the nearest *even* number of turns would be chosen, to make the sections equal.

Note 2   When transformer cores are supplied for the user to wind his own coils, it is usual, for convenience, to specify the magnetic limits at a particular frequency, in terms of the volts per turn. For this core it is 6/67.57 = 88.8 mV/turn or 11.26 turns per volt; at 50 Hz.

EXAMPLE 2.2

A 20-kVA, 3810/320-V, 50-Hz single-phase transformer operates at a maximum flux density of 1.25 teslas, for which the iron requires a value of $H = 0.356$ At/mm.

The core cross-section is 0.016 m^2 and the mean length of the magnetic path through the core is 1.4 m. The primary and secondary turns are 860 and 52 respectively. It is decided to use the transformer as an inductor and to keep the reactance substantially constant with current, the core is sawn through transversely and packed with brass to give an "air" gap. If the secondary winding is used, find the length of the air gap so that when carrying rated current, the maximum flux density is not exceeded. What is then the inductance and the reactance at 50 Hz?

$$\text{Rated current} = \frac{20\,000}{230} = 86.96 \text{ A r.m.s.}$$

The peak m.m.f. exerted by this current is : $\sqrt{2} \times 86.96 \times 52 = 6394.7$ At

At peak flux density, the m.m.f. absorbed by the iron is $H \times l = 0.356 \times 1.4 \times 10^3 = 498.4$ At.

$\therefore$ m.m.f. available for the air gap $= 6394.7 - 498.4 = 5896.3$ At.

Neglecting air-gap fringing so that the flux density is assumed to be the same as in the iron:

$$\text{Air-gap m.m.f.} = H \times l = \frac{B}{\mu_0} \times l = \frac{1.25}{4\pi/10^2} \times l = 5896.3$$

from which $l = 5.93$ mm.

The effective permeance of the core + gap =

$$\Lambda = \frac{\text{flux}}{\text{m.m.f.}} = \frac{1.25 \times 0.016}{6394.7}$$
$$= 3.128 \times 10^{-6} \text{ Wb/At}$$

so inductance $= N^2\Lambda = 52^2 \times 3.128 \times 10^{-6} = 8.458$ mH

and reactance $= 2\pi \times 50 \times 8.458 \times 10^{-3} = 2.657\,\Omega$

Alternatively, the e.m.f. $= 4.44 \times (1.25 \times 0.016) \times 50 \times 52 = 230.9$ V
and the impedance $= 230.9/86.96 = 2.656\,\Omega$

Note 1 Resistance has been neglected in the above calculation; it would be relatively small.

Note 2 The inductance is not quite constant with current, but at the maximum value, the iron absorbs less than 8% of the total m.m.f. At lower currents, the linearity will improve since the iron will absorb proportionately less At.

EXAMPLE 2.3

A 230/6-V, single-phase transformer is tested with its secondary winding short circuited. A low voltage (20 V) is applied to the primary terminals and it then takes an input current of 1 A; the power supplied being 10 watts. Calculate the values of leakage reactance and resistance, referred to the primary side and then to the secondary side. If the magnetising impedance is neglected, calculate the secondary terminal voltage when a load impedance of value $0.12 + j0.09\,\Omega$ is connected.

On s.c. test, the input power factor is: $\dfrac{P}{VI} = \dfrac{5}{20 \times 1} = 0.5 = \cos\varphi_{sc}$

and the impedance is: $\dfrac{V}{I} = \dfrac{20}{1} = 20\,\Omega = Z_{sc}$

$\therefore$ impedance referred to the primary side $= Z_{sc}(\cos\varphi_{sc} + j\sin\varphi_{sc})$

$$= 20(0.5 + j0.866) = \underline{10 + j17.32\,\Omega}$$

Impedance referred to the secondary side $= Z_{sc}\left(\dfrac{N_2}{N_1}\right)^2 = \left(\dfrac{6}{230}\right)^2$

$$= \underline{0.0068 + j0.0118\,\Omega.}$$

It is convenient, to solve for the load test with the impedance referred to the secondary side. The diagram shows the equivalent circuit connected to the load, and the phasor diagram—not to scale.

The load current would be: $\dfrac{6}{0.1268 + j0.1018} = \dfrac{6(0.1268 - j0.1018)}{(0.1268)^2 + (0.1018)^2}$

$$= 28.77 - j23.1 = 36.9\underline{/-38°8}\ \text{A}$$

Voltage at secondary terminals, i.e. across the load $= 36.9\sqrt{0.12^2 + 0.09^2}$

$$= \underline{5.535\ \text{V}}$$

An alternative approach is to calculate the drop of voltage due to the transformer internal impedance; the so-called regulation. From the phasor diagram as drawn, this is approximately equal to $RI\cos\varphi - XI\sin\varphi = |E - V|$ ($\sin\varphi$ is −ve.)

The load power-factor is $\dfrac{0.12}{\sqrt{0.12^2 + 0.09^2}} = 0.8 = \cos\varphi.\ \therefore\ \sin\varphi = -0.6$

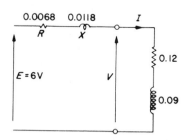

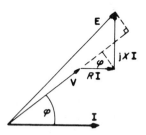

FIG. E.2.3.

27

Regulation = 36.9(0.0068 × 0.8 + 0.0118 × 0.6) = 0.462 V

So load voltage = 6 − 0.462 = 5.38 V

Note 1   In this case there is enough information to calculate V from $E − ZI$ where, with E as the reference phasor, the phase angle of I with respect to E could be found from the total series impedance. If only the load power-factor φ is known however, this information is not available and the regulation expression must be used. A more accurate regulation expression can be derived.[1]

Note 2   If the load power-factor had been leading, $−\sin \varphi$ would have been negative and the load voltage could have been *higher* than the open-circuit voltage (E).

EXAMPLE 2.4

A 3-phase, 50-Hz transformer is to have primary, secondary and tertiary windings for each phase. The specification is as follows: Primary to be 6600 V and delta connected. Secondary to be 1000 V and delta connected. Tertiary to be 440 V and star connected. Determine suitable numbers of turns to ensure that the peak flux does not exceed 0.03 Wb.

If the secondary is to supply a balanced load of 100 kVA at 0.8 p.f. lagging and the tertiary is to supply a balanced load of 50 kW at u.p.f., determine the primary line-current and power factor for this condition. Neglect all transformer imperfections.

This is the first 3-phase problem in the book and it is an excellent opportunity to become absolutely familiar with the basic circuit relationships. It is always helpful to draw a circuit diagram as on the figure, where these relationships become obvious. Note that it is standard practice to specify line voltages, line currents and total power for 3-phase devices so that, as in this case, conversion to phase values may be necessary. For example, the turns ratio is the phase-voltage ratio and is usually specified for the no-load condition.

Using the e.m.f. equation and as before, designing the low-voltage winding first:
$$440/\sqrt{3} = 4.44 \times 0.03 \times 50 \times N_3$$

from which $N_3 = 38.14$ say <u>39 turns per phase</u>—to keep the flux below the specified level.

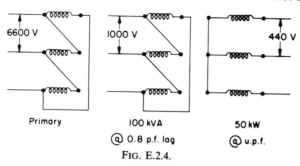

Primary   IOO kVA   50 kW

@ 0.8 p.f. lag   @ u.p.f.

FIG. E.2.4.

For the secondary: $\dfrac{N_2}{N_3} = \dfrac{1000}{440/\sqrt{3}}$ from which $N_2 = 153.5$ say <u>154 turns per phase</u>

For the primary: $\dfrac{N_1}{N_3} = \dfrac{6600}{440/\sqrt{3}}$ from which $N_1 = 1013.2$ say <u>1013 turns per phase</u>

Load condition

Tertiary current per phase $= \dfrac{\text{power per phase}}{\text{voltage per phase}} = \dfrac{50\,000/3}{440/\sqrt{3}} = 65.6$ A

Referred to primary; $I_3' = 65.6 \times \dfrac{39}{1013} = 2.525$ A

But since referred currents are required in order to calculate the total primary current, it is simpler to go directly to this by dividing the tertiary kVA by primary voltage.

i.e. $I_3' = \dfrac{50\,000/3}{6600}$ and since power factor is unity, $I_3' = 2.525 + j0.$

Similarly $I_2' = \dfrac{10\,000/3}{6600}(0.8 - j0.6)$ since p.f. is 0.8 lagging. $I_2' = \underline{4.04 - j3.03}$

So $I_1 = I_2' + I_3' + I_0 (= 0) = \underline{6.565 - j3.03}$

and the primary is delta connected so line current $= \sqrt{3} \times \sqrt{6.565^2 + 3.03^2}$

$= \sqrt{3} \times 7.23 = \underline{12.52\ A}$

Power factor $= \cos \varphi = 6.565/7.23 = \underline{0.908 \text{ lagging.}}$

EXAMPLE 2.5

On open circuit, a 3-phase, star/star/delta, 6600/660/220-V transformer takes 50 kVA at 0.15 p.f. What is the primary input kVA and power factor when, for balanced loads, the secondary delivers 870 A at 0.8 p.f. lagging and the tertiary delivers 260 line A at unity power factor? Neglect the leakage impedances.

The connections are different here from the previous example and a sketch of the circuit diagram appropriately modified would be instructive.

The data given permit I_0 to be calculated from $kVA/(\sqrt{3} \times kV)$:

$$I_0 = \frac{50}{\sqrt{3} \times 6.6}(\cos \varphi - j\sin \varphi) = 4.374(0.15 - j0.9887) = 0.656 - j4.324$$

$$I_2' = 870(0.8 - j0.6) \times \frac{660/\sqrt{3}}{6600/\sqrt{3}} \qquad\qquad = 69.6 - j52.2$$

$$I_3' = \frac{260}{\sqrt{3}}(1 + j0) \times \frac{220}{6600/\sqrt{3}} \qquad\qquad = 8.667 + j0$$

$$I_1 = I_0 + I_2' + I_3' \qquad\qquad\qquad = 78.92 - j56.52$$

$$I_1 = \sqrt{78.92^2 + 56.52^2} = 97.07 \text{ A at } \cos \varphi = 78.92/97.07 = \underline{0.813 \text{ lag}}$$

Input $kVA = \sqrt{3} \times 6.6 \times 97.07 = \underline{1109.6\,kVA}$.

EXAMPLE 2.6

A 3-phase, 3-winding, delta/delta/star, 33 000/1100/400-V, 200-kVA transformer carries a secondary load of 150 kVA at 0.8 p.f. lagging and a tertiary load of 50 kVA at 0.9 p.f. lagging. The magnetising current is 4% of rated current; the iron loss being 1 kW total. Calculate the value of the primary current and power factor and input kVA when the other two windings are operating on the above loads.

Again the leakage impedances will be neglected. See reference 2 for an exact equivalent circuit for the 3-winding transformer.

Power component of $I_0 = \dfrac{1\,kW/3}{33\,kV} = 0.01$ A

Magnetising component of $I_0 = \dfrac{4}{100} \times \dfrac{200/3}{33} = 0.081$ A

$$\therefore I_0 \qquad\qquad = 0.01 - j0.081$$

$$I_2' = \frac{150/3}{33}(0.8 - j0.6) \qquad = 1.212 - j0.909$$

$$I_3' = \frac{50/3}{33}(0.9 - j0.436) \qquad = \underline{0.455 - j0.22}$$

$$I_1 = \underline{1.677 - j1.21}$$

Line current $= \sqrt{3} \times \sqrt{1.677^2 + 1.21^2} = \sqrt{3} \times 2.07 = \underline{3.58 \text{ A}}$

at power factor $\qquad\qquad\qquad 1.677/2.07 = \underline{0.81 \text{ lagging}}$

and input $\qquad\qquad kVA = \sqrt{3} \times 33 \times 3.58 = \underline{204.6\,kVA}$

EXAMPLE 2.7

The following are the light-load test readings on a 3-phase, 100-kVA, 400/6600-V, star/delta transformer:

Open circuit; supply to low-voltage side   400 V,   1250 W

Short circuit; supply to high-voltage side 314 V,   1600 W, full-load current.

Calculate the efficiencies at full load, 0.8 power factor and at half full load, u.p.f.

Calculate also the maximum efficiency. What is the percentage leakage impedance based on 100% = rated V/rated I?

The losses on a transformer are: Fe loss which varies very little at constant voltage and frequency and Cu loss which is proportional to (current)^2, or (load kVA)^2 at constant voltage.

At any load, λ times rated value (load here referring to load current or load kVA):

$$\text{Efficiency} = \frac{\text{Output}}{\text{Input}} = \frac{\lambda \times kVA \times \cos\varphi}{\lambda \times kVA \times \cos\varphi + \text{Losses}} \text{ where kVA is the rated value}$$

$$\eta = \frac{\lambda\,kVA\cos\varphi}{\lambda\,kVA\cos\varphi + \text{Fe loss} + \lambda^2(\text{Cu loss at full load})}$$

The maximum value of this expression is easily shown by differentiation, to occur when $\lambda = \sqrt{(\text{Fe loss})/(\text{Cu loss at full load})}$ at any particular power factor. The o.c. test gives the normal Fe loss since rated voltage is applied and the s.c. test gives the copper loss at full load since rated current is flowing.

For full load, 0.8 p.f.

$$\eta = \frac{1 \times 100 \times 0.8}{(1 \times 100 \times 0.8) + 1.25 + 1^2 \times 1.6} = \frac{80}{82.85} = 0.9656 = \underline{96.56\%}.$$

For half full load, u.p.f.

$$\eta = \frac{0.5 \times 100 \times 1}{(0.5 \times 100 \times 1) + 1.25 + (0.5)^2 \times 1.6} = \frac{50}{51.65} = 0.968 = \underline{96.8\%}.$$

Maximum efficiency when

$$\lambda = \sqrt{1.25/1.6} = 0.884 \text{ and power factor is unity.}$$

$$\text{Max. } \eta = \frac{0.884 \times 100 \times 1}{88.4 + 1.236 + (0.884)^2 \times 1.6} = \frac{88.4}{90.9} = 0.9725 = \underline{97.25\%}.$$

Leakage impedance

Rated secondary current per phase $= \dfrac{100\,000/3}{6600} = 5.05\text{A}.$

Short-circuit power factor $= \dfrac{1600/3}{314 \times 5.05} = 0.336.$

Z_{sc} (referred to secondary) $= \dfrac{314}{5.05}(0.336 + j0.9417) = 20.89 + j58.55\ \Omega.$

Base impedance $= 100\% = \dfrac{6600}{5.05} = 1306.9\ \Omega.$

Hence percentage impedance $= \dfrac{1}{1306.9}(20.89 + j58.55) \times 100$

$= (0.016 + j0.0448) \times 100 = \underline{1.6 + j4.48\%}.$

The value before multiplying by 100 is called the *per-unit* impedance; see Sections 3.3, 5.3 and Example (4.2d).

EXAMPLE 2.8

The following light-load, line-input readings were taken on a 3-phase, 150-kVA, 6600/440-V, delta/star-connected transformer:

Open-circuit test   1900 W,   440 V,   16.5 A
Short-circuit tests   2700 W,   315 V,   12.5 A.

(a) Calculate the equivalent-circuit parameters per phase, referred to the h.v. side.

(b) Determine the secondary terminal voltages when operating at rated and half-rated current if the load power-factor is 0.8 lagging. Calculate also the efficiencies for these loads.

(c) Determine the secondary terminal voltage when operating at rated current with a load power-factor of 0.8 leading and calculate the efficiency for this condition.

Although this problem is for a 3-phase transformer, once the equivalent-circuit parameters per phase have been determined correctly, it may proceed as for single-phase, making due allowance for the fact that the calculations will give phase currents and powers. A balanced load is assumed. The figure shows the circuit and the approximate equivalent circuit which should help to avoid confusion when analysing the tests.

Open-circuit test
Since iron loss is a function of voltage, this test must be taken at rated voltage if the usual parameters are required. The voltage is 440 V so it must have been taken on the low-voltage side. Referring I_0 to the primary will permit the magnetising parameters, referred to the h.v. side, to be calculated directly.

$$I_0 = 16.5 \times \frac{440/\sqrt{3}}{6600} = 0.635 \text{ A}$$

$$\cos \varphi_{oc} = \frac{1900}{\sqrt{3} \times 440 \times 16.5} = 0.151; \quad \sin \varphi_{oc} = 0.9985.$$

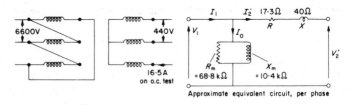

Approximate equivalent circuit, per phase

FIG. E.2.8.

Hence:

$$R_m = \frac{V}{I_0 \cos \varphi_{oc}} = \frac{6600}{0.635 \times 0.151} = 68.8 \text{ k}\Omega. \quad X_m = \frac{6600}{0.635 \times 0.9985} = \underline{10.4 \text{ k}\Omega}.$$

Short-circuit test
   This does not have to be taken at exactly rated current, since with unsaturated leakage reactance, a linear relationship between voltage and current can be assumed. Only a low voltage is required, so the readings show that the test was taken on the h.v. side.

$$\cos \varphi_{sc} = \frac{2700}{\sqrt{3} \times 315 \times 12.5} = 0.396; \quad \sin \varphi_{sc} = 0.918.$$

$$Z_{sc} = \frac{315}{12.5/\sqrt{3}}(0.396 + j0.918) = \underline{17.3 + j40 \ \Omega}.$$

Load conditions
   Rated current, by definition $= \dfrac{\text{Rated VA per phase}}{\text{Rated voltage per phase}} = \dfrac{150/3}{6.6} = 7.575$ A. The
same regulation expression can be used as in Example 2.3 and $\cos \varphi = 0.8$.
$\sin \varphi = -0.6$ for (b) and $+0.6$ for (c)

	(a)	(b)	(c)	
H.V. Load current per phase	= 7.575	3.787	7.575	A
$I \cos \varphi$	= 6.06	3.03	6.06	A
$I \sin \varphi$	= −4.545	−2.272	+4.545	A
Regulation = $17.3I \cos \varphi - 40I \sin \varphi$	= 286.7	143.3	−77	V
Terminal voltage = 6600 − regulation	= 6313.3	6456.7	6677	V
Referred to secondary [×440/($\sqrt{3} \times 6600$)]	= 243	248.5	257	V
Secondary terminal voltage (line)	= 420.9	430.4	445.1	V
Load current referred to secondary	= 196.8	98.4	196.8	A
Secondary (output) power = $\sqrt{3} VI \cos \varphi$	= 114.8	58.7	121.3	kW
Cu loss = $2.7 \times (I_{hv}/12.5\sqrt{3})^2$	= 2.97	0.74	2.97	kW
Total loss (+Fe loss = 1.9)	= 4.87	2.64	4.87	kW
Efficiency	= 95.93	95.7	96.14	%

Note that when calculating the efficiency, the changing secondary voltage has been allowed for, and this is higher than the o.c. voltage when the power factor is leading.

EXAMPLE 2.9

   A 3-phase transformer has a star-connected primary and a delta-connected secondary. The primary/secondary turns ratio is 2/1. It supplies a balanced, star-connected load, each phase consisting of a resistance of 4Ω in series with an inductive reactance of 3Ω.

(a) If the transformer was perfect, what would be the value of the load impedance per phase viewed from the primary terminals?

From a practical test, the following primary input-readings were taken:

	Total power	Line voltage	Line current
Secondary short circuited	12 W	7.75 V	2 A
Secondary load connected	745 W	220 V	2.35 A

(b) Deduce, from the readings, the equivalent circuit of the load viewed from the primary winding and explain why it differs from (a).

(a) The circuit diagram is shown on the figure and the first step is to transform the star-connected load to an equivalent delta; i.e. one that carries the same current as the secondary winding and has the same voltage across it, as indicated on the figure. Since the current per load-phase will thus be reduced by $\sqrt{3}$ and its voltage increased by $\sqrt{3}$, the effect will be to transform the impedance by a factor of 3 times, from that of the star-connection.

Hence $\qquad$ $\mathbf{Z} = 12 + j9 \; \Omega$ per phase.

It is now possible to treat each balanced phase separately, as a single-phase problem. The effect of the 2/1 turns ratio and a perfect transformer will be to decrease the current by 1/2 and increase the voltage by 2/1, giving an impedance transformation of 2^2; i.e. $(N_1/N_2)^2$. Viewed from the primary therefore, the load impedance will appear as:

$$\mathbf{Z}'_{load} = 48 + j36 \; \Omega \text{ per phase.}$$

(b) From the s.c. tests:

$$\cos \varphi_{sc} = \frac{12}{\sqrt{3} \times 7.75 \times 2} = 0.4469; \quad \sin \varphi_{sc} = 0.8845.$$

Hence

$$\mathbf{Z}_{sc} = \frac{7.75/\sqrt{3}}{2}(0.4469 + j0.8845) = 1 + j2 \; \Omega \text{ per phase.}$$

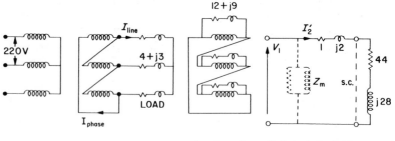

Transformed load   Equivalent circuit/ph

FIG. E.2.9.

34

From the load test:

$$\cos \varphi_{load} = \frac{745}{\sqrt{3} \times 220 \times 2.35} = 0.8319; \quad \sin \varphi_{load} = 0.555.$$

$$Z_{input} = \frac{220/\sqrt{3}}{2.35}(0.8319 + j0.555) = 45 + j30 \ \Omega \text{ per phase.}$$

Hence,

referred load impedance $= Z_{input} - Z_{sc} = \underline{44 + j28}$ per phase.

The equivalent circuit per phase from these results is shown on Fig. E.2.10, which includes the unknown magnetising impedance Z_m across the input terminals. A small part of the input current will flow through here so that the figure of 2.35 A used in calculating Z_{input} will be higher than the true value of I_2'. Hence, the above value of the referred load impedance will be lower than it should be, from part (a).

EXAMPLE 2.10

A 3-phase, 11 000/660-V, star/delta transformer is connected to the far end of a distribution line for which the near-end voltage is maintained at 11 kV. The effective leakage reactance and resistance per-phase of the transformer are respectively 0.25 Ω and 0.05 Ω referred to the low-voltage side. The reactance and resistance of each line are respectively 2 Ω and 1 Ω.

It is required to maintain the terminal voltage at 660 V when a line current of 260 A at 0.8 lagging power factor is drawn from the secondary winding. What percentage tapping must be provided on the h.v. side of the transformer to permit the necessary adjustment? The transformer magnetising current may be neglected and an approximate expression for the regulation may be used. Neglect also the changes to the impedance due to the alteration of the turns ratio.

The equivalent circuit per phase is shown on the figure. The line impedance can also be referred to the secondary side and included in the regulation expression.

Referred line impedance $= \left(\frac{660}{11\ 000/\sqrt{3}}\right)^2 \times (1 + j2) = 0.0108 + j0.0216 \ \Omega$ per phase.

The total impedance referred to the secondary $= 0.0608 + j0.2716 \ \Omega$ per phase.

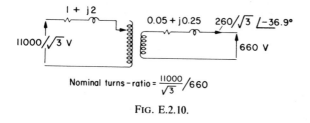

Nominal turns-ratio $= \dfrac{11000}{\sqrt{3}}/660$

Fig. E.2.10.

35

Voltage regulation per phase $= I(R \cos \varphi - X \sin \varphi) = \dfrac{260}{\sqrt{3}}(0.0608 \times 0.8 + 0.2716 \times 0.6)$

$$= 7.3 + 24.46 = 31.76 \text{ V}.$$

So o.c. voltage of transformer must be $660 + 31.76$

and turns ratio must be: $\dfrac{11\,000/\sqrt{3}}{660 + 31.76}$ instead of $\dfrac{11\,000/\sqrt{3}}{660}$

i.e.   9.18 instead of 9.623

h.v. tapping must be at: $\dfrac{9.18}{9.623} = \underline{95.4\%}$.

EXAMPLE 2.11

Two single-phase transformers operate in parallel to supply a load of $24 + j10\ \Omega$. Transformer A has a secondary e.m.f. of 440 V on open circuit and an internal impedance in secondary terms of $1 + j3\ \Omega$. The corresponding figures for Transformer B are 450 V and $1 + j4\ \Omega$. Calculate the terminal voltage, the current and terminal power-factor of each transformer.

The equivalent circuit is shown in the figure and yields the following equations:

$$\mathbf{E_A} - \mathbf{Z_A I_A} = \mathbf{V} = (\mathbf{I_A} + \mathbf{I_B})\mathbf{Z}$$
$$\mathbf{E_B} - \mathbf{Z_B I_B} = \mathbf{V} = (\mathbf{I_A} + \mathbf{I_B})\mathbf{Z}$$

Solving simultaneously gives:

$$\mathbf{I_A} = \frac{\mathbf{E_A Z_B} + (\mathbf{E_A} - \mathbf{E_B})\mathbf{Z}}{\mathbf{Z}(\mathbf{Z_A} + \mathbf{Z_B}) + \mathbf{Z_A Z_B}}$$

The expression for $\mathbf{I_B}$ is obtained by interchanging A and B in the above equation.

A reference phasor must be chosen and if the two transformers have a common primary voltage, the equivalent-circuit e.m.f.s ($\mathbf{E_{oc}}$) will be in phase, so will be a convenient choice.

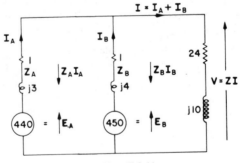

FIG. E.2.11.

Hence $\qquad E_A = 440 + j0$ and $E_B = 450 + j0$.

Substituting:

$$I_A = \frac{440(1 + j4) + (-10)(24 + j10)}{(24 + j10)(2 + j7) + (1 + j3)(1 + j4)} = \frac{200 + j1660}{-33 + j195} = \frac{1672/83°13}{197.8/99°6}$$
$$= 8.45/-16°5$$

$$I_B = \frac{450(1 + j3) + 10(24 + j10)}{197.8/99°6} = \frac{690 + j1450}{197.8/99°6} = \frac{1605.8/64°6}{197.8/99°6}$$
$$= 8.12/-35°$$

$I_A + I_B$		$= 8.1 - j2.4 + 6.65 - j4.66 = 14.75 - j7.06 = 16.35/-25°6.$
Load impedance	Z	$= 24 + j10 = 26/22°6.$
Terminal voltage	V	$= Z(I_A + I_B) = 425.1/-3°.$
Relative to	V, I_A	$= 8.45/-16°5 + 3° = \underline{8.45}$ A at cos $13°6 = 0.972$ p.f. lag.
Relative to	V, I_B	$= 8.12/-35° + 3° = \underline{8.12}$ A at cos $32° = 0.848$ p.f. lag.

Note 1 Although the two currents are similar, the power and reactive components of these currents are quite different. The transformers must be identical (in *per-unit* terms), if they are to share the load in proportion to their ratings. Calculations like the above determine whether any discrepancies are tolerable.

Note 2 To calculate the input primary currents, the secondary currents must be referred through the turns ratio and the corresponding components I_0 added.

Note 3 Two 3-phase transformers in parallel would be solved the same way, but using their *per-phase* equivalent circuits.

CHAPTER 3

D.C. MACHINES

FOR a first approach to the subject of electrical drives, the d.c. machine provides a simple introduction to the problems encountered since, for steady-state operation, it can be represented with reasonable accuracy, as a variable e.m.f. $E\alpha$(speed × flux), behind the armature-circuit resistance R_a. The field m.m.f. may be provided in various ways and with more than one field winding. Non-linearities, especially saturation effects, maybe involved in the calculations. The first three of the following examples bear somewhat lightly on machine-design aspects but the remainder are concerned with motoring, regenerating and braking. Chapter 6 deals with transient operation and Chapter 7 with d.c. machines in power-electronic circuits.

3.1 REVISION OF EQUATIONS

The average (d.c.) e.m.f. generated in a winding with z_s conductors connected in series, of active length l, rotating at velocity $v = \pi dn$ where d is the armature diameter and n the speed of rotation in rev/sec, is obtained from:

$$E = B_{av}lvz_s \text{ and } B_{av} = \frac{\text{Flux per pole}}{\text{Cylindrical area/No. of poles}} = \frac{\phi}{\pi d l/2p}$$

$$E = \frac{2p\phi}{\pi dl} \times l \times \pi dn \times z_s = 2p\phi nz_s \tag{3.1}$$

A d.c. machine armature-winding always has parallel paths and z_s is the total number of armature conductors Z, divided by the number of parallel paths. A simple wave winding has the smallest number, 2, and $z_s = Z/2$. For a simple lap winding, $z_s = Z/2p$.

Reference back to Section 1.4 will be helpful in understanding the following development of the power-balance equation. For simplicity at this stage, the brush loss—typically $2 \times I_a$ watts—will be assumed to be included in the R_a effect.

From the basic circuit equation for a motor:

$$V = E \qquad + RI_a \qquad (3.2)$$

Multiplying by I_a gives the power-balance equation:

$$VI_a = EI_a \qquad + RI_a^2 \qquad (3.3)$$

$$\text{Terminal power} = \text{Converted} + \text{Electrical}$$
$$\text{(air-gap)}$$
$$(P_{elec}) \qquad \text{power } P_{gap} \qquad \text{loss}$$

The power converted, EI_a, can be expressed in mechanical terms as $\omega_m T_e$ (rad/s $\times$ Nm) and hence by equating the expressions:

$$\frac{T_e}{I_a} = \frac{E}{\omega_m} = \frac{2p\phi nz_s}{2\pi n} = \frac{pz_s}{\pi}\phi = k_\phi \qquad (3.4)$$

Note that k_ϕ, the electromechanical conversion coefficient, is directly proportional to the flux per pole and has alternative units of e.m.f. per rad/s, or electromagnetic torque per ampere. It is sometimes called the speed constant or the torque constant and when SI units are used, these have the same numerical value, k_ϕ.

Hence:

$$E = k_\phi \omega_m \qquad (3.5)$$

$$T_e = k_\phi I_a \qquad (3.6)$$

and:

$$k_\phi = f(F_f, F_a)$$

where F_a, the armature m.m.f. per pole, has some demagnetising effect usually, and this is often greater than 10% of F_f. It will be neglected in the following examples except where special magnetisation curves are taken for series motors in Section 3.4. For a single field winding then:

39

$$k_\phi = f(I_f) \tag{3.7}$$

Several other equations may be derived from the above for the purpose of expressing a particular variable as the unknown. The most important is the speed/torque equation from:

$$\omega_m = \frac{E}{k_\phi} = \frac{V - RI_a}{k_\phi} = \frac{V}{k_\phi} - \frac{RT_e}{k_\phi^2} \tag{3.8}$$

I_a could be obtained from $(V - E)/R$ and k_ϕ from E/ω_m, but E (and I_a) are dependent variables, determined from power considerations and may have to be obtained from:

$$I_a = \frac{V - \sqrt{V^2 - 4R\omega_m T_m}}{2R} \tag{3.9}$$

and

$$k_\phi = \frac{V + \sqrt{V^2 - 4R\omega_m T_m}}{2\omega_m} \tag{3.10}$$

which are derived from eqns (3.3, 3.4 and 3.8). The choice of sign before the radical gives the lower current and higher flux, which is correct for the normal, low-resistance case. The opposite choice is applicable to high-resistance circuits; see Reference 1 and Example 3.12. Note that on steady state, $T_e = T_m$.

3.2   SOLUTION OF EQUATIONS

The following flow diagram has been prepared to act as a guide to thought while ascertaining a solution procedure. Not every possibility has been covered but the systematic approach indicated should be helpful in all cases. Non-linearities are taken into account either at the beginning or at the end of the solution. For example, if I_f is given, k_ϕ follows and hence leads to a solution of the linear equations for torque and speed, say. Alternatively, if k_ϕ is calculated from the linear equations, I_f follows from the magnetisation curve. On the mechanical side, if the non-linear relationship $T_m = f(\omega_m)$ is available, then any particular speed will yield the corresponding torque T_m which is the same as T_e on steady state. Alternatively, if $\omega_m = f(T_e)$ is calculated from the electromagnetic equations, then the intercept with the $T_m = f(\omega_m)$ curve determines the steady-state speed. Relationships for transient speed-calculations are also available from these two curves; see Chapter 6.

D.C. Machines Solution Programme

Input data from:

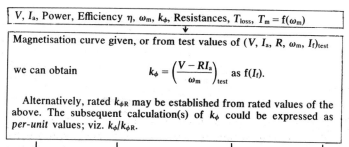

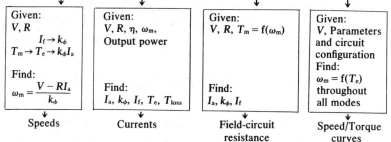

Given: V, R $\qquad I_f \to k_\phi$ $T_m \to T_e \to k_\phi I_a$ Find: $\omega_m = \dfrac{V - RI_a}{k_\phi}$	Given: $V, R, \eta, \omega_m,$ Output power Find: $I_a, k_\phi, I_f, T_e, T_{loss}$	Given: $V, R, T_m = f(\omega_m)$ Find: I_a, k_ϕ, I_f	Given: V, Parameters and circuit configuration Find: $\omega_m = f(T_e)$ throughout all modes
Speeds	Currents	Field-circuit resistance	Speed/Torque curves

EXAMPLE 3.1

A 4-pole d.c. armature wave winding has 294 conductors;
(a) What flux per pole is necessary to generate 230 V when rotating at 1500 rev/min?
(b) What is the electromagnetic torque at this flux when rated armature current of 120 A is flowing?

(c) How many interpole ampere turns are required with this current if the interpole gap density is to be 0.15 tesla and the effective radial air gap is $l_g = 8$ mm? Neglect the m.m.f. absorbed by the iron.

(d) Through what mechanical angle must the brushes be moved away from the quadrature axis if it is required to produce a direct-axis magnetisation of 200 At/pole?

(a) From eqn (3.1) $\qquad 2 \times p \times \phi \times n \times z_s$

substituting: $\qquad 230 = 2 \times 2 \times \phi \times \dfrac{1500}{60} \times \dfrac{294}{2}$

from which: $\qquad \underline{\phi = 0.0156 \text{ Wb.}}$

(b) From eqns (3.4) and (3.6) $T_e = k_\phi \cdot I_a = \dfrac{p \cdot z_s}{\pi} \cdot \phi \cdot I_a$

$$= \frac{2 \times 147}{\pi} \times 0.0156 \times 120 = \underline{175.7 \text{ Nm.}}$$

(c) On the interpolar (quadrature) axis, maximum armature At per pole F_a occurs, and the interpole m.m.f. must cancel this and also provide sufficient excess to produce the required commutating flux opposing that of the armature.

$$F_a = \frac{\text{Total ampere turns}}{\text{No. of poles}} = \frac{\text{amps/conductor} \times \text{conductors}/2}{2p}$$

$$= \frac{120/2 \times 294/2}{4} = 2205 \text{ At/pole}$$

Required

$$H = \frac{At}{l_g} = \frac{B}{\mu_0}. \text{ Hence At} = \frac{B \cdot l_g}{\mu_0} = \frac{0.15 \times 8 \times 10^{-3}}{4\pi/10^7} = 955 \text{ At/pole}$$

Hence total interpole m.m.f. required $= 2205 + 955 = \underline{3160 \text{ At/pole}}$

(d) From the diagram, a brush axis shift of α produces a demagnetising (or magnetising) m.m.f. of $F_a \times 2\alpha/180$ At/pole. Hence:

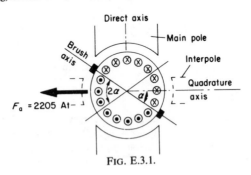

FIG. E.3.1.

42

so:
$$200 = 2205 \times 2\alpha/180$$
$$\alpha = 8.16 \underline{\text{ electrical degrees}}$$
$$= 8.16/p = \underline{4.08 \text{ mechanical degrees}}$$

EXAMPLE 3.2

A d.c. shunt-wound generator rated at 220 V and 40 A armature current has an armature resistance of 0.25 Ω. The shunt field resistance is 110 Ω and there are 2500 turns per pole. Calculate:

(a) the range of external field-circuit resistance necessary to vary the voltage from 220 V on full load to 170 V on no load when the speed is 500 rev/min;

(b) the series-winding m.m.f. required to give a level-compound characteristic at 220 V when running at 500 rev/min;

(c) the maximum voltage on o.c. if the speed is reduced to 250 rev/min and all external field resistance is cut out.

Armature reaction and brush drops may be neglected.

The following open-circuit characteristic was obtained when running at 500 rev/min with the shunt field excited:

E.M.F.	71	133	170	195	220	232 V
Field current	0.25	0.5	0.75	1.0	1.5	2.0 A

ω_m at 500 rev/min = $500 \times 2\pi/60$ = 52.36 rad/s; at 250 rev/min ω_m = 26.18 rad/s.

Hence k_ϕ = e.m.f. (above)/52.36 = 1.36   2.54   3.25   3.72   4.2   4.43

The k_ϕ/I_f curve is plotted on the diagram, F_f being the field current × 2500.

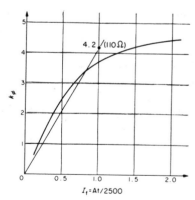

FIG. E.3.2.

43

(a) The e.m.f. must be calculated at the two limits to determine the range of field current and hence of field-circuit resistance variation.

	No load	Full load
$E = V + R \cdot I_a =$	170 V	$220 + 40 \times 0.25 = 230$ V
$k_\phi = E/52.36 =$	3.25	4.39
I_f from curve $=$	0.75	1.86
$R_F = 220/I_f =$	293.3 Ω	118.3 Ω
External field-circuit resistance $= R_F - 110 = $	183.3 Ω	8.3 Ω

(b) The terminal voltage must be 220 V on no load and on full load.

V	$= 220$	220
$E = V + R \cdot I_a$	$= 220$	230
Required k_ϕ at $\omega_m = 52.36$	$= 4.2$	4.39
Field m.m.f. required, from curve	$= 1.5 \times 2500$	1.86×2500
Difference $=$ series m.m.f. required $= (1.86 - 1.5) \times 2500 = $ 840 At/pole		

(c) The open-circuit curve could be redrawn in terms of e.m.f. against field current with the e.m.f. reduced in the ratio 250/500. Alternatively, the k_ϕ curve can be used, since it is the e.m.f. at 250 rev/min scaled down by the divisor 26.18 rad/s. The slope of the resistance line (V/I_f) for 110 Ω must also be reduced, to 110/26.18 ($=4.2$) as shown. The field line intersects the characteristic at a k_ϕ ($=$e.m.f./26.18) of 3.38. Hence the voltage on open circuit— which is the terminal voltage neglecting the very small R_a I_f drop—is $3.38 \times 26.18 = 88.5$ V.

EXAMPLE 3.3

The machine of the last question is to be run as a motor from 220 V. A speed range of 2/1 by field control is required. Again neglecting the effect of armature reaction and brush drop and assuming $I_a = 0$ on no load, calculate:

(a) the range of external field-circuit resistance required, as a shunt motor, to permit speed variation from 500 rev/min on load to 1000 rev/min with the armature carrying its rated current of 40 A;

(b) the value of the series-field ampere turns required to cause the speed to fall by 10% from 500 rev/min on no load, when full-load current is taken;

(c) the speed regulation (no load to 40 A load) with this series winding in circuit and the shunt field set to give 1000 rev/min on no load.

(d) By how much would this series winding increase the torque at 40 A compared with condition (a) at the minimum field setting?

Parts (a) and (b) require calculation of the k_ϕ range to find the excitation needs.

(a)

	$I_a = 0$ A, no load	$I_a = 40$ A
Speed	500	1000 rev/min

	52.36	104.7 rad/s
$E = 220 - 0.25 \times I_a$	220	210 V
$k_\phi = E/\omega_m$	4.2	2.0 Nm/A
I_f from mag. curve	1.5	0.38 A
$R_F = 220/I_f$	146.7	579 Ω
External resistance $= R_F - 110 =$	36.7	469 Ω

(b) Speed

	500	450 rev/min
ω_m	52.36	47.12 rad/s
$E = 220 - 0.25 \times I_a$	220	210 V
$k_\phi = E/\omega_m$	4.2	4.46 Nm/A
Field ampere turns from mag. curve $= 1.5 \times 2500$		2.05×2500

Difference is required series m.m.f. $= (2.05 - 1.5) \times 2500 = \underline{1375 \text{ At/pole}}$

(c) The speed will be obtained from $\omega_m = E/k_\phi$.

On no load, $k_\phi = 220 \text{ V}/104.7 \text{ rad/s} = 2.1$.

From mag. curve this requires $0.4 \text{ A} \times 2500 = 1000 \text{ At/pole}$ shunt excitation.

On load, the total excitation is therefore $1000 + 1375 = 2375$ At/pole.

k_ϕ will therefore correspond to $2375/2500 = 0.95$ A giving: 3.65 N_m/A.

Hence, ω_m on load will be $\dfrac{E}{k_\phi} = \dfrac{210}{3.65} = 57.5 \text{ rad/s} = 549 \text{ rev/min}$

Speed regulation from 1000 rev/min is therefore $\dfrac{1000 - 549}{1000} \times 100 = \underline{45.1\%}$.

Note the great increase from the 500 rev/min condition because of the weak shunt field.

(d) $T_e = k_\phi, I_a$. At minimum field, 1000 rev/min $T_e = 2 \times 40 = 80$ Nm

With additional series excitation $T_e = 3.65 \times 40 = 146$ Nm

So although the speed has fallen considerably, due to the series winding, the electromagnetic torque has increased by $66/80 = \underline{82\%}$ for the same reason and the air-gap power is the same.

EXAMPLE 3.4

In the shunt motor of the last question, the no-load armature current was neglected. In fact, the total no-load input current is 5 A when both field and armature are directly connected across the 220 V supply, the output (coupling) torque being zero, so that the only torque is that due to the friction, windage and iron losses. Calculate the speed, output power and efficiency when the load has increased to demand rated armature current, 40 A.

The no-load condition is shown on the first diagram where it is seen that the armature current is 3 A, the field taking $220/110 = 2$ A.

The value of k_ϕ from the o.c. curve at 2 A is 4.43 Nm/A.

The no-load e.m.f. is $220 - 0.25 \times 3 = 219.25$ V.

Hence speed $\omega_m = E/k_\phi = 219.25/4.43 = 49.49 \text{ rad/s} = 473 \text{ rev/min}$.

The air-gap power $P_{gap} = \omega_m \cdot T_e = E \cdot I_a = 219.25 \times 3 = 658$ watts is consumed in friction, windage and iron losses and corresponds to $T_{loss} = 658/49.49 = 13.3$ Nm.

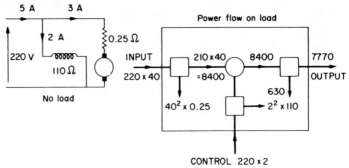

FIG. E.3.4.

For the load condition, with 40 A in the armature, the second diagram is a useful representation of the power flow. The explanation of the numerical values involves a few minor calculations which can be understood by reference back to Fig. 1.10.

Speed $= E/k_\phi = 210/4.43 = 47.4$ rad/s $= \underline{453 \text{ rev/min}}$.
If we neglect any small change in loss torque with this speed fall then
Mechanical loss $= \omega_m \cdot T_{loss} = 47.4 \times 13.3 = 630$ watts.
Output power $= P_{gap} -$ mechanical loss $= 210 \times 40 - 630 = \underline{7.77 \text{ kW}} = 10.4$ hp.
Input power $= 220(40 + 2) = 9.24$ kW so efficiency $= 7.77/9.24 = \underline{84.1\%}$.

EXAMPLE 3.5

In the back-to-back test circuit shown, Machine 1 is a motor driving Machine 2 which is a generator. The generated power is fed back into the common 250-V line

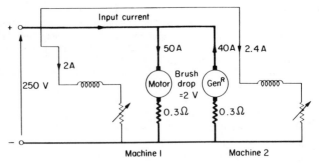

FIG. E.3.5.

46

so that only the machine losses have to be supplied. Currents in various parts of the circuit, together with the resistances, are shown. Allow for brush drop of 2 V total per machine and calculate the efficiency of each machine. It may be assumed that the mechanical losses are the same for both machines.

Input current = 50 − 40 = 10 A.

Input power to armature circuits = 250 × 10 = 2500 watts.

Total machine losses, excluding friction, windage and iron losses = $50^2 × 0.3 + 2 × 50 + 40^2 × 0.3 + 2 × 40 = 1410$ watts.

∴ Total mechanical loss = 2500 − 1410 = 1090 watts = 545 watts per machine

$$\text{Motor efficiency} = \frac{\text{Input} - \text{losses}}{\text{Input}} = 1 - \frac{(50^2 × 0.3) + (2 × 50) + 545 + (250 × 2)}{250(50 + 2)}$$

$$= 1 - \frac{1895}{13000}$$

$$= \underline{85.42\%}$$

$$\text{Generator efficiency} = \frac{\text{Output}}{\text{Output} + \text{losses}}$$

$$= \frac{250 × 40}{(250 × 40) + (40^2 × 0.3) + (2 × 40) + 545 + (250 × 2.4)}$$

$$= \frac{10000}{11705} = \underline{85.43\%}$$

The most convenient expressions to suit the data have been chosen. It is a coincidence that efficiencies are the same. The motor has the higher copper loss and the generator the higher flux and hence field loss and, in practice, a slightly higher iron loss also. But note also that efficiency is a function of output and for the generator this is 10 kW whereas for the motor it is 11.105 kW.

The next few examples illustrate the consequences of changing the machine parameters, sometimes with the object of achieving a certain speed against a specified mechanical load characteristic. This brings in the overall drive viewpoint and the interaction of mechanical and machine speed/torque characteristics. It leads on to the treatment of machine equations in *per-unit* terms which is often helpful in assessing drive characteristics.

EXAMPLE 3.6

A 500-V, 60-hp, 600-rev/min d.c. shunt motor has a full-load efficiency of 90%. The resistance of the field itself is 200 Ω and rated field current is 2 A. $R_a = 0.2\,Ω$. Calculate the full-load (rated) current I_{aR} and in subsequent calculations, maintain this value. Determine the loss torque.

The speed is to be increased up to 1000 rev/min by field weakening. Calculate the extra resistance, over and above the field winding itself to cover the range 600–1000 rev/min. Determine the output torque and power at the top speed, assuming that the loss torque varies in proportion to speed. For the magnetisation curve use the empirical expression below, which is an approximation to the curve shape.

$$\text{Field-current ratio} = \frac{(1-a) \times \text{flux ratio}}{1 - a \times \text{flux ratio}} \text{ with } a = 0.4$$

where the flux ratio is that between a particular operating flux (E/ω_m) and rated flux $(k_{\phi R})$. The field-current ratio is that of the corresponding field currents.

The data are assembled on the figure as a convenient aide-memoire, together with a skeleton power-flow diagram from which:

Full-load efficiency

$$\eta_R = \frac{P_{\text{mech}}}{P_{\text{elec}} + P_{\text{control}}} = \frac{60 \times 746}{500 \times I_{aR} + 500 \times 2} = \frac{90}{100}$$

from which: $I_{aR} = \underline{97.5 \text{ A}}$

Hence: $k_{\phi R} = \dfrac{E_R}{\omega_{mR}} = \dfrac{500 - 0.2 \times 97.5}{20\pi}$ $= 7.65 \text{ Nm/A}$

and: $T_{eR} = k_{\phi R} \cdot I_{aR} = 7.65 \times 97.5$ $= 745.9 \text{ Nm}$

$$T_{\text{coupling}} = \frac{60 \times 746}{20\pi} \qquad = \underline{712.4 \text{ Nm}}$$

$$T_{\text{loss}} = T_{eR} - T_{\text{coupling}} \qquad = \underline{33.5 \text{ Nm}}$$

At 1000 rev/min, $T_{\text{loss}} = 33.5 \times 1000/600$ $= 56 \text{ Nm}$

At 1000 rev/min, $k_\phi = \dfrac{500 - 0.2 \times 97.5}{1000 \times 2\pi/60} = 4.59 \text{ Nm/A}$

∴ flux ratio $= 4.59/7.65 = 0.6$.

Hence, field-current ratio $= \dfrac{I_{f(1000)}}{2 \text{ A}} = \dfrac{0.6 \times 0.6}{1 - 0.4 \times 0.6}$

from which: $I_{f(1000)} = 0.947 \text{ A}$

and: $R_F = 500/0.947 = 528 \text{ }\Omega$ so external resistance $= \underline{328 \text{ }\Omega}$

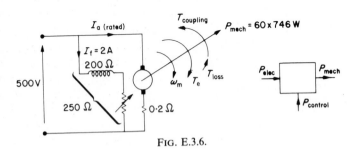

FIG. E.3.6.

48

Coupling torque $= T_e - T_{loss} = 4.59 \times 97.5 - 56 = \underline{392\ Nm}$
Mechanical output power $= \omega_m \cdot T_{coupling} = 104.7 \times 392 = \underline{41\ kW} = 55\ hp$

EXAMPLE 3.7

A 500-V, 500-rev/min d.c. shunt motor has a full-load (rated) armature current of 42 A. $R_a = 0.6\ \Omega$ and $R_f = 500\ \Omega$. It is required to run the machine under the following conditions by inserting a single resistor for each case.
(a) 300 rev/min while operating at rated electromagnetic torque;
(b) 600 rev/min at the same torque;
(c) 800 rev/min while operating at the same gross power ($\omega_m \cdot T_e$) as in condition (b).
For each condition, find the appropriate value of the resistor.
The following magnetisation curve was taken on open circuit at 500 rev/min:

Field current	0.4	0.6	0.8	1.0	1.2 A
Generated e.m.f.	285	375	445	500	540 V

The test speed $\omega_{m(test)}$ $\quad = 500 \times 2\pi/60 = 52.36\ rad/s.$
$k_\phi = E/\omega_{m(test)} = E/52.36 \quad = 5.44 \quad 7.16 \quad 8.5 \quad 9.56 \quad 10.3\ Nm/A$

$$\text{Rated } k_\phi (k_{\phi R}) = \frac{V_R - R \cdot I_{aR}}{\omega_{mR}} = \frac{500 - 0.6 \times 42}{52.36} = 9.07\ Nm/A$$

Rated $T_e(T_{eR}) = k_{\phi R} \cdot I_{aR} = 9.07 \times 42 = 381\ Nm.$
Rated field current from curve at $k_\phi = 9.07$, is 0.9 A $\therefore R_F = 500/0.9 = 555\ \Omega$

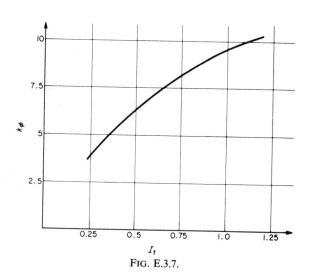

FIG. E.3.7.

Now consider the speed/torque equation (3.8): $\omega_m = \dfrac{V}{k_\phi} - \dfrac{R \cdot T_e}{k_\phi^2}$

It can be seen that at a fixed terminal voltage V, any increase of speed beyond the rated value can only be obtained by reduction of flux; i.e. by inserting extra resistance in the field circuit. A reduction of speed, without exceeding the flux limit imposed by saturation, can only be obtained by operating on the second term—in practice this means increasing R since reduction of k_ϕ would give rise to excessive armature currents unless R is relatively high—see Reference 1 and speed/flux curves of Example 3.12.

Hence, for (a), rearranging the equation: $R = \dfrac{(V - k_\phi \cdot \omega_m)}{T_e / k_\phi} \left(= \dfrac{V - E}{I_a} \right)$

Since $\omega_m = 300 \times 2\pi/60 = 10\pi$, $\quad R = \dfrac{500 - 9.07 \times 10\pi}{381/9.07}$

$$= 5.12\,\Omega, \text{ an extra } 5.12 - 0.6 = \underline{4.52\,\Omega}$$

For (b) we require k_ϕ, not knowing the armature current and hence eqn (3.10) will have to be used. At 600 rev/min $\omega_m = 20\pi$ so:

$$k_\phi = \frac{V + \sqrt{V^2 - 4 \times R \times \omega_m \times T_e}}{2\omega_m} = \frac{500 + \sqrt{500^2 - 4 \times 0.6 \times 20\pi \times 381}}{2 \times 20\pi}$$

$$= 7.47\ \text{Nm/A}$$

From the magnetisation curve, this requires $I_f = 0.64$ A and $R_F = 500/0.64 = 781\,\Omega$. Hence extra field-circuit resistance is $781 - 555 = \underline{226\,\Omega}$

For (c), since the same $\omega_m T_e$ product is specified, the only difference in the k_ϕ equation above is to the denominator which becomes $2 \times 800 \times 2\pi/60 = 167.6$.

k_ϕ is therefore 5.602 requiring an I_f of 0.41 A and $R_F = 500/0.41 = 1219\,\Omega$.

$\therefore$ extra resistance is $1219 - 555 = \underline{664\,\Omega}$

EXAMPLE 3.8

A 220-V, 1000-rev/min, 10-hp, d.c. shunt motor has an efficiency of 85% at this rated, full-load condition. The total field-circuit resistance is then $100\,\Omega$ and $R_a = 0.4\,\Omega$. Calculate the rated values of current, flux and electromagnetic torque; (I_{aR}, $k_{\phi R}$ and T_{eR}). Express your answers to the following questions in *per unit* where appropriate by dividing them by these reference or base values, which are taken as 1 *per unit*. Take 220 V (V_R) as 1 *per unit* voltage.

(a) Find the applied voltage to give half rated speed if T_m is proportional to ω_m^2; k_ϕ and R_a unchanged.

(b) Find the extra armature-circuit resistance to give half rated speed if T_m is proportional to speed; k_ϕ and V being 1 *per unit*.

(c) Find the *per-unit* flux to give 2000 rev/min and the armature current if $V = 1$ *per unit* and R_a is the normal value.

(d) What electromagnetic torque is developed if the voltage, flux and speed are at half the rated values and there is an extra $2\,\Omega$ in the armature circuit?

50

The data could usefully be assembled on a diagram as for Example 3.6. Referring also to the associated power-flow diagram:

$$\text{Motor efficiency } \eta_R = \frac{P_{mech}}{P_{elec} + P_{control}}$$

$$0.85 = \frac{10 \times 746}{220 \times I_{aR} + 220^2/100}$$

from which: $I_{aR} = \underline{37.7 \text{ A}}$.

Hence: $k_{\phi R} = \dfrac{220 - 0.4 \times 37.7}{1000 \times 2\pi/60} = \underline{1.957}$ and therefore $T_{eR} = 1.957 \times 37.7 = \underline{73.8 \text{ Nm}}$

The remaining questions can all be answered from the speed/torque equation:

$$\omega_m = \frac{V}{k_\phi} - \frac{R \cdot T_e}{k_\phi^2} \text{ where } T_e = T_m \text{ on steady state.}$$

(a) At half speed, $\omega_m = 52.36$ rad/s and $T_m = (\tfrac{1}{2})^2 \times 73.8$

From the equation: $V = k_\phi \cdot \omega_m + \dfrac{R \cdot T_m}{k_\phi} = 1.957 \times 52.36 + \dfrac{0.4}{1.957} \times \dfrac{73.8}{4}$
$$= 106.2 \text{ V} = \underline{0.48 \text{ per unit}}$$

(b) A different mechanical characteristic applies so $T_m = \tfrac{1}{2} \times 73.8 = 36.9$ Nm

From the equation: $R = \dfrac{V - k_\phi \cdot \omega_m}{T_e/k_\phi} \left(= \dfrac{V - E}{I_a} \right) = \dfrac{220 - 1.957 \times 52.36}{36.9/1.957}$
$$= 6.23 \ \Omega. \text{ i.e. an extra } 6.23 - 0.4 = \underline{5.83 \ \Omega}$$

(c) $k_\phi = \dfrac{V + \sqrt{V^2 - 4 \cdot R \cdot \omega_m \cdot T_m}}{2\omega_m} = \dfrac{220 + \sqrt{220^2 - 4 \times 0.4 \times 104.7 \times 73.8}}{2 \times 2000 \times 2\pi/60}$
$$= 0.9784 \text{ Nm/A} = 0.9784/1.957 = \underline{0.5 \text{ per unit}}$$

Note that rated power and speed have been used under the radical because for this mechanical load, the power is stated to be constant. Check $I_a = I_{aR}$.

(d) $T_e = k_\phi \cdot \dfrac{(V - k_\phi \cdot \omega_m)}{R} = \dfrac{1.957}{2} \dfrac{(110 - 0.978 \times 52.36)}{2 + 0.4} = 24$ Nm
$$= 24/73.8 = \underline{0.325 \text{ per unit}}$$

and $I_a = 24/0.978 = 24.5$ A

3.3 PER-UNIT NOTATION

The last question introduced the idea of expressing quantities in *per-unit*, i.e. as fractions of some base or reference quantity. It is possible to solve the question throughout in *per-unit* notation and after the following explanation, it would be a good exercise to try this. The method is sometimes convenient, especially when integrating the mechanical system parameters into the drive and in simplifying scaling factors for computer solutions. For a d.c. machine, with the appropriate choice of base values, the equations, apart from being dimensionless, are the same as those used for actual values as explained in Reference 1. The most convenient base values are:

Rated voltage $V_R = 1$ *per-unit* voltage

Rated current $I_{aR} = 1$ *per-unit* current

Rated flux $k_{\phi R} = 1$ *per-unit* flux

From these:

Rated torque $= k_{\phi R} \cdot I_{aR}$ is also 1 *per-unit* torque

Rated power $= V_R \cdot I_{aR}$ is also 1 *per-unit* power

and 1 *per-unit* resistance $= V_R/I_{aR}$, since only three of the seven practicable quantities, derived from the products and quotients of the first three, can be defined independently. It follows also that 1 *per-unit* speed is predetermined as $V_R/k_{\phi R}$, since these two parameters have been chosen. Therefore rated speed is not 1 *per unit* but:

$$\frac{E_R}{k_{\phi R}} = \frac{V_R - R \cdot I_{aR}}{k_{\phi R}} = \frac{1 - R \times 1}{1} = 1 - R \ per \ unit.$$

Per-unit resistance is:

$$\frac{\text{ohmic value}}{\text{base value}} = \frac{R}{V_R/I_{aR}} = \frac{R \cdot I_{aR}}{V_R},$$

which is the fraction of base voltage, which is absorbed across the armature-circuit resistance at base current.

In the following example, the field current is also expressed in *per unit* using the same empirical expression as in Example 3.6.

EXAMPLE 3.9

A d.c. shunt motor runs at 1000 rev/min when supplied from rated voltage, at rated flux and drives a total mechanical load, including the loss torque, which has coulomb friction, viscous friction and square-law components given by the following expression:

$$T_m = 30 + 30\left(\frac{rev/min}{1000}\right) + 30\left(\frac{rev/min}{1000}\right)^2 Nm$$

The armature resistance is 0.06 *per-unit* and the magnetisation curve can be approximated by the empirical expression:

$$I_f \text{ per unit} = \frac{0.6 \times \phi \text{ per unit}}{1 - 0.4 \times \phi \text{ per unit}}$$

Calculate:

(a) The values of 1 *per-unit* torque in Nm and 1 *per-unit* speed in rev/min;

(b) the required I_f and the value of I_a in *per unit*, if the speed is to be 600 rev/min with the terminal voltage set at 0.5 *per unit*;

(c) the required I_f and the value of I_a in *per unit* when the terminal voltage is set at the rated value and the speed is adjusted to (i) 1200 rev/min; (ii) 0.8 *per unit*;

(d) the required terminal voltage in *per unit* if the resistance is increased to 0.2 *per unit*, the field current is reduced to 0.6 *per unit* and the speed is to be set at the rated value.

In this comprehensive question, since the non-linear $T_m = f(\omega_m)$ relationship is given and $T_e = T_m$ in the steady state, then T_e follows if the speed is specified and conversely, any particular torque will correspond to a particular speed. Thereafter, the solution is just applying the various equations developed at the beginning of this chapter. The quadratic expression for I_a must be used because the power is given, not the value of e.m.f. or flux.

(a) 1 *per unit* torque, from the question, must occur at a speed of 1000 rev/min

viz. $$30\left(1 + \frac{1000}{1000} + \frac{1000^2}{1000^2}\right) = \underline{90\,Nm}$$

Rated speed = 1 − R *per unit* is 1000 rev/min.

$$\therefore 1 \text{ *per unit* speed} = \frac{1000}{1 - 0.06} = \underline{1064\,rev/min}$$

53

Preliminary calculation of $T_e (= T_m)$ at stated speeds:

Part	Rev/min	p.u. speed $= \dfrac{\text{rev/min}}{1064}$	Torque, Nm	p.u. torque $= \dfrac{T_m}{90}$
	1064	1		1
(d)	1000	0.94	90	1
(b)	600	0.564	$30(1 + 0.6 + 0.6^2) = 58.8$	0.653
(c)(i)	1200	1.128	$30(1 + 1.2 + 1.2^2) = 109.2$	1.213
(c)(ii)	851	0.8	$30(1 + 0.851 + 0.851^2) = 77.3$	0.858

Calculations for parts:	(b)	(c)(i)	(c)(ii)
ω_m	0.564	1.128	0.8
T_e	0.653	1.213	0.858
Power $= \omega_m T_e$	0.368	1.368	0.686
$X = V^2 - 4R \cdot \omega_m T_e$	$0.5^2 - 0.24 \times 0.368$ $= 0.1616$	$1^2 - 0.24 \times 1.368$ $= 0.6716$	$1^2 - 0.24 \times 0.686$ $= 0.835$
$I_a = \dfrac{V - \sqrt{X}}{2R}$	0.8166	1.504	0.717
$k_\phi = T_e / I_a$	0.8	0.807	1.196
$I_f = \dfrac{0.6 k_\phi}{1 - 0.4 k_\phi}$	0.706	0.715	1.376

(d) The field current is set at 0.6 *per unit* $= \dfrac{0.6 k_\phi}{1 - 0.4 k_\phi}$ hence $k_\phi = 0.714$

The speed is to be the rated value (0.94 *per unit*)
The torque will therefore be 1 *per unit*.
Hence $I_a = T_e / k_\phi = 1/0.714 = 1.4$ *per unit*
Required $V = k_\phi \cdot \omega_m + R \cdot I_a = 0.714 \times 0.94 + 0.2 \times 1.4 = \underline{0.951 \; per \; unit}$

Note that the answers to part (c) show that field control of speed is not satisfactory with this mechanical load because the armature current becomes excessive at high speeds and the field current is excessive at speeds lower than rated. Part (d) shows a similar situation.

EXAMPLE 3.10

A d.c. shunt motor is being considered as a drive for different mechanical loads having the following characteristics: (a) Constant power ($\omega_m T_m$); (b) constant torque and (c) torque proportional to speed. It is desired to know the effects on armature current and speed of making various changes on the electrical side. Taking as a basis that rated voltage, rated armature current and field current give rated speed and torque, express armature current and speed in *per unit* when the following changes are made:

(i)   field current reduced to give half flux;
(ii) armature supply-voltage halved;
(iii) armature voltage and field flux both halved.

Consider loads (a), (b) and (c) in turn and neglect all machine losses.

The required equations for current and speed are: $I_a = T_e/k_\phi$ and $\omega_m = V/k_\phi$ and all calculations are in *per unit*.

Mechanical load characteristic	(a) $\omega_m T_m$ const. i.e. $T_m \alpha 1/\omega_m$	T_m const. (b)	$T_m \alpha$ speed (c)
(i) $k_\phi = 0.5$; $V = 1$.			
$\omega_m = V/k_\phi$	2	2	2
$T_e = T_m$	0.5	1	2
$I_a = T_e/k_\phi$	1	2	4
(ii) $V = 0.5$; $k_\phi = 1$.			
ω_m	0.5	0.5	0.5
T_m	2	1	0.5
I_a	2	1	0.5
(iii) $V = 0.5$; $k_\phi = 0.5$			
ω_m	1	1	1
T_m	1	1	1
I_a	2	2	2

Again, this example shows, in a simple manner, what is, and what is not a feasible strategy in the control of d.c. machines and how the nature of the mechanical load determines this; one armature-current overload is as high as four times the rated value.

EXAMPLE 3.11

A d.c. motor has a *per-unit* resistance of 0.05. Determine the two values of current and of flux at which rated torque can be developed at rated speed when supplied from rated voltage.

$$I_a = \frac{V \mp \sqrt{V^2 - 4R \cdot \omega_m \cdot T_e}}{2R} = \frac{1 \mp \sqrt{1^2 - 4 \times 0.05 \times (1 - 0.05) \times 1}}{2 \times 0.05}$$

$$= \frac{1 \mp \sqrt{0.81}}{0.1} = \underline{1 \text{ per unit}} \text{ or } \underline{19 \text{ per unit}}$$

The numerator is the same for $k_\phi = \dfrac{1 \pm \sqrt{0.81}}{2 \times (1 - 0.05)} = \underline{1 \text{ per unit}}$ or $\underline{\dfrac{1}{19} \text{ per unit}}$

Clearly, the only practical solution is the first one with $k_\phi = I_a = 1$ *per unit*, even though the same torque of 1 *per unit* is given by the second solution. This is a relatively low-resistance machine. The next example shows the effect of an increased armature-circuit resistance, when, as on some small servo motors and with "constant" current supplies, speed increase is obtained by increasing the field current, working on the rising part of the speed/flux characteristic; see Reference 1.

EXAMPLE 3.12

For a separately excited d.c. motor which at rated voltage, flux and armature current delivers rated torque at rated speed $(1 - R_a)$ *per unit*, show that the maximum speed which can be obtained by field weakening is:

(a) $V^2/4R$ *per-unit* for a constant-torque load equal to rated torque and:

(b) $V \times \sqrt{(1 - R_a)/4R}$ *per-unit* if rated torque is the same, but is proportional to speed and the circuit resistance is R which is not necessarily equal to R_a.

(c) Calculate for resistances of $R_a = 0.05$ and for $R = 0.5$, the values of ω_{max} in *per unit* and the values of armature current and flux at this speed, for the constant-torque load. Repeat the calculation, but this time for the case of load torque proportional to speed.

(d) For the same motor determine the required circuit resistance to permit continuous speed increase by field increase up to rated flux with rated voltage applied. Consider both mechanical load-characteristics as before.

(a) For the constant-torque load, $T_m = 1$ and the equation is $\omega_m = \dfrac{V}{k_\phi} - \dfrac{R}{k_\phi^2}$

$$\frac{d\omega_m}{dk_\phi} = -\frac{V}{k_\phi^2} + 2 \times \frac{R}{k_\phi^3}$$

and for maximum speed, this must be zero; i.e. $V = 2R/k_\phi$ or $k_\phi = 2R/V$. Substituting in the speed equation:

$$\omega_{max} = \frac{V^2}{2R} - \frac{V^2}{4R} = \frac{V^2}{4R}.$$

(b) For the case of torque proportional to speed, by considering the identical ratios of torque and speed to their rated values:

$$\frac{T_m}{1} = \frac{\omega_m}{\omega_{mR}}; \text{ so } T_m = \frac{\omega_m}{1 - R_a}$$

and substituting in the speed equation:

$$\omega_m = \frac{V}{k_\phi} - \frac{R \times [\omega_m/(1 - R_a)]}{k_\phi^2}$$

and by rearrangement:

$$\omega_m = \frac{k_\phi \cdot V}{k_\phi^2 + \dfrac{R}{1 - R_a}}$$

differentiating:

$$\frac{d\omega_m}{dk_\phi} = -\frac{V \cdot \left(k_\phi^2 + \dfrac{R}{1 - R_a}\right) - k_\phi \cdot V \cdot (2k_\phi)}{(\text{denominator})^2}$$

and this zero when $k_\phi^2 = R/(1 - R_a)$ and this is the condition for maximum speed. Substituting in the re-formed speed expression for this load;

$$\omega_{max} = \frac{V \sqrt{\left(\dfrac{R}{1 - R_a}\right)}}{\dfrac{R}{1 - R_a} + \dfrac{R}{1 - R_a}}$$

so

$$\omega_{max} = V \cdot \sqrt{\frac{1 - R_a}{4R}}$$

Before dealing with the numerical part of this question, it is worth noting that the point of maximum speed is the changeover between the rising and falling parts of the speed/flux characteristic. If this changeover is required to occur at rated flux, so that speed increase by increasing flux can be obtained, the expression for k_ϕ to give ω_{max} will also yield the required resistance to meet this condition; by substituting $k_\phi = 1$. For the constant-torque load, required $R = V/2$ and for $T_m \alpha \omega_m$, $R = 1 - R_a$. This information is relevant to the final

57

part (d) of the question but generally, it will be found that at ω_{max}, $E = k_\phi\omega_{max} = V/2$; i.e., for maximum speed the apparent "load" resistance, E/I_a, is equal to the source (series), resistance $(V/2)/I_a$, cf. maximum power-transfer theorem.

(c) *Numerical solution*

		T_m constant			$T_m \; \alpha \; \omega_m$		
		$R = 0.05$	$R = 0.5$			$R = 0.05$	$R = 0.5$
Speed at rated torque $= (1-R)$		0.95	0.5			0.95	0.5
ω_{max}	$\dfrac{V^2}{4R} =$	5	0.5	$V\sqrt{\dfrac{1-R_a}{4R}} =$		2.18	0.689
T_m at ω_{max}		1	1	$\dfrac{\omega_{max}}{1-R_a} =$		2.29	0.725
Power $= \omega_{max}T_m$		5	0.5			5	0.5
$\sqrt{1-4R} \times$ Power		0	0			0	0
$I_a = \dfrac{1 \mp \sqrt{}}{2R}$		10	1			10	1
$k_\phi = \dfrac{1 \pm \sqrt{}}{2\omega_{max}}$		0.1	1			0.229	0.725
$T_e = k_\phi \cdot I_a = T_m$		1	1			2.29	0.725

The above results are shown in outline on the accompanying speed/torque and speed/flux curves. It can be seen that the high-resistance circuit keeps the current and speed within rated limits though the power and the speed and/or torque cannot reach rated values. The zero for the square-root term confirms that the maximum conditions have been reached, with only one solution for I_a and k_ϕ.

In the solution of the final part of the question, maximum speed ω_{max} will be reached at maximum flux by suitable adjustment of the resistance. The solution is also shown on the accompanying diagram.

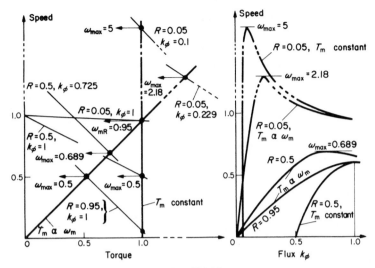

FIG. E.3.12.

(d) For constant-torque load, required resistance for continuous increase of speed
with flux $= V/2 = 0.5$ *per unit* for rated voltage. The solution has already been
covered above.

For the case of $T_m \propto \omega_m$, the required resistance is $1 - R_a = 1 - 0.05 = 0.95$ *per
unit*, see below.

$\omega_{max} = V\sqrt{\dfrac{1-R_a}{4R}}$ $= \sqrt{(1-0.05)/(4 \times 0.95)}$		$= 0.5$
T_m at this speed $= \omega_{max}/(1-R_a) = 0.5/(0.95)$		$= 0.526$
Power $= \omega_{max} \cdot T_m = 0.526 \times 0.5$		$= 0.263$
$\sqrt{1 - 4R \times \text{Power}} = 1 - 4 \times 0.95 \times 0.526$		$= 0$
$\therefore I_a = 1/2R$ $= 1/1.9$		$= 0.526$
$k_\phi = 1/2\omega_{max}$ $= 1/(2 \times 0.5)$		$= 1$
$T_e = k_\phi \cdot I_a = T_m$ $= 1 \times 0.526$		$= 0.526$

3.4 SERIES MOTORS

The special characteristics of the series motor make it suitable for many applications requiring high overload-torque per ampere as in traction, together with its falling speed/torque curve limiting the power demand, this being suitable also for crane and fan drives with simple resistance control of the characteristic. Two examples neglecting saturation will be followed by calculations of speed/torque curves allowing for the non-linearities due to armature reaction, saturation and the mechanical load.

EXAMPLE 3.13

A 220-V d.c. series motor runs at 700 rev/min when operating at its full-load current of 20 A. The motor resistance is 0.5 Ω and it may be assumed unsaturated. What will be the speed if:

    (a) the load torque is increased by 44%?

    (b) the motor current is 10 A?

Speed is given by $E/k_\phi = (V - RI_a)/k_\phi$ and for the series machine, neglecting saturation $k_\phi \propto I_a$ since $I_a = I_f$. Hence, $T_e = k_\phi \cdot I_a \propto I_a^2$.

If the torque is increased to 1.44, this will be achieved by an increase of current by a factor of $\sqrt{1.44} = 1.2$. The same increase of flux will occur.

Thus $\quad \dfrac{\omega_{m1}}{\omega_{m2}} = \dfrac{E_1}{E_2} \cdot \dfrac{k_{\phi 2}}{k_{\phi 1}} = \dfrac{220 - 0.5 \times 20}{220 - 0.5 \times (20 \times 1.2)} \times \dfrac{1.2}{1} = 1.212$

$$\therefore \text{ new speed} = 700/1.212 = 578 \text{ rev/min}$$

For a current of 10 A: $\dfrac{\omega_{m1}}{\omega_{m2}} = \dfrac{220 - 0.5 \times 20}{220 - 0.5 \times 10} \times \dfrac{10}{20} = 0.488$

$$\therefore \text{ new speed} = 700/0.488 = 1433 \text{ rev/min}$$

EXAMPLE 3.14

A d.c. series motor has a *per-unit* resistance of 0.05 based on rated voltage, rated current and rated flux as reference quantities. Assuming the machine is unsaturated, i.e. k_ϕ in *per unit* $= I_a$ in *per unit*, calculate:

    (a) The *per-unit* speed and current when the torque is 0.5 *p.u.*

    (b) The *per-unit* speed and torque when the current is 0.5 *p.u.*

    (c) The *per-unit* current and torque when the speed is 0.5 *p.u.*

(a) Since torque $= k_\phi \cdot I_a$ and the machine is unsaturated, torque in *per unit* $= I_a^2$

Hence $I_a^2 = 0.5$ so $I_a = \underline{0.707}$

$$\omega_m = \frac{E}{k_\phi} = \frac{1 - 0.05 \times 0.707}{0.707} = \underline{1.36}$$

(b) $I_a = 0.5$ so $T_e = 0.5^2 = \underline{0.25}$

$$\omega_m = \frac{E}{k_\phi} = \frac{1 - 0.05 \times 0.5}{0.5} = \underline{1.95}$$

(c) $I_a = \dfrac{V - E}{R} = \dfrac{V - k_\phi \cdot \omega_m}{R}$ and since $k_\phi = I_a$:

$$I_a = \frac{1 - I_a \times 0.5}{0.05} \text{ from which } I_a = \underline{1.82}$$

$$T_e = I_a^2 = 1.82^2 = \underline{3.3}$$

Series Machine Speed/torque Curves

To allow for non-linearities in the magnetic circuit, these curves must be worked out point by point. The general method is to get expressions for E, I_a and k_ϕ as $f(I_f)$. Hence, for any particular value of I_f, $\omega_m = E/k_\phi$ and $T_e = k_\phi \cdot I_a$.

The magnetisation curve necessary to determine the k_ϕ/I_f relationship can readily be obtained—with allowance for armature reaction included—by loading the machine as a motor, with provision for varying the terminal voltage whilst the speed is held constant, preferably by adjusting the mechanical load. Alternatively, if the series field can be separately excited and the machine is loaded as a generator, the same information can be obtained if the armature current is maintained at the same value as the field current, as this is increased. Hence $E_{\text{test}} = V \pm R \cdot I_a$ and k_ϕ at each value of I_f is $E_{\text{test}}/\omega_{\text{test}}$, where $\omega_{\text{test}} = (2\pi/60) \times \text{test rev/min}$. A test on open-circuit would not of course include armature reaction effects but would be a good approximation to the true curve. In the following examples, for convenience, the magnetisation curve data are given at the end of the question and the k_ϕ/I_f curve is derived at the beginning of the solution.

EXAMPLE 3.15

A 250-V d.c. series motor has an armature-circuit resistance $R_a = 1.2\,\Omega$. Plot its speed/torque and speed/power curves from the following data and determine the torque and mechanical power developed at 600 rev/min. Also calculate the value of additional series resistance to limit the starting torque at full voltage to 120 Nm. The following magnetisation curve was taken when running as a motor from a variable terminal voltage and rotating at a constant speed of 500 rev/min.

Terminal voltage	114	164	205	237	259	278	V
Field current	8	12	16	20	24	28	A

Test speed $\omega_{test} = 500 \times 2\pi/60 = 52.36$ rad/s

$E_{test} = V - 1.2I_f$	104.4	149.6	185.8	213	230.2	244.4	V
$k_\phi = E_{test}/\omega_{test}$	2	2.86	3.55	4.07	4.4	4.67	Nm/A

Having determined the $k_\phi = f(I_f)$ characteristic, speed and torque will be calculated for the specified terminal voltage. The e.m.f. will be $250 - 1.2I_f$ and $I_a = I_f$.

E	240.4	235.6	230.8	226	221.2	216.4	V
$\omega_m = E/k_\phi$	120.2	82.4	65	55.5	50.3	46.3	rad/s
$N = \omega_m \times 60/2\pi$	1148	787	621	530	480	442	rev/min
$T_e = k_\phi \cdot I_f$	16	34.3	56.8	81.4	105.6	130.8	Nm
Power $= \omega_m \cdot T_e$	1.93	2.83	3.7	4.52	5.31	6.06	kW

Speed/torque and speed/power curves are plotted from the above results. At 600 rev/min:

$$\text{Torque} = \underline{63\ Nm} \text{ and Power} = \underline{3.8\ kW}$$

For the second part of the question, it will be necessary to plot the T_e/I_a curve noting that any particular value of T_e occurs at a unique value of I_a. These data are available in the above table and from the curve at 120 Nm, $I_a = 26.3$ A. Hence, the required series resistance to limit and starting current to this value at full voltage, with e.m.f. zero $= 250/26.3 = 9.51\,\Omega$, an extra $9.51 - 1.2 = \underline{8.31\,\Omega}$.

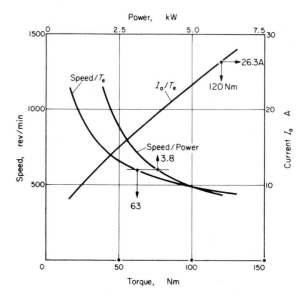

FIG. E.3.15.

EXAMPLE 3.16

A d.c. series motor has an armature resistance of 0.08 Ω and the field resistance is the same value.

(a) Find the speed at which a torque of 475 Nm will be developed when supplied at 250 V.

(b) The motor is driving a hoist and the load can "overhaul" the motor so that its speed can be reversed to operate in the positive-torque, negative-speed quadrant. How much external armature-circuit resistance will be necessary to hold the speed at −400 rev/min when the torque is 475 Nm? Note that this will demand a current of the same value as in (a), but the e.m.f. is now reversed, supporting current flow; the machine is generating and the total resistance is absorbing $V + E$ volts. Calculate and draw the speed/torque curve to check that the chosen resistance is correct.

The magnetisation curve was taken by running the machine as a separately-excited generator, field and armature currents being adjusted together to the same value. The following readings were obtained at a constant test speed of 400 rev/min:

63

Terminal voltage	114	179	218	244	254	V
Field current	30	50	70	90	110	A

$\omega_{test} = 400 \times 2\pi/60 = 41.89$ rad/s. $E_{test} = V + 0.08\, I_f$ ($I_a = I_f$ but field is not in series)

E_{test}	116.4	183	223.6	251.2	262.8	
$k_\phi = E_{test}/41.89$	2.79	4.37	5.34	6	6.27	Nm/A
$T_e = k_\phi \cdot I_a = k_\phi \cdot I_f$	83.7	218.5	373.8	540	689.7	Nm

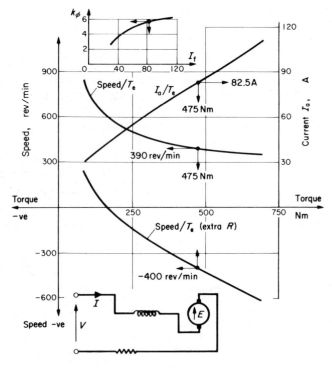

FIG. E.3.16.

64

(a)

$E = 250-0.16I_f$	245.2	242	238.8	235.6	232.4	V
$\omega_m = E/k_\phi$	87.9	55.4	44.7	39.3	37.1	Rad/s
$N = \omega_m \times 60/2\pi$	839	529	427	375	354	rev/min

Speed/torque and T_e/I_a curves are plotted from the above table. At a torque of 475 Nm, the speed is 390 rev/min and a current of $I_a = 82.5$ A is taken.

(b) When overhauling, the circuit conditions are as shown on the graph with E reversed, but using the motoring convention, E is still calculated from: $E = V - RI_a$ and will be negative.

From the k_ϕ/I_f curve at 82.5 A, $k_\phi = 5.78$.

$$E = k_\phi \cdot \omega_m = 5.78 \times (-400) \times 2\pi/60 = -242 \text{ V}$$

so $\qquad -242 = 250 - 82.5R$, from which $R = 5.96$; an extra 5.8 Ω.

For the above field currents in the table, the torque will be the same but the e.m.f. is now $250 - 5.96I_f$ and this permits the new speed points to be found:

E	71.2	−48	−167.2	−286.4	−405.6	V
$\omega_m = E/k_\phi$	25.5	−11	−31.3	−47.7	−64.7	rad/s
N	244	−105	−299	−456	−618	rev/min

From the plotted curve, the speed at 475 Nm is in fact −400 rev/min. Note that the machine is really operating in a braking mode, the machine is generating but the circuit as a whole is dissipative. The mode will be met again in Examples 3.19, 4.7, and 6.7.

EXAMPLE 3.17

For the same machine as in Example 3.15, calculate the speed/torque curves for the following circuit conditions, the supply voltage being 250 V throughout:

(a) with a 5Ω series resistor and a 10 Ω diverter resistor across the machine terminals;

(b) with a 5 Ω series resistor and with the 10 Ω diverter across the armature terminals only;

(c) with a single resistor of 1.8 Ω, diverting current from the field winding;

65

(d) without diverters but with the series winding tapped at 75% of the full series turns. Allow for the reduced circuit resistance.

These circuits are all used in practice, to change the characteristic for various control purposes, but the problem is also a good exercise in simple circuit theory. The various configurations are shown on the figure below together with the derivations of the required equations relating E and I_a to the field current I_f, which is not always the same as I_a. The magnetisation data are transferred from Example 3.15.

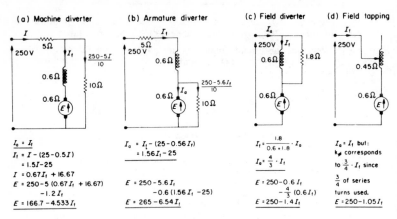

(a) Machine diverter

$$I_a = I_f$$
$$I_f = I - (25 - 0.5I)$$
$$= 1.5I - 25$$
$$I = 0.67I_f + 16.67$$
$$E = 250 - 5(0.67I_f + 16.67)$$
$$-1.2I_f$$
$$E = 166.7 - 4.533I_f$$

(b) Armature diverter

$$I_a = I_f - (25 - 0.56I_f)$$
$$= 1.56I_f - 25$$

$$E = 250 - 5.6I_f$$
$$-0.6(1.56I_f - 25)$$
$$E = 265 - 6.54I_f$$

(c) Field diverter

$$I_f = \frac{1.8}{0.6 + 1.8} \cdot I_a$$
$$I_a = \frac{4}{3} \cdot I_f$$
$$E = 250 - 0.6I_f$$
$$-\frac{4}{3}(0.6I_f)$$
$$E = 250 - 1.4I_f$$

(d) Field tapping

$I_a = I_f$ but:
k_ϕ corresponds
to $\frac{3}{4} \cdot I_f$ since
$\frac{3}{4}$ of series
turns used.
$$E = 250 - 1.05I_f$$

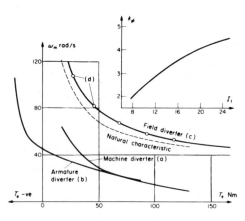

Fig. E.3.17.

66

Field current	8	12	16	20	24	28	A
k_ϕ	2	2.86	3.55	4.07	4.4	4.67	Nm/A
(a) $E = 166.7 - 4.533I_f$	130.4	112.3	94.1	76	57.9	39.7	V
$\omega_m = E/k_\phi$	65.2	39.3	26.5	18.7	13.2	8.5	rad/s
$T_e = k_\phi \cdot I_f$	16	34.3	56.8	81.4	105.6	130.8	Nm
(b) $I_a = 1.57I_f - 25$	-12.5	-6.3	-0.04	6.2	12.4	18.7	A
$E = 265 - 6.54I_f$	212.7	186.5	160.4	134.2	108	81.9	V
ω_m	106	65.2	45.1	33	24.6	17.5	rad/s
$T_e = k_\phi \cdot I_a$	-25	-18	-0.1	25.2	54.6	87.3	Nm
(c) $I_a = 1.333I_f$	10.7	16	21.3	26.7	32	37.3	A
$E = 250 - 1.4I_f$	238.8	233.2	227.6	222	216.4	210.8	V
ω_m	119.4	81.5	64.1	54.5	49.1	45.1	rad/s
T_e	21.4	45.8	75.6	108.7	140.8	174.2	Nm
(d) k_ϕ at $I_f \times 3/4$		2.2	2.86	3.4	3.85	4.15	Nm/A
$E = 250 - 1.05I_f$		237.4	233.2	229	224.8	220.6	V
ω_m		108	81.5	67.4	58.4	53.2	rad/s
T_e		26.4	45.8	68	92.4	116.2	Nm

The four characteristics are plotted on the graph, together with the natural characteristic from Example 3.15. Curve (d) lies on top of curve (c) since in each case, the series m.m.f. is reduced to 3/4 of the normal value and the resistance drop across the field terminals is the same. For a given armature current, the speed is higher and the torque is lower than with the natural characteristic. Curves (a) and (b) give a lower speed for a given torque and for the armature diverter, there is a finite no-load speed as it crosses into the regenerative region. Rapid braking from the natural characteristic to curve (b) is therefore possible.

EXAMPLE 3.18

A 500-V d.c. series motor has an armature circuit resistance of 0.8 Ω. The motor drives a fan, the total mechanical torque being given by the expression:

$$T_m = 10 + \frac{(\text{rev/min})^2}{2250} \text{ lbf ft.}$$

Plot the speed/torque curves and hence find the steady-state speed and torque under the following conditions:

(a) when an external starting resistance, used to limit the starting current to 60A at full voltage, is left in circuit;

(b) when all the external resistance is cut out;

(c) when only 2/3 of the series winding turns are used, a field tapping being provided at this point in the winding. The armature-circuit resistance may be considered unchanged at 0.8 Ω.

67

The magnetisation curve at 550 rev/min is as follows:

Field current	20	30	45	55	60		A
Generated e.m.f.	309	406	489	521	534	554	V

Test speed $\omega_{test} = 550 \times 2\pi/60 = 57.6$ rad/s.
Required starting resistance for 60 A = 500/60 = 8.33 Ω; i.e. 8.33 − 0.8 = 7.53 Ω extra.

k_ϕ = gen. e.m.f./57.6	5.36	7.05	8.49	9.05	9.27	9.46 Nm/A

For case (a) $I_a = I_f$ and $E = 500 - 8.33I_f$
For case (b) and (c) $I_a = I_f$ and $E = 500 - 0.8I_f$
But for (c), the value of k_ϕ must be reduced to that corresponding to $2/3I_f$.
Hence, for the various operating conditions:

(a) $E = 500 - 8.33I_f$	333.4	250.00	125.1	41.85	0.2	− 62.3	V
$\omega_m = E/k_\phi$	62.2	35.47	13.82	4.62	0.02	− 6.58	rad/s
$N = \omega_m \times 60/2\pi$	594	339	141	44	0.2	− 63	rev/min
T_e for (a) and (b)	107	212	382	498	556	639	Nm

(b) $E = 500 - 0.8I_f$	484	476	464	456	452	446	V
ω_m	90.3	67.5	54.7	50.4	48.8	47.1	rad/s
N	862	645	522	481	466	450	rev/min

(c) k_ϕ at $2/3I_f$		5.36	7.05			8.49	Nm/A
$T_e = k_\phi \cdot I_a$		161	317			573	Nm
$\omega_m = E(b)/k_\phi$		88.8	65.8			52.5	rad/s
N		848	628			502	rev/min

The mechanical load characteristic is given in lbf ft and the conversion factor to Nm is 746/550. It is a straightforward matter now to plot T_m in Nm for the

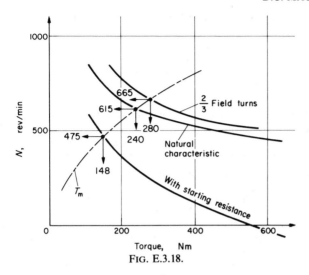

FIG. E.3.18.

converted expression: $T_m = 13.6 + (\text{rev/min})^2/1659$ Nm and this has been done along with the speed/T_e curves from the above table. The intersections of the T_m and T_e curves give the steady-state points as:

(a) 475 rev/min, 148 Nm; (b) 615 rev/min, 240 Nm; (c) 665 rev/min, 280 Nm.

3.5 BRAKING CIRCUITS

If when motoring, the circuit conditions are so changed that current I_a (or flux k_ϕ) reverses polarity, the torque T_e will reverse. Being then in the same sense as T_m, which opposes rotation, the speed will fall, T_m being assisted by this electrical braking action. Depending on the circuit and the nature of T_m, the rotation may reverse after falling to zero, to run up again as a motor in this changed direction. Reversal of flux is sometimes employed with certain power-electronic drives but the time constant for ϕ is relatively long by comparison with the armature-current time-constant. Further, since I_a would increase excessively as k_ϕ was

69

reduced for ultimate reversal, armature current must first be zeroed for the reversal period, usually less than a second, and during this "dead time", motor control is lost. Consider the expression for I_a:

$$I_a = \frac{V - E}{R} = \frac{V - k_\phi \omega_m}{R}$$

Reversal of I_a and T_e can be achieved by four different methods:

(1) Increase of $k\phi\omega_m$, the motor becoming a generator pumping power back into the source. This regeneration would only be momentary if k_ϕ was increased, being limited by saturation and the fall of speed. If T_m is an active load, e.g. a vehicle drive, then gravity could cause speed to increase, and be controlled by controlling the regenerated power.

(2) Reversal of V. This would have to include a limiting resistor to control the maximum current. Such reverse-current braking (plugging) is very effective but consumes approximately three times the stored kinetic energy of the system in reducing the speed to zero, and would run up as a motor in reverse rotation unless prevented. See Tutorial Example T.6.5.

(3) Short circuiting the machine, making $V = 0$, would also require a limiting resistor. Again the machine is generating in what is called a dynamic (or rheostatic) braking mode and this time, the resistor and the machine losses just dissipate the stored kinetic energy. Braking is slower, especially if T_m is small.

(4) Far superior to any of the above methods is to provide the relatively expensive facility of controlling V, using a separate generator or power-electronic circuit in what is called the Ward-Leonard system, after its inventor. Rapid control of current, torque and speed in any of the four quadrants is made available. The next example illustrates all the methods above, showing them on the 4-quadrant diagram.

EXAMPLE 3.19

A 250 V, 500 rev/min d.c. separately-excited motor has an armature resistance of 0.13 Ω and takes an armature current of 60 A when delivering rated torque at rated flux. If flux is maintained constant throughout, calculate the speed at which a braking torque equal to the full-load torque is developed when:

(a) regeneratively braking at normal terminal voltage;

(b) plugging, with extra resistance to limit the peak torque on changeover to 3 *per unit*;

(c) dynamically braking, with resistance to limit the current to 2 *per unit*;

(d) regeneratively braking at half rated terminal voltage.

(e) What terminal voltage would be required to run the motor in reverse rotation at rated torque and half rated speed?

It is first necessary to calculate rated flux and thereafter the speed is given by:

$$\omega_m = \frac{V - RI_a}{k_\phi} \text{ or } \frac{V}{k_\phi} - \frac{RT_e}{k_\phi{}^2}$$

with the appropriate values of R, V and I_a or T_e.

$$k_{\phi(rated)} = \frac{250 - 0.13 \times 60}{2\pi \times 500/60} = \frac{242.2}{52.36} = 4.626 \text{ Nm/A or V/rad/s}$$

Substituting this value of k_ϕ will give all the answers from the general expression for the speed/torque curve.

(a) $I_a = -60$ A. $\omega_m = \dfrac{250 - 0.13(-60)}{4.626} = 55.73 \text{ rad/s} = \underline{532 \text{ rev/min}}$

(b) I_a must be limited to $3(-60)$ A, and $V = -250$ V. Assuming that speed does not change in the short time of current reversal: $I_a = \dfrac{V - E}{R}$ so $R = \dfrac{-250 - 242.2}{3(-60)} = 2.734 \,\Omega$, the e.m.f. $k_\phi\omega_m$ being unchanged momentarily.

This is the total circuit resistance which means an external resistor of 2.6 Ω is required.

Speed for full-load torque $= \dfrac{-250 - 2.734(-60)}{4.626} = -18.6 \text{ rad/s} = \underline{-177 \text{ rev/min}}$

(c) I_a limited to $2(-60)$ A and $V = 0$ so: $R = \dfrac{0 - 242.2}{2(-60)} = 2.018 = $ extra 1.89 Ω.

Speed for full-load torque $= \dfrac{0 - 2.018(-60)}{4.626} = 26.18 \text{ rad/s} = \underline{250 \text{ rev/min}}$.

(d) $I_a = -60$ A; $V = 125$ V. $\omega_m = \dfrac{125 - 0.13(-60)}{4.626} = 28.7 \text{ rad/s} = \underline{274 \text{ rev/min}}$.

(e) $I_a = -60$ A; $\omega_m = \dfrac{-52.36}{2}$. $V = k_\phi\omega_m + RI_a = 4.626 \times (-26.18) + 0.13(-60) = \underline{-128.9 \text{ V}}$.

Note that the motoring equation has been used throughout, even though most modes are generating. This simplifies the concepts but requires the insertion of a

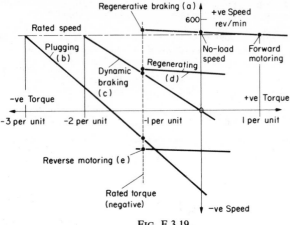

FIG. E.3.19.

negative sign for current, torque or power if these are specified. Alternatively, if the correct signs of speed, voltage and flux are inserted the signs of I_a, T_e and P will come out naturally in the calculations.

The speed/torque curves for each setting are shown on the attached 4-quadrant diagram (Fig. E.3.19) and the above answers at one particular torque (-1 *per unit*) are indicated. The dynamic changeover between quadrants and curves will be illustrated by examples in Chapter 6.

EXAMPLE 3.20

A d.c. series motor drives a hoist. When lowering a load, the machine acts as a series generator, a resistor being connected directly across the terminals—dynamic braking mode. Determine:

(a) the range of resistance required so that when lowering maximum load (450 lbf ft) the speed can be restrained to 400 rev/min, and for light load (150 lbf ft), the speed can be allowed to rise to 600 rev/min.

(b) What resistance would be required if the light-load speed was maintained instead at 400 rev/min and what would then be the saving in external resistance loss at this load? What total mechanical power is gravity providing under this condition? Neglect the mechanical losses. Armature-circuit resistance 0.1 Ω.

72

Before giving the magnetisation data, it should be pointed out that the machine is going to be operating as a self-excited series generator and a step-by-step calculation will be required. A braking condition with a series motor driving a hoist has already been encountered in Example 3.16. The mode here was "plugging"; also with forward torque and reverse speed, but a different circuit connection.

The following magnetisation curve was taken at a speed of 400 rev/min; i.e. $\omega_{m(test)} = 41.89$.

Field current	30	50	70	90	110	A
Generated e.m.f.	114	179	218	244	254	V
$k_\phi = E/41.89$	2.72	4.27	5.2	5.83	6.06	Nm/A
Torque $T_e = k_\phi I_f$	81.6	213.5	364	524.7	666.6	Nm

Flux and torque are plotted against current on Fig. E.3.20. The question specifies torque so the curves will be used to read k_ϕ and $I_a\,(= I_f)$ at the T_e values.

For 450 lbf ft = $450 \times \dfrac{746}{550} = 610.4$ Nm; $I_a = 102$ A and $k_\phi = 6$ Nm/A

For 150 lbf ft $= 203.4$ Nm; $I_a = 49$ A and $k_\phi = 4.2$ Nm/A

For dynamic braking: $I_a = \dfrac{0 - k_\phi \omega_m}{R}$ so required resistance is $R = \dfrac{-k_\phi \omega_m}{I_a}$

(a) For 400 rev/min and 450 lbf ft; $R = \dfrac{-6 \times \dfrac{2\pi}{60} \times 400}{-102} = 2.464\ \Omega$; extra $\underline{2.364\ \Omega}$

For 600 rev/min and 150 lbf ft; $R = \dfrac{-4.2 \times 20\pi}{-49} = 5.386\ \Omega$; extra $\underline{5.286\ \Omega}$

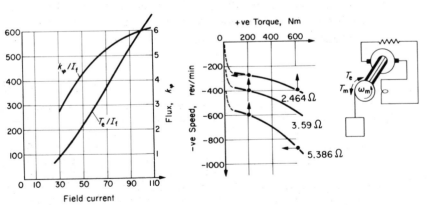

FIG. E.3.20.

73

(b) For 400 rev/min and 150 lbf ft; $R = \dfrac{-4.2 \times 40\pi/3}{-49} = 3.59\,\Omega$; extra $\underline{3.49\,\Omega}$

Difference in power loss $= (5.286 - 3.49) \times 49^2 = \underline{4.31\,\text{kW}}$
Total mechanical power is that dissipated; i.e. $3.49 \times 49^2 = \underline{8.62\,\text{kW}} = E \cdot I_a$

The various features of interest are shown on the speed/torque curves which, as an exercise, could be plotted from the above data following a few additional calculations of speed $\omega_m = -RT_e/k_\phi^2$.

CHAPTER 4

INDUCTION MACHINES

FOR drives, the important characteristic is that relating speed and torque. Using the same axes as for the d.c. machine, with $\omega_m = f(T_e)$ as the dependent variable, the basic speed/torque curve on a 4-quadrant diagram is shown on Fig. 4.1a. It can be compared with that shown for the d.c. machine in Example 3.19. Basic operation as a motor is at speeds near to synchronous, $n_s = f/p$ rev/sec, with small values of slip $s = (n_s - n)/n_s$. There are other significant operational modes however, e.g. starting, generating and braking. Adopting a motoring convention, i.e. P_{elec} and P_{mech} both positive, the various modes are shown, covering slip variations from small negative values (generating) to larger values $s \to 2$, where braking occurs. Changing the ABC supply sequence to the primary— usually the stator winding—will reverse the rotation of the magnetic field and give a mirror-image characteristic as indicated. Note also the typical mechanical characteristic; $T_m = f(\omega_m)$, its intersection with the $\omega_m = f(T_e)$ characteristic which determines the steady-state speed, and its reversal, as a passive load, if rotation reverses. Although the natural induction-machine characteristic as shown is quite typical, it is possible to change it by various means, for example to cause change of speed or improve the starting torque. The later questions in this chapter are much concerned with such changes.

4.1 REVISION OF EQUATIONS

Figure 4.1b shows a power-flow diagram for the induction machine and Fig. 4.1c the "exact" (Tee) equivalent circuit, per

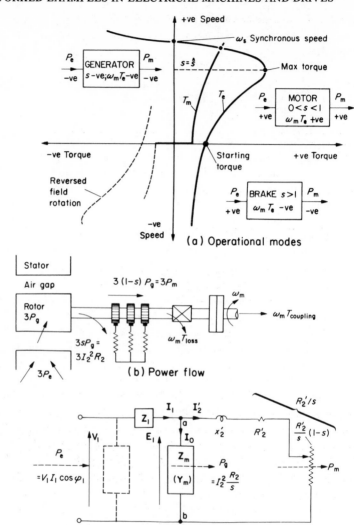

(a) Operational modes

(b) Power flow

(c) Equivalent circuit per phase

FIG. 4.1. 3-phase induction machine.

76

phase, the approximate circuit being indicated by the transfer of the magnetising branch to the terminals. These are not the only ways of presenting the equivalent circuit but they have the advantage of preserving the identity of important physical features like the magnetising current I_m, and the winding impedances. $z_1 = R_1 + jx_1$ and $Z_2' \times R_2'/s + jx_2'$. The magnetising branch admittance Y_m is $1/R_m + 1/jX_m$. The approximate circuit makes calculations very easy and is justified if a general idea of performance is required, having an accuracy within about 10%. The worked examples in this chapter apart from Example 4.18, refer to 3-phase machines under balanced conditions, but the values per-phase would apply to any polyphase machine.

The power-balance equation yields the important relationships:

Electrical terminal power per phase

$$= P_e = V_1 I_1 \cos \varphi_1 = E_1 I_2' \cos \varphi_2 + \text{Stator loss}$$

Air-gap power per phase

$$= P_g \qquad = E_1 I_2' \cos \varphi_2 = I_2'^2 R_2'/s \qquad (4.1)$$

Hence: rotor-circuit power per phase

$$= I_2^2 R_2 = s P_g \qquad (4.2)$$

and: mechanical power per phase

$$= P_m = (1 - s)P_g = \frac{(1 - s)}{s} I_2^2 R_2 \qquad (4.3)$$

from which: electromagnetic torque

$$= T_e = \frac{3P_m}{\omega_m} = \frac{3P_g(1 - s)}{\omega_s(1 - s)} = \frac{3}{\omega_g} P_g = \frac{3}{\omega_s} \frac{I_2^2 R_2}{s} \qquad (4.4)$$

From the expressions for P_e, P_g and P_m it can be seen that P_e and P_m are both positive (motoring) when $0 < s < 1$. When s is negative P_e and P_m are negative (generating), and when $s > 1$, P_e is positive but P_m is negative, i.e. power flow inwards at both sets of "terminals", which is a braking condition. The mechanical "coupling" power is:

$$P_{coupling} = 3I_2^2 R_2 \frac{(1-s)}{s} - \omega_m T_{loss}$$

Note that the rotor-circuit power-loss can be expressed either as $3I_2^2 R_2$ or $3I_2'^2 R_2'$, and the rotor is assumed to carry the secondary winding, the usual arrangement. If the approximate circuit is used:

$$T_e = \frac{3}{2\pi \times f/p} \times \frac{V_1^2}{(R_1 + R_2'/s)^2 + (x_1 + x_2')^2} \times \frac{R_2'}{s} \text{ Nm} \qquad (4.5)$$

where: $\quad I_2' = \dfrac{V_1 + j0}{(R_1 + R_2'/s) + j(x_1 + x_2')} = (Real) - j(Imag.) \qquad (4.6)$

$$\mathbf{I}_0 = \frac{V_1}{R_m} - j\frac{V_1}{X_m} \qquad\qquad = I_p - jI_m \qquad (4.7)$$

and $\mathbf{I}_1 = \mathbf{I}_2' + \mathbf{I}_0 = [(Real) + I_p] - j[(Imag.) + I_m] = I_1 \cos\varphi_1 + jI_1 \sin\varphi_1$. Note that φ_1 and $\sin\varphi_1$ are taken as $-$ve for lagging p.f. For a generator with s negative, the expression for I_2' is of the form:

$$\frac{V_1}{-A + jB} \times \frac{-A - jB}{-A - jB} \text{ which becomes of the form: } V_1(-a - jb),$$

the real part of the current being negative. The machine is not a "positive" motor as the motoring-convention equations have assumed, but a "negative" motor indicating reverse power flow. If we reverse the convention, changing the signs, the real part becomes positive, and also the imaginary part, showing that as a generator, the induction machine operates at leading power factor.

For calculations using the "exact" circuit, the following arrangement preserves the connection with the equivalent circuit as a useful reference:

$$\mathbf{Z}_{input} = z_1 + \mathbf{Z}_{ab}$$

$$= R_1 + jx_1 + \cfrac{1}{\cfrac{1}{R_m} + \cfrac{1}{jX_m} + \cfrac{1}{R_2'/s + jx_2'}} \qquad (4.8)$$

$$= R_1 + jx_1 + R_{ab} + jX_{ab}$$

$$= R_{input} + jX_{input}$$

Hence:

$$\mathbf{I}_1 = \frac{V_1}{Z_{input}}\left(\frac{R_{in.}}{Z_{in.}} - j\frac{X_{in.}}{Z_{in.}}\right) = I_1 \cos\varphi_1 + jI_1 \sin\varphi_1$$

$$\mathbf{E}_1 = \mathbf{V}_1 \times \frac{\mathbf{Z}_{ab}}{\mathbf{Z}_{input}} \text{ and } \mathbf{I}_0 = \frac{E_1}{R_m} - \frac{jE_1}{X_m} \qquad (4.9), (4.10)$$

$$I_2'^2 = \frac{E_1^{\,2}}{(R_2'/s)^2 + x_2'^2} \qquad (4.11)$$

From these equations, the majority of the Chapter 4 examples are solved, but other special equations are developed later as required. For example, an important quantity is the maximum torque. This can be obtained from the approximate expression above, either by differentiating or considering the condition for maximum power transfer, taking the load as the power consumed $(I_2'^2 R_2'/s)$ in the apparent rotor resistance. From these considerations, $R_2'/\hat{s}$ must be equal to:

$$R_2'/\hat{s} = \sqrt{R_1^{\,2} + (x_1 + x_2')^2}, \qquad (4.12)$$

giving a maximum torque on substitution of $\hat{s}$ as:

$$\text{Max } T_e = \frac{3}{\omega_s} \times \frac{V_1^{\,2}}{2[\pm\sqrt{(R_1^{\,2} + (x_1 + x_2')^2)} + R_1]} \qquad (4.13)$$

which is seen to be independent of the value of R_2'.

4.2 SOLUTION OF EQUATIONS

As for the d.c. machine, the following flow diagram has been prepared to act as a guide to the kind of problems which might be

Induction-machine Solution Programme

Input data from:

V_1, I_1, $\cos\varphi_1$, f, p, Power, Efficiency η, ω_m, s, Z, N_{stator}/N_{rotor}, T_{loss}, $T_m = f(\omega_m)$

Equivalent circuit given, or s.c. and o.c. tests to obtain it, OR ω_m/T_e curve.

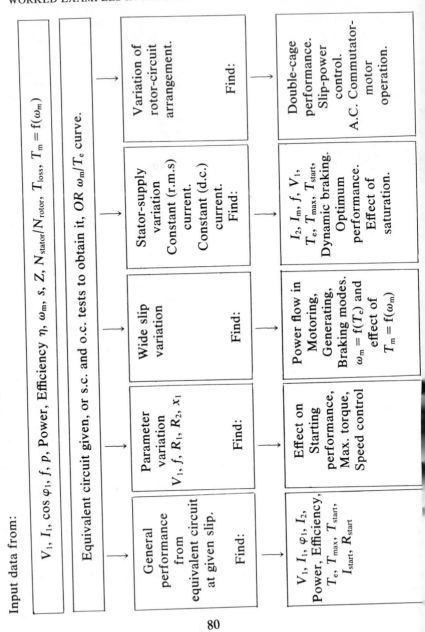

General performance from equivalent circuit at given slip.	Parameter variation V_1, f, R_1, R_2, x_1	Wide slip variation	Stator-supply variation Constant (r.m.s) current. Constant (d.c.) current.	Variation of rotor-circuit arrangement.
Find:	Find:	Find:	Find:	Find:
V_1, I_1, φ_1, I_2, Power, Efficiency, T, T_{max}, T_{start}, I_{start}, R_{start}	Effect on Starting performance, Max. torque, Speed control	Power flow in Motoring, Generating, Braking modes. $\omega_m = f(T_e)$ and effect of $T_m = f(\omega_m)$	I_2, I_m, f, V_1, T_e, T_{max}, T_{start}, Dynamic braking. Optimum performance. Effect of saturation.	Double-cage performance. Slip-power control. A.C. Commutator-motor operation.

ɔosed, and to indicate in a general way the approach to solutions.
The reader must also be prepared to refer back to the equations
ust developed when trying to understand the solutions in the
following examples.

EXAMPLE 4.1

The equivalent circuit of a 440-V, 3-phase, 8-pole, 50-Hz star-connected induction
motor is given on the figure. The short-circuit test is conducted with a locked rotor
and a line current of 80 A. The "open-circuit" test is conducted by supplying the
primary winding at rated voltage and at the same time driving the rotor in the same
direction as the rotating field, at synchronous speed; $s = 0$. Determine:

(a) the line voltage and power factor on the short-circuit test;

(b) the line current and power factor on the "open-circuit" test;

(c) the equivalent circuit per-phase if these tests were analysed on an approximate
basis; i.e. neglecting the magnetising branch when analysing the s.c. test and
neglecting the series leakage impedances for analysis of the o.c. test.

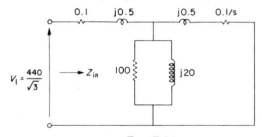

FIG. E.4.1.

a) Input impedance $Z_{in} = z_1$ $\qquad + Z_{ab}(1/Y_{ab})$

$$= 0.1 + j0.5 \qquad + \cfrac{1}{\cfrac{1}{100} + \cfrac{1}{j20} + \cfrac{1}{0.1 + j0.5}}$$

$$\cfrac{1}{0.01 - j0.05 + \cfrac{0.1 - j0.5}{0.1^2 + 0.5^2}}$$

$$\cfrac{1}{0.395 - j1.973}$$

$$= 0.1 + j0.5 \qquad + 0.097 + j0.487$$

$$= 0.197 + j0.987 = 1.006\underline{/78°7}\ \Omega \text{ per phase}$$

Input voltage on s.c. $= \sqrt{3} \times 1.006 \times 80 = \underline{140 \text{ Line V at } 0.1957 \text{ power factor}}$

(b) Input impedance $(R_2/s = \infty)$ $= 0.1 + j0.5 + \dfrac{1}{0.01 - j0.05}$ $(1/Y_m)$

$$= 0.1 + j0.5 + 3.85 + j19.23$$

$$= 3.95 + j19.73 = 20.1\underline{/78°7}\ \Omega \text{ per phase}$$

$$\text{Input current } I_0 = \frac{440/\sqrt{3}}{20.1} = \underline{12.64 \text{ A at } 0.1963 \text{ p.f.}}$$

(c) $Z_{sc} = \dfrac{140/\sqrt{3}}{80}\underline{/\cos^{-1} 0.1957} = 1.006\,(0.196 + j0.98) = \underline{0.197 + j0.987\ \Omega}$

Dividing this equally between stator and rotor: $z_1 = z_2' = 0.0985 + j0.494\ \Omega$

From "o.c. test": $R_m = \dfrac{V}{I_0 \cos \varphi_{oc}} = \dfrac{440/\sqrt{3}}{12.64 \times 0.1963} = \underline{102.4\ \Omega}$

$$X_m = \frac{V}{I_0 \sin \varphi_{oc}} \qquad \frac{440/\sqrt{3}}{12.64 \times 0.98} = \underline{20.5\ \Omega}$$

The largest errors with this approximation are in the magnetising-circuit parameters, about 2.5%, and are less than this for the series-impedance elements, which are more decisive on overall performance. The errors depend on the relative magnitudes of the parameters and are not always so small. Note that test information would usually be given in terms of line voltage and current and total power. The power factor would have to be calculated from:

$$\cos \varphi = \frac{\text{Total power}}{\sqrt{3} \times V_{\text{line}} \times I_{\text{line}}}$$

In the questions above, the o.c. and s.c. power factors are about the same, but this is not usually so. Note also that it is not usually convenient to drive the machine for the "o.c. test". Running on no load, where the slip is very small, is a close approximation and allowance can be made for the error in assuming $z_2' = \infty$ as described in Reference 1.

EXAMPLE 4.2

For the machine and equivalent circuit given in Example 4.1, calculate, at a slip of 3%, the input stator-current and power factor; the rotor current referred to the stator; the electromagnetic torque; the mechanical output power and the efficiency. Also calculate the starting torque. Take the mechanical loss as 1 kW. Consider:

(a) the equivalent circuit neglecting stator impedance altogether;

(b) the approximate circuit;

(c) the"exact" circuit.

(d) Repeat (c) working in *per-unit* taking the calculated output, rated voltage and synchronous speed as base quantities.

Synchronous speed $\omega_s = 2\pi \times f/p = 2\pi \times 50/4 = 78.54 \text{ rad/s}$. $\omega_m = \omega_s(1 - 0.03) = 76.18 \text{ rad/s}$.

	(a) Stator impedance neglected	(b) Approximate equivalent circuit
$I_2' =$	$\dfrac{254}{1/0.03 + j0.5} = 74.5 + j11.15$	$\dfrac{254}{(0.1 + 0.1/0.03) + j1} = 68.2 - j19.9$
$I_0 =$	$\dfrac{254}{100} - \dfrac{j254}{20} = 2.54 - j12.7$	$= 2.54 - j12.7$
$I_1 =$	$I_2' + I_0 = 77.04 - j23.85$	$70.74 - j32.6$
$=$	80.6 A at $\cos \varphi_1 = 0.955$	77.9 A at $\cos \varphi_1 = 0.908$
$I_2' =$	$\sqrt{74.5^2 + 11.15^2} = 75.32 \text{ A}$	$\sqrt{68.2^2 + 19.9^2} = 71 \text{ A}$
$T_e =$	$\dfrac{3}{78.54} \times 75.32^2 \times \dfrac{0.1}{0.03} = 722.2 \text{ Nm}$	$\dfrac{3}{78.54} \times 71^2 \times \dfrac{0.1}{0.03} = 641.8 \text{ Nm}$
$P_{mech} =$	$76.18 \times 722.2 - 1000 = 55.7 \text{ kW}$	$76.18 \times 641.8 - 1000 = 49.41 \text{ kW}$
$P_{elec} =$	$\sqrt{3} \times 440 \times 77.04 = 58.7 \text{ kW}$	$\sqrt{3} \times 440 \times 70.74 = 53.9 \text{ kW}$
Effy. $\eta =$	$55.7/58.7 = 94.9\%$	$49.41/53.9 = 91.7\%$
$T_{start} =$	$\dfrac{3}{78.54} \times \dfrac{254^2}{0.1^2 + 0.5^2} \times \dfrac{0.1}{1} = 947.8 \text{ Nm}$	$\dfrac{3}{78.54} \times \dfrac{254^2}{0.2^2 + 1^2} \times \dfrac{0.1}{1} = 236.9 \text{ Nm}$

It can be seen that neglecting stator impedance gives appreciable differences in the answers and at starting they are utterly erroneous. From the next, exact-circuit calculation, it will be found that the approximate circuit gives answers well within 10% of these correct results.

(c) Impedance across points"ab" $= Z_{ab} = \dfrac{1}{\dfrac{1}{100} + \dfrac{1}{j20} + \dfrac{1}{\dfrac{0.1}{0.03} + j0.5}} =$

$= \dfrac{1}{0.01 - j0.05 + 0.293 - j0.044} = 3.01 + j0.934 = 3.15\underline{/17^\circ.2}$

Adding stator impedance z_1: $Z_{in} = 3.11 + j1.434 = 3.42\underline{/24°7}$

$$I_1 = \frac{254}{3.42\underline{/24°7}} = 74.3 \text{ A at } 0.908 \text{ power-factor lagging}$$

$$E_1 = \frac{|Z_{ab}|}{|Z_{in}|} \times V_1 = \frac{3.15}{3.42} \times 254 = 234 \text{ V. } \therefore I_2' = \frac{234}{\sqrt{33.3^2 + 0.5^2}} = 69.4 \text{ A}$$

$$I_0 = E_1/R_m - jE_1/X_m = \underline{2.34 - j11.7 \text{ A}}$$

Torque $T_e = \dfrac{3}{78.54} \times 69.4^2 \times 3.33 = \underline{613.6 \text{ Nm}}$

P_{mech} $= 76.18 \times 613.6 - 1000 = \underline{45.66 \text{ kW}}$

P_{elec} $= \sqrt{3} \times 440 \times 74.3 \times 0.908$ $= \underline{51.4 \text{ kW}}$

Efficiency $\eta = 45.66/51.4 = \underline{88.8\%}$

For starting torque, $s = 1$, some data are already available from Example 4.1:

$Z_{AB} = \sqrt{0.097^2 + 0.487^2} = 0.496 \text{ }\Omega$ and $Z_{in} = 1.006 \text{ }\Omega$

Hence $T_{start} = \dfrac{3}{78.54} \times \left(\dfrac{0.496}{1.006} \times 254\right)^2 \times \dfrac{1}{0.5^2 + 1^2} \times \dfrac{0.1}{1} = \underline{230.4 \text{ Nm}}$

(d) For the *per-unit* notation, we must first establish the base quantities:

Rated output $= 45.66 \text{ kW} = P_{base}$ (total) or 15.22 kW (phase value)

Rated voltage $= 440 \text{ V}$ $= V_{base}$ (line) or 254 V (phase value)

Synchronous speed $= 2\pi \times f/p = 78.54 \text{ rad/s} = $ Speed $(\omega_m)_{base} = \omega_s$.

These are the usual base quantities chosen for induction motors and the rest follow as below:

$$I_{base} \text{ (per phase)} = \frac{P_{rated}/3}{V_{rated}/\text{phase}} \quad (= 59.9 \text{ A}).$$

$$I_{rated} = \frac{P_{rated}/3}{V_{rated} \times \cos\varphi_{rated} \times \eta_{rated}} \quad (= 74.3 \text{ A})$$

$$I_{rated} \text{ in } per \ unit = \frac{I_{rated}}{I_{base}} = \frac{1}{\cos\varphi_{rated} \times \eta_{rated}} \quad (= 1.24 \ per \ unit)$$

$\omega_{m(rated)} = \omega_s(1 - s_{rated})$; so $\omega_{m(rated)}$ in *per unit* $= 1 - s_{rated}$

$$\text{Torque}_{base} = \frac{P_{base}}{\omega_{m(base)}} \quad \text{and} \quad \text{Torque}_{rated} = \frac{P_{rated}/\omega_{m(rated)}}{P_{rated}/\omega_{m(base)}} = \frac{1}{1 - s_{rated}} \quad \text{in}$$

per unit.

$$Z_{base} = \frac{V_{base}(\text{per phase})}{I_{base}(\text{per phase})} = \frac{V_{base}}{P_{base}(\text{per phase})/V_{base}} = \frac{V_{base}^2}{P_{base}} \text{ ohms}$$

Applying these relationships to the question: $Z_{\text{base}} = \dfrac{(440/\sqrt{3})^2}{45\,660/3} = 4.24\,\Omega$

Hence $R_1 = R_2' = \;\; 0.1/4.24 \;\; = \;\; 0.02358 \; per\ unit$

$\qquad x_1 = x_2' = \;\; 0.5/4.24 \;\; = \;\; 0.11792 \; per\ unit$

$\qquad\quad R_m = \;\; 100/4.24 \; = 23.58 \qquad per\ unit$

$\qquad\quad X_m = \quad 20/4.24 \;\; = \;\; 4.717 \quad per\ unit$

Mechanical loss $= 1000/45\,660 = 0.0219 \; per\ unit$

Calculations now proceed as in part (c) but $V = 1$; $\omega_s = 1$ and all other quantities are in *per unit*.

$$\mathbf{Z}_{ab} = \cfrac{1}{\cfrac{1}{23.58} + \cfrac{1}{j4.717} + \cfrac{1}{0.02358/0.03 + j0.11792}}$$

$$= \cfrac{1}{0.0424 - j0.212 + 1.2443 - j0.18677}$$

$$= 0.7091 + j0.2197 \quad = 0.74235 \;(\text{modulus})$$

add z_1: $\qquad \underline{0.02358 + j0.11792}$

$\qquad \mathbf{Z}_{in} = \underline{0.7327 + j0.3376} \quad = 0.80674 \;(\text{modulus})$

Hence $I_1 = \dfrac{1}{0.80674} = 1.24 \; per\ unit$ at $\cos\varphi_1 = 0.7327/0.80674 = 0.908$ lagging

$E_1 = \dfrac{0.74235}{0.80674} \times 1 = 0.92$

$I_2' = \dfrac{0.92}{\sqrt{0.786^2 + 0.1179^2}} = 1.157$ (Check from actual values $69.4/59.9 = 1.158$)

$\mathbf{I}_0 = \dfrac{0.92}{23.58} - \dfrac{j0.92}{4.717} = 0.039 - j0.195.$

Coupling torque $= \dfrac{1}{1} \times 1.157^2 \times \dfrac{0.02358}{0.03} - 0.0219$ (mech. loss) $= 1.03\ [\times 1/(1 - 0.03)]$

$P_{\text{elec}}\ (V \times I \times \cos\varphi) = 1 \times 1.24 \times 0.908 = 1.126 \; per\ unit$ so $\eta = 1/1.126 = 0.888$

All the *per-unit* values check with part (c). The final calculations are somewhat neater and the method has advantages when many repetitive calculations are required, comparisons are being made or large systems are being studied. For computer simulations, especially for transient analyses, the scaling problem is eased considerably.

EXAMPLE 4.3

A 3-phase, 440-V, delta-connected, 4-pole 50-Hz induction motor runs at a speed of 1447 rev/min when operating at its rated load. The equivalent circuit has the following per-phase parameters:

$$R_1 = 0.2\,\Omega, \quad R_2' = 0.4\,\Omega; \quad x_1 = x_2' = 2\,\Omega; \quad R_m = 200\,\Omega; \quad X_m = 40\,\Omega$$

(a) Using the approximate circuit, determine, for rated load, the values of line current and power factor, torque, output power and efficiency. The mechanical loss is 1000 watts.

(b) Determine the same quantities, if the machine is run as a generator with the same numerical value of slip.

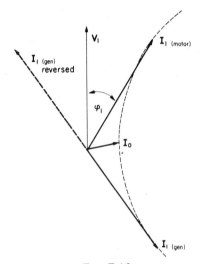

FIG. E.4.3.

(a) Full-load slip $= \dfrac{60 \times f/p - 1447}{60 \times 50/2} = \dfrac{1500 - 1447}{1500} = 0.0353$

$I_2' = \dfrac{440}{(0.2 + 0.4/0.0353) + j(2 + 2)} \doteqdot 34.05 - j11.8$

$I_0 = \dfrac{440}{200} + \dfrac{440}{j40} \qquad\qquad = \underline{2.2 \quad - j11}$

$I_1 = \qquad\qquad\qquad\qquad\qquad I_1 = \underline{36.25 - j22.8}$

86

Line current $= \sqrt{3 \times (36.25^2 + 22.8^2)} = \underline{74.2 \text{ A}}$ at $36.25/42.8 = \underline{0.847 \text{ p.f.}}$

$T_e = \dfrac{3}{2\pi \times 50/2} \times (34.05^2 + 11.8^2) \times \dfrac{0.4}{0.0353} = \dfrac{3}{157.1} \times 36.04^2 \times 11.33 = \underline{281 \text{ Nm}}$

$P_{mech} = (1 - 0.0353) \times 157.1 \times 291 - 1000$ (mech. loss) $= \underline{41.59 \text{ kW}} = 55.75 \text{ h.p.}$

$P_{elec} = 3 \times 440 \times 36.25 = 47.85 \text{ kW}$. Efficiency $= 41.59/47.85 = \underline{86.9\%}$

(b) As a generator, slip $= -0.0353$; hence:

$I_2' = \dfrac{440}{(0.2 - 0.4/0.0353) + j4} = \dfrac{440}{-11.13 + j4} = -35 \quad - j12.6$

$I_0 = \qquad\qquad\qquad\qquad\quad = \quad 2.2 - j11$

$I_1 = \qquad\qquad\qquad\qquad I_1 = -32.8 - j23.6$

Line current $= \sqrt{3 \times (32.8^2 + 23.6^2)} = \underline{70 \text{ A}}$ at $-32.8/40.4 = \underline{0.81 \text{ p.f.}}$ $(-144°)$

Note, that since a motoring equation has been used, the real part of I_1 is negative. If the convention is reversed it will be positive and can be seen that I_1 is at leading power factor. Phasor diagrams are helpful here and are shown alongside. The current locus is circular and circle diagrams can be used for rapid solutions. They are less important nowadays but the technique, with numerical illustration, is dealt with in Reference 1.

$T_e = \dfrac{3}{157.1} \times (35^2 + 12.6^2) \times (-11.33) = \underline{-299.4 \text{ Nm}}$

$P_{mech} = (1 + 0.0353) \times 157.1 \times (-299.4) - 1000 = \underline{-49.7 \text{ kW}}$

$P_{elec} = 3 \times 440 \times (-32.8) = -43.3 \text{ kW}$. Efficiency $= 43.3/49.7 = \underline{87.1\%}$

Note again that the motoring convention results in negative signs in the answers.

EXAMPLE 4.4

In a certain 3-phase induction motor, the leakage reactance is five times the resistance for both primary and secondary windings. The primary impedance is identical with the referred secondary impedance. The slip at full load is 3%. It is desired to limit the starting current to three times the full-load current. By how much must:

(a) R_1 be increased?

(b) R_2 be increased?

(c) x_1 be increased?

How would the maximum torque be affected if the extra impedance was left in circuit?

87

This question gives minimum information but can be solved most conveniently by taking ratios and thus cancelling the common constants. Let the new impedances be expressed as k_aR_1, k_bR_2' and k_cx_1 respectively, and $R_1 = R_2' = R$; $x_1 = x_2' = 5R$.

Full-load current $= \dfrac{V}{\sqrt{(R + R/0.03)^2 + (5R + 5R)^2}} = \dfrac{V/R}{\sqrt{1278.8}}$

Starting current $= \dfrac{V}{\sqrt{(k_aR + k_bR)^2 + 5^2(k_cR + R)^2}} = \dfrac{V/R}{\sqrt{(k_a + k_b)^2 + 25(k_c + 1)^2}}$

Current ratio $\dfrac{I_s}{I_{fl}} = \sqrt{\dfrac{1278.8}{(k_a + k_b)^2 + 25(k_c + 1)^2}}$; $-$required to be 3.

(a) and (b) If $k_c = 1$ and either k_a or $k_b = 1$:

$$1278.8 = 9 \times [(k + 1)^2 + 100]$$
$$\text{so } k \ (= k_a \text{ or } k_b) = \underline{5.49} \qquad (5.49R_1 \text{ or } 5.49R_2)$$

(c) If $k_a = k_b = 1$: $1278.8 = 9 \times [2^2 + 25(k_c + 1)^2]$ from which $k_c = \underline{1.35}$ $(1.35x_1)$

Expression for full-load torque $= \dfrac{3V_1^2}{\omega_s \times [(R + R/0.03)^2 + (10R)^2]} \times \dfrac{R}{0.03}$
[eqn (4.5)]

$$= \dfrac{3V_1^2}{\omega_sR} \times \dfrac{1}{38.36}$$

Expression for starting torque $= \dfrac{3V_1^2 \times R}{\omega_s \times [(k_aR + k_bR)^2 + 25(k_cR + R)^2]}$
[eqn (4.5), $s = 1$]

$$= \dfrac{3V_1^2}{\omega_sR} \times \dfrac{1}{(k_a + k_b)^2 + 25(k_c + 1)^2}$$

Expression for maximum torque $= \dfrac{3V_1^2}{\omega_s \times 2[\sqrt{(k_aR)^2 + 25(k_cR + R)^2} + k_aR]}$
[eqn (4.13)]

$$= \dfrac{3V_1^2}{\omega_sR} \times \dfrac{1}{2[\sqrt{k_a^2 + 25(k_c + 1)^2} + k_a]}$$

Ratio $\dfrac{\text{Starting torque}}{\text{Full-load torque}} = \dfrac{T_s}{T_{fl}} = \dfrac{38.36}{(k_a + k_b)^2 + 25(k_c + 1)^2}$

Ratio $\dfrac{\text{Maximum torque}}{\text{Full-load torque}} = \dfrac{T_{max}}{T_{fl}} = \dfrac{38.36}{2[\sqrt{k_a^2 + 25(k_c + 1)^2} + k_a]}$

Results	$k_c = 1.35$; $k_a = k_b = 1$ x_1 increased	$k_b = 5.49$; $k_a = k_c = 1$ R_2 increased	$k_a = 5.49$; $k_b = k_c = 1$ R_1 increased	$k_a = k_b = k_c$ $= 1$ No change
T_s/T_{fl}	0.27	0.27	0.27	0.369
T_{max}/T_{fl}	1.5	1.735	1.135	1.735
T_s/I_{fl}	3	3	3	3.507

The table shows that there is no loss of maximum torque if the starting current is limited by rotor resistance. Based on considerations of maximum-torque loss alone, x_1 is a preferable alternative to R_1 as a limiting impedance, but it must be remembered that this question is meant to illustrate the use of the equations rather than draw profound conclusions from a much restricted investigation into starting methods.

EXAMPLE 4.5

A 3-phase, 200-hp, 3300-V, star-connected induction motor has the following equivalent-circuit parameters per-phase:

$$R_1 = R'_2 = 0.8\,\Omega \quad x_1 = x'_2 = 3.5\,\Omega$$

Calculate the slip at full load if the friction and windage loss is 3 kW. How much extra resistance would be necessary to increase the slip to three times this value with the full-load torque maintained? How much extra stator resistance would be necessary to achieve the same object and what loss of peak torque would result?

Mechanical power $= 3P_g(1 - s) -$ mechanical loss

$$200 \times 746 \qquad = \frac{3 \times V_1^{\,2}}{(R_1 + R'_2/s)^2 + (x_1 + x'_2)^2} \times \frac{R'_2}{s}(1 - s) - 3000 \text{ (mech. loss)}$$

$$146\,200 \qquad = \frac{3 \times (3300/\sqrt{3})^2}{(0.8 + 0.8/s)^2 + 7^2} \times \frac{0.8(1 - s)}{s}$$

$$0.01747\left(0.64 + \frac{1.28}{s} + \frac{0.64}{s^2} + 49\right) = \frac{1}{s} - 1$$

$$167.26 - \frac{87.445}{s} + \frac{1}{s^2} \qquad = 0$$

solving the quadratic: $\dfrac{1}{s} = \dfrac{87.445 \pm \sqrt{87.445^2 - 4 \times 167.26}}{2}$

from which the lower value of s comes from $\dfrac{1}{s} = 85.5;\ \underline{s = 0.0117}$

From the torque equation it can be seen that torque will be a fixed value, with all other parameters constant, if the quantity R'_2/s is unchanged; i.e. if R'_2 changes in proportion to any slip change, the torque will be unaltered. In this case, the slip is to be $3\times$, so the extra rotor resistance, referred to the primary, will be $2 \times 0.8 = 1.6\,\Omega$. Maximum torque is unaffected by change of R'_2.

For increase of stator resistance, $\dfrac{3}{\omega_s} \times I_2^{\,2} \times \dfrac{R'_2}{s}$ to be unchanged; i.e. $\dfrac{V_1^{\,2}}{Z^2} \times \dfrac{R'_2}{s}$ must be the same so, since V_1 and R'_2 are unchanged then: $1/(Z^2 \times s)$ must be the same for the same torque. Equating:

$$\frac{1}{\{[R_1 + 0.8/(3 \times 0.01117)]^2 + 49\} \times (3 \times 0.0117)} = \frac{1}{\{(0.8 + 0.8/0.0117)^2 + 49\} \times 0.0117}$$

$$\frac{1}{519.5 + 45.584R_1 + R_1^2 + 49} = \frac{3}{4675.2 + 49}$$

from which: $R_1^2 + 45.584R_1 + 1043 = 0$ and the lowest value of $R_1 = 16.6 \, \Omega$.
Extra stator resistance required is therefore $\underline{15.8 \, \Omega}$

Now maximum torque $= \dfrac{3V_1^2}{2\omega_s[\sqrt{R_1^2 + (x_1 + x_2')^2} + R_1]}$
[eqn (4.13)]

proportional to: $\dfrac{1}{\sqrt{R_1^2 + (x_1 + x_2')^2} + R_1}$

so torque ratio $= \dfrac{\sqrt{0.8^2 + 7^2} + 0.8}{\sqrt{16.6^2 + 7^2} + 16.6} = \dfrac{7.845}{34.6} = 0.226 = \underline{77.4\% \text{ reduction}}$

EXAMPLE 4.6

A 3-phase, 4-pole, 3300-V, 50-Hz, star-connected induction motor has identical primary and referred secondary impedances of value $3 + j9 \, \Omega$ per phase. The turns-ratio per-phase is 3/1 (stator/rotor), and the rotor winding is connected in delta and brought out to slip rings. Calculate:

(a) the full-load torque at rated slip of 5%;

(b) the maximum torque at normal voltage and frequency;

(c) the supply voltage reduction which can be withstood without the motor stalling;

(d) the maximum torque if the supply voltage and frequency both fall to half normal value;

(e) the increase in rotor-circuit resistance which, at normal voltage and frequency will permit maximum torque to be developed at starting. Express this: (i) as a fraction of normal R_2 and (ii) as (3) ohmic values to be placed in series with each of the slip-ring terminals and star connected.

The approximate circuit may be used and the magnetising branch neglected.

(a) Full-load torque $= \dfrac{3 \times (3300/\sqrt{3})^2}{2\pi \times 50/2} \times \dfrac{1}{(3 + 3/0.05)^2 + 18^2} \times \dfrac{3}{0.05} = \underline{969 \text{ Nm}}$

(b) Maximum torque $= 69328 \times \dfrac{1}{2 \times (\sqrt{3^2 + 18^2} + 3)}$ $= \underline{1631 \text{ Nm}}$

(c) With voltage reduced, the torque must not fall below 969 Nm, and since $T_e \propto V^2$
[eqn (4.5)]

$$\frac{969}{1631} = \left(\frac{\text{Reduced } V}{\text{Normal } V}\right)^2 \quad \text{so: Reduced } V = \sqrt{\frac{969}{1631}} = 0.77 \text{ per unit} = \underline{23\% \text{ reduction}}$$

(d) This situation could arise if the supply-generator speed was to fall without change of its excitation; both voltage and frequency would fall together. Correcting all affected parameters in the appropriate equations:

$$\hat{s} = \frac{3}{\sqrt{3^2 + (18 \times \frac{1}{2})^2}} = 0.316; \text{ eqn (4.12), allowing for the reduced frequency.}$$

Substituting in the first equation:

$$\text{Max. } T_e = \frac{3 \times (\frac{1}{2} \times 3300/\sqrt{3})^2}{2\pi \times (\frac{1}{2} \times 50)/2} \times \frac{1}{(3 + 3/0.316)^2 + (18/2)^2} \times \frac{3}{0.316} = \underline{1388 \text{ Nm}}$$

The answer could have been obtained directly by substituting the reduced parameters into the second equation used, (4.13), in part (b).

(e) Normally, maximum torque occurs at a slip of $\hat{s} = \dfrac{3}{\sqrt{3^2 + 18^2}}$

The required value of R_2 could be obtained by substituting $\hat{s} = 1$ in eqn (4.12), or alternatively, since R_2/s is a constant for any given torque:

$$\frac{\text{New } R_2'}{1} = \frac{3}{0.1644} \quad \text{Hence} \quad \frac{\text{New } R_2'}{\text{Old } R_2'} = \frac{1}{0.1644} = 6.082$$

Hence, additional R_2 required = 5.082 times original R_2. Since the turns ratio is 3/1, the actual additional resistance per rotor phase must be $5.082 \times 3\,\Omega/3^2 = 1.694\,\Omega$. However, this would carry the phase current and either by considering the delta/star transformation or the fact that the line current of a star-connected load across the slip rings would carry $\sqrt{3}$ times the phase current, three external line resistors of value $1.694/3 = \underline{0.565\,\Omega}$ would dissipate the same power and avoid the necessity of bringing out expensive additional connections and slip rings, if inserting resistance in each phase.

EXAMPLE 4.7

Using the approximate circuit for the motor of Example 4.1, calculate the mechanical coupling power at speeds of 0, 720, 780 and −720 rev/min; positive speed being taken as in the direction of the rotating field. For the last case show, on a power-flow diagram, all the individual power components, to prove that the total input power is absorbed in internal machine losses. Take the mechanical loss as constant at all speeds other than zero, where it too is zero.

Synchronous speed $= N_s = 60 \times f/p = 60 \times 50/4 = 750$ rev/min

Series-circuit impedance $= \sqrt{(0.1 + 0.1/s)^2 + 1^2} = Z.$

Mechanical coupling power $= 3P_m - \text{mech. loss} = 3\dfrac{I_2'^2 R_2'}{s}(1 - s) - 1000 = P_{\text{coupling}}$

91

Speed, rev/min.	0	720	780	−720
Slip $= \dfrac{750 - \text{Speed}}{750}$	1	0.04	−0.04	1.96
$R'_2/s = 0.1/s$	0.1	2.5	−2.5	0.051
Z	1.02	2.786	2.6	1.011
$I'_2 = \dfrac{440/\sqrt{3}}{Z}$ A	249	91.2	97.7	251.2
$3P_m$ kW	0	59.86	−74.45	−9.268
$P_{\text{coupling}} = P_{\text{mech}}$	0	58.86	−75.45	−10.268
$T_e = \dfrac{3}{2\pi \times 50/4} \times \dfrac{I_2^2 R'_2}{s}$ Nm	236.8	790.8	−911.5	122.9

These four sets of readings correspond to four significant points on the speed/torque curve; starting, motoring at full load, generating at the same, but negative slip, and reverse-current braking (plugging). In this last case, the values are those which would occur momentarily if the motor, running at full speed in the reverse sense, suddenly had its phase sequence and rotating field reversed. The values of currents, powers and torques should be studied to gain better understanding of induction machine operation.

For −720 rev/min $\cos \varphi = (R_1 + R'_2/s)/Z = 0.1493$ and $\sin \varphi = -0.9888$.

$\therefore \mathbf{I}'_2 = 251.2\underline{/-84°3}$ $= 37.5 - j248.4$

and $\mathbf{I}_0 = \dfrac{440/\sqrt{3}}{100} - \dfrac{j440/\sqrt{3}}{20}$ $= \underline{2.54 - j12.7}$

$\therefore \mathbf{I}_1$ $= 40.04 - j261.1$

$P_{\text{elec}} = \sqrt{3} \times 440 \times 40.04$ $= 30.51 \text{ kW}$

Stator Cu loss = Rotor Cu loss = $3 \times 251.2^2 \times 0.1$ $= 18.93$

Stator Fe loss = $3 \times (254)^2/100$ $= \underline{1.94}$

Total stator loss $= 20.87$

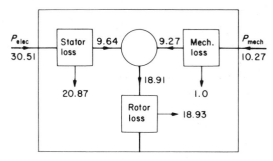

Figures in kW. Actual directions shown
FIG. E.4.7.

Mechanical loss = 1 kW + rotor Cu loss (18.93 kW) = 19.93
Total machine loss = 40.8 kW
Total machine input = $P_{elec} + P_{mech} = 30.51 + 10.27 = 40.78$ kW

The slight differences, e.g. between the input and the loss, are due to rounding-off errors. The figure shows the power distribution for this braking condition.

EXAMPLE 4.8

A 3-phase, 6-pole, 50-Hz induction motor has a peak torque of 6 Nm and a starting torque of 3 Nm when operating at full voltage. Maximum torque occurs at a slip of 25%. When started at 1/3 of normal voltage the current is 2 A.

(a) What is the mechanical power, at peak torque when operating at normal voltage?

(b) What maximum torque would the machine produce at 1/3 of normal voltage?

(c) What starting current would the machine take when supplied with normal voltage?

(d) What extra rotor-circuit resistance, as a percentage, would be required to give maximum torque at starting and what would then be the current, in terms of that at peak torque without external resistance?

This is basically a simple problem, to bring out certain elementary relationships. The curves sketched on Fig. E.4.8 indicate the main points for the solution. No additional equations from the ones used previously are involved.

(a) Power at maximum torque = $\omega_m T_e = 2\pi \times \dfrac{50}{3} \times (1 - 0.25) \times 6 = \underline{0.471\ kW}$

(b) Torque $\propto V^2$ hence, reduced maximum torque = $(1/3)^2 \times 6 = \underline{2/3\ NM}$

(c) Current $\propto V$, hence $I_{start} = 3 \times 2 = \underline{6\ A}$

WEEMD - H

93

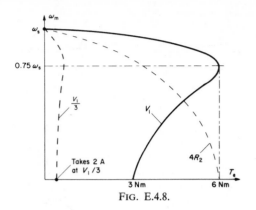

FIG. E.4.8.

(d) R_2'/s is constant for same torque. Since s changes from 0.25 to 1, then the total rotor circuit resistance must change in the same ratio; i.e. by 4 times. Hence extra rotor resistance = <u>300%R_2</u>.

Since R_2'/s is constant and since this is the only equivalent-circuit impedance varying with speed, the total impedance presented to the terminals is unchanged and so the current is the same as at $s = 0.25$.

EXAMPLE 4.9

An induction motor has the following speed/torque characteristic:

Speed	1470	1440	1410	1300	1100	900	750	350	0 rev/min
Torque	3	6	9	13	15	13	11	7	5 Nm

It drives a load requiring a torque, including loss, of 4 Nm at starting and which increases linearly with speed to be 8 Nm at 1500 rev/min.

(a) Determine the range of speed control obtainable, without stalling, by providing supply-voltage reduction.
(b) If the rotor was replaced by one having the same leakage reactance but with a doubled resistance, what would then be the possible range of speed variation with voltage control?

For each case, give the range of voltage variation required.

This is a "drives" problem and must be solved graphically from the data given. The solution depends on the simple relationships that $T_e \propto V^2$, and for any given torque R_2'/s is constant, if all other parameters are constant; eqn (4.5).

(a) Plotting the speed = $f(T_e)$ and $T_m = f(\omega_m)$ characteristics from the data gives the normal steady-state speed at their intersection. The T_e characteristic is reduced proportionally until maximum T_e intersects the T_m characteristic. This occurs at

94

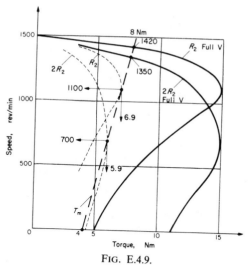

FIG. E.4.9.

a torque of 6.9 Nm and speed of 1100 rev/min. Hence voltage reduction is $\sqrt{15/6.9} = 1.47/1$ or 100% to 68% volts, giving a speed reduction from 1420 to 1100 rev/min.

(b) At various values of T_e, the slip, which is proportional to the speed difference from the synchronous value, is noted and a new speed plotted for this same T_e but with this speed difference doubled, since R_2 is doubled. Again, from the intersections of the T_m characteristic with the two new curves, the speed range is seen to be 1350 to 700 rev/min. The torque value on the reduced curve for $2R_2$ is 5.9, so the ratio of peak torques gives the appropriate voltage reduction as $\sqrt{15/5.9} = 1.59/1$ or 100% to 63% volts. This greater speed range, for a similar voltage reduction, is obtained at the penalty of additional rotor-circuit losses, but nevertheless such schemes are sometimes economically suitable because of their simplicity, for certain types of load where torque falls off appreciably with speed.

The curves also show the speed range obtainable with resistance control; in this case, doubling the rotor resistance reduces the speed from 1420 to 1350 rev/min.

EXAMPLE 4.10

A 440-V, 3-phase, 6-pole, 50-Hz, delta-connected induction motor has the following equivalent-circuit parameters at normal frequency:

$$R_1 = 0.2\,\Omega; \quad R_2' = 0.18\,\Omega; \quad x_1 = x_2' = 0.58\,\Omega\text{—all per phase values.}$$

(a) The machine is subjected in service to an occasional fall of 40% in both voltage and frequency. What total mechanical load torque is it safe to drive so that the machine just does not stall under these conditions?

(b) When operating at normal voltage and frequency, calculate the speed when delivering this torque and the power developed. Calculate also the speed at which maximum torque occurs.

(c) If V and f were both halved, what would be the increase in starting torque from the normal direct-on-line start at rated voltage and frequency?

(d) If now the machine is run up to speed from a variable-voltage, variable-frequency supply, calculate the required terminal voltage and frequency to give the "safe" torque calculated above: (i) at starting and (ii) at 500 rev/min.

(e) Repeat (d) for the machine to develop a torque equal to the maximum value occurring at rated voltage and frequency. In both (d) and (e), the criteria is that the air-gap flux per pole is maintained constant for any particular torque.

(a) The question asks effectively for the maximum torque with voltage and frequency reduced to 0.6 of rated values. Substituting in the maximum-torque eqn. (4.13) with appropriate correction of parameters:

$$\text{Max. } T_e = \frac{3}{2\pi \times 0.6 \times 50/3} \times \frac{(0.6 \times 440)^2}{2[\sqrt{0.2^2 + (0.6 \times 1.16)^2} + 0.2]} = \underline{1800\ \text{Nm}}$$

(b) From the general torque expression eqn. (4.5), with normal supply, the required slip to produce this torque is obtained by equating:

$$1800 = \frac{3}{2\pi \times 50/3} \times \frac{440^2}{(0.2 + 0.18/s)^2 + 1.16^2} \times \frac{0.18}{s}$$

giving: $1.803\left(0.04 + \dfrac{0.072}{s} + \dfrac{0.0324}{s^2} + 1.3456\right) = \dfrac{1}{s}$

from which: $\dfrac{1}{s^2} - \dfrac{214.9}{s} + 42.77 = 0$

and the smaller value of s on solution is 0.0907 corresponding to a speed of:

$$1000(1 - s) = \underline{909\ \text{rev/min.}}$$

Power developed $= \dfrac{2\pi}{60} \times 909 \times 1800 = \underline{171.3\ \text{kW}} = \underline{230\ \text{hp}}$

Speed for maximum torque from eqn. (4.12) $\hat{s} = \dfrac{0.18}{\sqrt{0.2^2 + 1.16^2}} = 0.1529$ so

speed $= \underline{847\ \text{rev/min.}}$

(c) The expression for starting torque is: $\dfrac{3}{2\pi \times f/p} \times \dfrac{V^2}{(R_1 + R_2')^2 + (x_1 + x_2')^2} \times \dfrac{R_2'}{1}$

Using ratios to cancel the constants in the expression:

96

$$\frac{\text{Starting torque at } \frac{1}{2}V \text{ and } f}{\text{Normal starting torque}} = \frac{1}{(f/2)/f} \times \frac{[(V/2)/V]^2}{(0.38^2 + (1.16/2)^2)/(0.38^2 + 1.16^2)}$$

$$= 2 \times \frac{0.25}{0.1478/1.497} = \underline{1.55 \text{ times normal}}.$$

(d) and (e) As will be shown in the next example, if the flux per pole (E_1/f) is maintained constant by adjustment of voltage and frequency, any particular torque occurs at a unique value of slip frequency f_2 and rotor current I_2'.

Further, since: $n_s = n + sn_s$

$$pn_s = pn + p \times \frac{f_2}{f_{supply}} \times n_s$$

$f_{supply} = pn + f_2$ since pn_s is the supply frequency. $\cdot$

The questions ask for the supply frequency and voltage to produce the maximum torque, and a torque of 1800 Nm, at two different speeds, 500 rev/min and zero. The required values of f_2 and I_2 can be deduced from those occurring at normal voltage and frequency for these particular torques. The supply voltage required will be $I_2'Z$ where the reactive elements in the impedance will be corrected for f_{supply} as calculated. Parts (d) and (e) are worked out in the following table.

	Starting $n = 0$		Speed $n = 500/60$ rev/s	
	1800 Nm	Max. torque	1800 Nm	Max. torque
Slip at 50 Hz	0.0907	0.1529	0.0907	0.1529
Slip frequency $f_2 = s \times 50$	4.535	7.645	4.535	7.645
Supply frequency $= pn + f_2$	4.535	7.645	2.535	32.645
$I_2' = \dfrac{440}{\sqrt{(0.2 + 0.18/s)^2 + 1.16^2}}$	177.9	244.4	177.9	244.4
Actual slip $= f_2/f_{supply}$	1	1	0.1536	0.234
R_2'/s	0.18	0.18	1.172	0.7692
$X = 1.16 \times f_{supply}/50$	0.1052	0.177	0.6812	0.757
$Z = \sqrt{(0.2 + R_2'/s)^2 + X^2}$	0.3943	0.4192	1.532	1.23
$V_{supply} = I_2'Z$	70.1	102.5	272.5	300.6

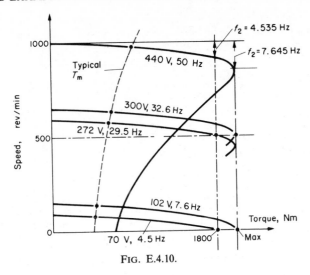

FIG. E.4.10.

The various speed/torque curves are sketched on the figure, for the criteria of constant flux per pole. It can be seen that they are very suitable for speed-controlled applications, with maximum torque being available over the whole range.

4.3 CONSTANT-(PRIMARY) CURRENT OPERATION: IMPROVED STARTING PERFORMANCE

This is a very interesting mode, though in practice, operation is confined to starting, with variable-frequency supplies, and rheostatic braking where the constant current is usually of zero frequency. The value of primary impedance is only required for the calculation of supply voltage and does not influence the electromechanical performance. Consequently, for such calculations, the equivalent circuit can omit the primary impedance. The magnetising resistance will also be omitted, without significant loss of accuracy. It must be emphasised that the induction machine equivalent circuit can be used at any frequency over a wide range (including approximate allowance for the time harmonics by superposition), providing *all* frequency-sensitive parameters are given their appropriate values. However, it is sometimes useful to define, and, after modification, work with the parameters specified at a particular frequency f_{base}, which will usually be the rated value.

EXAMPLE 4.11

The values of E_1 and x_2' for a particular induction motor are known at a frequency f_{base}.

(a) Develop the expressions which show that the rotor current and torque are independent of the supply frequency but depend on the slip frequency, f_2; providing that the flux (E_1/f) is constant.

(b) Show also, independently of the above, that for any given primary current I_1, the rotor current I_2' is governed by f_2 and explain how this is related to the constant-flux condition.

(c) Finally, derive the expression for the slip $\hat{s} = f_2/f$ at which maximum torque occurs for a constant-current drive and hence show that the maximum torque capability is independent of both supply and slip frequencies.

(a) At any frequency f, and slip f_2/f, then sx_2' becomes: $(f_2/f)(x_2' \times f/f_{base}) = x_2' \times f_2/f_{base}$. With constant flux per pole, the referred secondary e.m.f. E_1 at standstill is proportional to the supply frequency f, so sE_1 becomes: $(f_2/f)(E_1 \times f/f_{base}) = E_1 \times f_2/f_{base}$.
Hence rotor current:

$$I_2' = \frac{E_1 \times f_2/f_{base}}{R_2' + j(x_2' \times f_2/f_{base})} = \frac{E_1}{\dfrac{R_2'}{f_2/f_{base}} + jx_2'} \qquad (4.14)$$

At any frequency, with the appropriate values of e.m.f.s and reactances, the general torque expression, eqn. (4.4), is

$$\frac{3}{2\pi \times f/p} \times I_2'^2 \times \frac{R_2'}{f_2/f} \times \frac{(f_{base})}{(f_{base})}$$

99

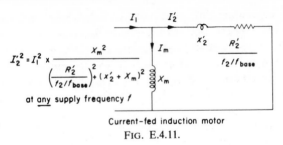

Current-fed induction motor
FIG. E.4.11.

By incorporating f_{base} in a unity multiplier, cancelling f and rearranging:

$$T_e = \frac{3}{2\pi \times f_{\text{base}}/p} \times I_2'^2 \times \frac{R_2'}{f_2/f_{\text{base}}} \qquad (4.15)$$

showing that since I_2' is independent of f, eqn. (4.14), then so is T_e.

(b) From the rules for parallel circuits and correcting for frequency on the circuit of Fig. E.4.11:

$$I_2' = I_1 \times \frac{jX_m(f/f_{\text{base}})}{R_2'/(f_2/f) + j(x_2' + X_m)(f/f_{\text{base}})}$$

Dividing throughout by f/f_{base} and squaring:

$$I_2'^2 = I_1^2 \times \frac{X_m{}^2}{\left(\dfrac{R_2'}{f_2/f_{\text{base}}}\right)^2 + (x_2' + X_m)^2} \qquad (4.16)$$

A similar expression, with $X_m{}^2$ replaced by $\left[\left(\dfrac{R_2'}{f_2/f_{\text{base}}}\right)^2 + x_2'^2\right]$, will give $I_m{}^2$.

The expression for I_2' indicates that its value depends on f_2, not on supply frequency, whether or not the flux is constant. However, at a particular slip frequency f_2, eqn (4.16) modified for I_m^2 shows that I_m has a unique value related to I_1 and hence corresponds to a particular flux. Hence, for a given I_1 and f_2, there is a unique value of I'_2 and of I_m, flux ϕ and torque T_e from eqns. (4.15) and (4.16). Alternatively if voltage and frequency are controlled to give constant flux (E_1/f), any particular f_2 will define the currents and the torque. This gives an easy method of deriving the variable-frequency ω_m/T_e characteristic from that at a particular frequency (see Ref. 1).

(c) Inserting the expression for I'^2_2 into the torque expression, T_e will be found to have a form similar to eqn. (4.5) for the approximate circuit, with I_1X_m as the constant replacing V_1. By comparing expressions or by differentiating, the maximum value of T_e occurs when $R_2/(f_2/f_{base}) = x'_2 + X_m$ so for maximum torque:

$$\frac{\hat{f}_2}{f_{base}} = \frac{R'_2}{x'_2 + X_m}$$

hence, the slip for maximum torque

$$\hat{s} = \frac{\hat{f}_2}{f} \times \frac{f_{base}}{f_{base}} = \frac{R'_2}{x'_2 + X_m} \times \frac{f_{base}}{f} \tag{4.17}$$

Substituting the value of $\hat{f}_2/f_{base}$ in the torque equation (4.15) gives:

$$\text{Maximum } T_e = \frac{3I_1^2}{2\pi f_{base}/p} \times \frac{X_m^2}{(x'_2 + X_m)^2 + (x'_2 + X_m)^2} \times (x'_2 + X_m)$$

$$= \frac{3I_1^2}{2\pi \times f_{base}/p} \times \frac{X_m^2}{2(x'_2 + X_m)} \tag{4.18}$$

which is independent of both f and f_2, though f_2 must have the value given above, $\hat{f}_2$, to achieve this capability and it does depend on the value of I_1^2.

Note that in the relevant expressions derived, the variable f_2/f_{base} replaces $s = f_2/f$ used in the previous constant-frequency expressions. This quantity will be given the symbol S and is particularly useful when the constant primary-current is d.c. The machine is then generating at a rotor frequency $f_2 = pn$, showing that when $n_s = n_{s(base)}$:

$$S = pn/f_{base} = pn/pn_{s(base)} = n/n_s = n_s(1 - s)/n_s = 1 - s.$$

In this dynamic braking mode, the current I_1 is the equivalent r.m.s. primary current giving the same m.m.f. as I_{dc}. In the usual 2-lead connection for primary d.c. supply, the equivalent $I_1 = \sqrt{(2/3)}I_{dc} = 0.816I_{dc}$. The speed/torque curves for dynamic braking are only in the 1st and 3rd quadrants with negative speed × torque product, and a shape similarity with the motoring curves, see Ref. 1. A torque maximum occurs at a value of $\hat{S} = R_2'/(x_2' + X_m)$ usually at a very low speed because $S = 1 - s$.

EXAMPLE 4.12

A 3-phase, 8-pole, 50-Hz, star-connected, 500-V induction motor has the equivalent-circuit per phase shown. Calculate the torques produced at slips of 0.005, 0.025, 0.05, 1 and the maximum torque, for the following two conditions:

(a) Constant(r.m.s.)-voltage drive at 500 line V;

(b) Constant(r.m.s.)-current drive at the same primary current occurring for slip = 0.05 in (a).

The role of X_m in the calculations becomes important at very low slips where R_2'/s is large and becomes a dominant parameter. For the constant-voltage mode the approximate circuit will be used because maximum torque occurs at much higher slips than for the constant-current mode. Low-slip values need not be calculated in the first case, for this general comparison of the two modes.

$$\text{For const. } V \quad \hat{s} = \frac{R_2'}{\sqrt{R_1^2 + (x_1 + x_2')^2}} = \frac{0.13}{\sqrt{0.13^2 + 1.2^2}} = 0.1077$$

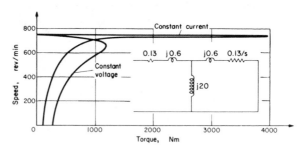

FIG. E.4.12.

102

$s =$	0.005	0.00631	0.025	0.05	0.1077	1
rev/min =	746	745	731	712.5	669	0
R_2'/s	26	20.6	5.2	2.6	1.207	0.13
$R_1 + R_2'/s = R =$			5.33	2.73	1.337	0.26
$x_2' + x_2' = X =$			1.2	1.2	1.2	1.2
$Z = \sqrt{R^2 + X^2} =$			5.46	2.98	1.8	1.228
$I_2' = 500/\sqrt{3}\,Z =$			52.8	96.8	160.6	235.1
$I_2' =$			$5.3 - j52.5$	$88.7 - j38.8$	$119 - j107.5$	$49.8 - j229.8$
$I_0 = 288.7/j20 =$			$-j14.4$	$-j14.4$	$-j14.4$	$j14.4$
$|I_1| = |I_2' + I_0|$			67.1	103.4	170.3	249.2
T_e at 500 V =			553	930	1188	274
$Z^2 = \dfrac{R_2'^2}{s^2} + (x_2' + X_m)^2 =$	1100	848.7	451.4	431.1		424.4
$X_m^2/Z^2 =$	0.364	0.471	0.886	0.928		0.943
$I_2'^2 = (103.4)^2 \dfrac{X_m^2}{Z^2} =$	3887	5039	9473	9920		10 077
T_e at 103.4 A	3856	3961	1880	985		50

(a)

(b)

103

For const. $I_1 = \hat{s} = \dfrac{R_2'}{x_2' + X_m} = \dfrac{0.13}{0.6 + 20} = 0.00631$

$T_e = \dfrac{3}{2\pi \times 50/4} \times I_2'^2 \times \dfrac{R_2'}{s} = \dfrac{I_2'^2}{26.2} \times \dfrac{R_2'}{s}$

The two speed/torque curves are sketched from the above results. They have the same torque approximately at $s = 0.05$, since the primary currents are the same. The difference is due to the approximations in the constant voltage case. The higher maximum torque for the constant-current case and the smaller speed-regulation look attractive, but the voltage required greatly exceeds the rated value as will be shown in the next question.

EXAMPLE 4.13

For the motor of the last question, and for the constant current of 103.4 A calculate, using the available results where appropriate:

(a) the values of I_m and I_2' for maximum torque;

(b) the required supply voltage to sustain this primary current at $s = 0.05$;

(c) the required supply voltage to sustain this primary current at $s = 0.00631$.

The approximate circuit may be used to estimate the supply voltage.

(a) $I_2' = I_1 \times \dfrac{jX_m}{(x_2' + X_m) + j(x_2' + X_m)} = 103.4 \times j20\dfrac{(20.6 - j20.6)}{20.6^2 + 20.6^2} = 50.2 + j50.2$

$= 71$ A

$I_m = I_1 - I_2' = 103.4 + j0 - 50.2 - j50.2 = 53.2 - j50.2 \quad = 73.1$ A

(b) $V = \sqrt{3} \times Z \times I_2' = \sqrt{3} \times 2.98 \times \sqrt{9920} \quad\quad\quad = 514$ V

(c) $V \quad\quad = \sqrt{3} \times \sqrt{20.6^2 + 1.2^2} \times \sqrt{5039} \quad = 2553$ V

Clearly, the maximum-torque, low-slip condition is not a practicable possibility. Furthermore, with a magnetising current of 73.1 A, instead of the normal 14.4 A, saturation would be considerable and X_m would fall. Example 4.15 makes some allowance for this. The next example (4.14) shows that this maximum torque can be obtained at lower frequencies since then, the slip $\hat{f}_2/f$ is higher and the component of voltage drop $I_2'R_2'/\hat{s}$ required is lower.

EXAMPLE 4.14

(a) Derive an expression for the required frequency to give maximum torque with a constant-current supply.

(b) Using the same motor data as for Example 4.12, calculate the required supply frequency and voltage to give this maximum torque with constant-current drive (i) at starting; (ii) at 20% of normal synchronous speed.

(c) For the same motor data, but with constant flux maintained instead, at the value corresponding to normal operation, determine the required voltage and frequency to give maximum torque.

(a) From Example 4.10 $\hat{s} = \dfrac{R_2'}{x_2' + X_m} \times \dfrac{f_{base}}{f}$ [eqn. (4.17)]

and, since $s = \dfrac{n_s - n}{n_s} = \dfrac{f/p - n}{f/p} = \dfrac{f - pn}{f}$, cancelling f after equat-

ing these two expressions gives $\hat{f} = \dfrac{R_2' \times f_{base}}{x_2' + X_m} + pn$

(b)

	(b)(i)	(b)(ii)
$\hat{f} =$	$\dfrac{0.13 \times 50}{0.6 + 20} = 0.3155$ Hz	$\dfrac{0.13 \times 50}{20.6} + 4 \times \dfrac{50}{4 \times 5}$ $= \underline{10.3155}$
$\mathbf{Z}_2' = \dfrac{R_2'}{s} + jx_2'\dfrac{\hat{f}}{f_{base}} =$	$0.13 + j0.6 \times \dfrac{0.3155}{50}$	$\dfrac{0.13}{0.3155/10.3155} + j0.6 \times \dfrac{10.3155}{50}$
$\mathbf{Z}_{input} = \mathbf{z}_1 + \dfrac{1}{\mathbf{Y}_m + \dfrac{1}{\mathbf{Z}_2'}} =$	$0.1913 + j0.0687 = 0.2033\,\Omega$	$2.132 + j2.247 = 3.097\,\Omega$
V_{supply} $= \sqrt{3} \times 103.4 \times Z_{input}$	$\underline{36.4 \text{ V at } 0.3155 \text{ Hz}}$	$\underline{555 \text{ V at } 10.3155 \text{ Hz}}$

All the detailed calculations are not shown and note that $\mathbf{Y}_m = 1/jX_m$ must also be corrected for the frequency change from 50 Hz values. The exact circuit must be used because of the high value of $I_m = 73.1$ A, from Example 4.13. Note that normal supply voltage of 500 V limits constant-current operation at 103.4 A to rather less than 20% of normal synchronous speed.

(c) From Example 4.11, any particular torque, at constant flux, is obtained at a unique slip frequency. In this case we require maximum torque, which from Example 4.12 occurs at $\hat{s} = 0.1077$ and therefore $\hat{f}_2 = 0.1077 \times 50 = 5.385$ Hz.

Because this is a constant, rated-flux condition, I_m is relatively small and the approximate circuit may be used to calculate the supply voltage from $\sqrt{3} \times Z \times I_2'$ using the results of Example 4.12. From Example 4.12 part (a), the rotor current will be the same ($I_2' = 160.6$ A) and the maximum torque too will be unchanged at 1188 Nm.

Hence, $Z_{input} = 0.13 + j(0.6 + 0.6) \times \dfrac{5.385}{50} + 0.13 = 0.26 + j0.1292 = 0.29 \ \Omega$

$V_{supply} = \sqrt{3} \times 0.29 \times 160.6 = \underline{80.8 \text{ V at } 5.385 \text{ Hz}}$

$I_m = \dfrac{80.8/\sqrt{3}}{20 \times 5.385/50} = 21.6$ A (difference from 14.4 A is due to approximations)

It will be noticed that the maximum torque is very much less than obtained with the constant-current drive. Even with the lower (constant) primary current of 103.4 A the torque is 3961 Nm, as against 1188 Nm. This is because the frequency is very much lower at 0.3155 Hz and more of the current I_1 is therefore passed through the reduced X_m. This improvement is offset partly, since the value of X_m collapses due to saturation at the high magnetising current. The next example illustrates this point.

EXAMPLE 4.15

Once again, using the motor data of the previous examples, calculate, for a constant-current drive of 103.4 A, the maximum starting torque (i) neglecting saturation and (ii) assuming the value of X_m is reduced to 1/3 of its normal value due to saturation. Make an approximate comparison of the flux levels for (i) and (ii) compared with normal operation at slip = 0.05.

In Example 4.10 it was shown that the maximum torque under constant-current drive conditions is:

$$T_e = \frac{3I_1^2}{2\pi f_{base}/p} \times \frac{X_m^2}{2(x_2' + X_m)}$$

This expression is independent of all frequencies except that x_2' and X_m correspond to f_{base}. It is sufficient for the purpose of answering this question. By correcting the second term for the specified saturated change of X_m, the effect of saturation of maximum torque is found simply. It is a useful exercise to check this, however, by working out the value of $\hat{s}$ for the saturated condition and hence the values of f_2, Z_2', Z_{input}, I_2' and I_m. They are as follows—using the exact circuit for solutions:

	$\hat{s}$	$\hat{f}_2$	Z_2'	Z_{input}	I_2'	I_m	$T_{e(max)}$	X_m
Unsaturated	1	0.3155	$0.061 + j0.065$	0.203	71	73.1	3961	20
Saturated	1	0.8944	$0.055 + j0.065$	0.199	67.1	73.4	1250	6.667

The unsaturated values have been worked out in previous examples. For the saturated value:

$$X_m \text{ reduced to: } 20 \times 1/3 = 6.667 \ \Omega$$

$$\hat{f}_2 = \frac{R_2'}{x_2' + X_m} \cdot f_{base} = \frac{0.13 \times 50}{0.6 + 6.667} = 0.8944 \text{ Hz}$$

$$\text{Maximum } T_e = \frac{3 \times 103.4^2}{2\pi \times 50/4} \times \frac{6.667^2}{2(0.6 + 6.667)} = \underline{1250 \text{ Nm}}$$

Using a lower frequency than for the constant, rated-flux condition, it can be seen that in spite of saturating the magnetic circuit, the maximum torque is still higher at $I_1 = 103.4$ A than the 1188 Nm for $I_1 = 170.3$ A, when constant voltage is the supply condition. To check that the saturation allowance is reasonable, the flux will be worked out from $E_1/f = I_m X_m/f$.

For normal rating, flux proportional to: $12.6 \times 20/50$ $= 5.04$

For starting (unsat.) ,, $73.1 \times \dfrac{20 \times 0.3155}{50} \Big/ 0.3155 = 29.4$

For starting (sat.) ,, $73.4 \times \dfrac{6.67 \times 0.8944}{50} \Big/ 0.8944 = 9.79$

The flux ratio allowing for saturation is $9.79/5.04 = \underline{1.94}$

The I_m ratio is: $73.4/12.6 = \underline{5.8}$

By the empirical formula used in Example 3.6, this flux ratio should give an I_m ratio of:

$$\frac{0.6 \times 1.94}{1 - 0.4 \times 1.94} = \underline{5.2}$$

which is close to 5.8 above and suggests that the saturation allowance is reasonable. For an exact calculation, the magnetisation characteristic ϕ/I_m would have to be available and an iterative program devised to approach the exact solution, since the value of I_1 in the maximum torque expression is not known until the value of X_m is known. A similar method to that used for the d.c. series motor can be adopted. Here, the nonlinearity of the magnetisation curve was dealt with at the beginning by taking various values of I_f

and k_ϕ. In the present case, a series of I_m values would define a series of corresponding X_m values. Referring to the various expressions developed in Example 4.11, each X_m will define $\hat{s}$, $\hat{f}_2$, E_1 ($= I_m X_m$), I'_2 (from E_1/Z'_2) and I_1 from the parallel-circuit relationships. The maximum torque follows for the various values of I_1 calculated.

The last five examples have shown, through the circuit equations, the special characteristics of the induction motor when under controlled frequency and voltage. A simple way of summarising the behaviour is through study of the m.m.f. diagram represented by the I_1, I'_2 and I_m triangle. As will be shown later in Section 5.5, which compares induction and synchronous machines, the torque is proportional to the product of any two currents and the sine of the angle between them. Now consider the two phasor diagrams of Fig. 4.2. The first one is for the maximum-torque condition deduced from the constant-supply-voltage equations in Examples 4.11 and 4.12. I_1 and I'_2 are relatively high but I_m remains at the level corresponding to rated flux. The voltage diagram is drawn for the approximate-circuit calculation. If this maximum-torque is required over a range of frequencies down to zero speed, the m.m.f. diagram would be unchanged, with the constant-rated flux represented by I_m. This occurs, from Examples 4.11–4.13, at a constant slip-frequency of 5.385 Hz. I'_2, I_1 and I_m are all constant. Refer also to Example 4.10.

Figure 4.2b shows the condition for maximum torque deduced from the constant-supply current equations, for the rated current of $I_1 = 103.4$ A. Again this condition can be sustained over a range of frequencies, by suitable adjustment of V_1 and f_1. It will be noticed that I_m is very much higher, Example 4.13a, and the diagram has been constructed allowing for saturation as in Example 4.15. The voltage diagram has to be drawn this time from the exact circuit because I_m is so large. It is shown for the starting condition. V_1 was not calculated allowing for saturation but it was 36.4 line volts with saturation changes neglected in Example 4.14.

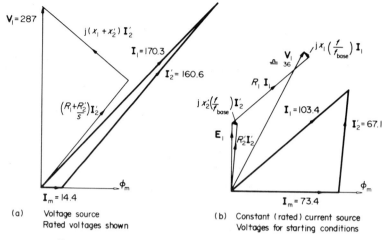

FIG. 4.2. Maximum torque with different supply conditions.

The starting frequency f_2 $(=f_1)$ was there calculated as 0.3155 Hz but in fact, allowing for saturation, f_2 should be 0.8944 Hz—Example 4.15. Even so this value is still much less than for Fig. 4.2a and therefore I_m is much higher. So is the maximum torque itself, though the supply current is only 103.4 A instead of 170.3 A in Fig. 4.2a. This is due to the currents being at a better displacement angle; I_2' and I_m are nearly perpendicular. Again, if it is desired to sustain the maximum torque of Fig. 4.2b up to the speed where the voltage reaches its maximum—about $f_1 = 10$ Hz, Example 4.14—f_2, and therefore all the currents, must be maintained constant. Thus for either constant-voltage or constant-current supplies, the condition for maximum torque is a particular constant flux, which is different for the two cases. Further discussion of this mode will be deferred till Sections 5.5 and 7.5.

EXAMPLE 4.16

Using the data and the "exact" circuit calculations for the motor of Example 4.2, investigate the following features of the performance when the machine is changed over from motoring at a slip of 3% to dynamic braking. D.C. excitation is applied to the stator, using the 2-lead connection; i.e. equivalent r.m.s. a.c. current I_1 equal to $\sqrt{2/3}I_{dc}$. For all cases the speed may be assumed unchanged until the switch changeover is completed. Further, the circuit is so adjusted as to retain initially the same value of rotor current as when motoring at 3% slip.

(a) Rotor-circuit resistance unchanged. Calculate the d.c. excitation voltage and current and find the initial braking torque on changeover and also the maximum torque produced during the run-down to zero speed. The d.c. excitation is maintained.

(b) Repeat the calculation for the condition where instead, the excitation is so adjusted that the air-gap flux (E_1/f) is maintained at the 3% slip value. Extra rotor-circuit resistance will now be required to keep the rotor current at the 3% value.

(c) Compare the initial braking torques and currents if instead of (b) or (c), two stator leads are reversed to cause reverse-current braking (plugging).

For (a) and (b), the magnetising resistance does not apply because the stator excitation is d.c. For part (c), the approximate circuit may be used.

(a) The equivalent circuit is shown on the figure but unlike Examples 4.11 to 4.15 the constant current is now d.c. and the relative motion is changed from $n_s - n$ to $n = Sn_s$ where $S = f_2/f_{base}$. The rotor frequency is now proportional to speed since the machine is operating as a variable-speed generator and $S = n/n_s = 1 - s$.

Before, and immediately after changeover,

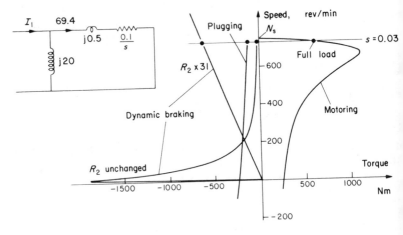

FIG. E.4.16.

$$N = (1 - s)N_s = (1 - 0.03) \times 60 \times 50/4 = 727.5 \text{ rev/min}$$
$$S = 727.5/750 = 0.97$$

From the parallel circuit relationships $I_2'^2 = I_1^2 \dfrac{20^2}{(0.1/0.97)^2 + (20 + 0.5)^2}$

and since I_2', from Example (4.2) $= 69.4$ A, $I_1 = 71.1$ A.

The d.c. current to give this equivalent I_1 is $71.1 \times \sqrt{(3/2)} = \underline{87.1 \text{ A}}$

and since two stator phases are in series, the required d.c. voltage is $2 \times 0.1 \times 87.1 = \underline{17.4 \text{ V}}$

The initial torque on changeover, using the general torque expression eqn. (4.15) developed in Example 4.10, is equal to:

$$\frac{3}{2\pi \times 50/4} \times 69.4^2 \times \frac{0.1}{0.97} = \underline{19 \text{ Nm}}$$

From the expression for maximum torque eqn. (4.18):

$$T_e = \frac{3}{2\pi \times 50/4} \times 71.1^2 \times \frac{20^2}{2(20 + 0.5)} = \underline{1884 \text{ Nm}}$$

and this occurs at a value of $\hat{S} = 0.1/(20 + 0.5) = 0.0049$, i.e. at speed 3.9 rev/min.
The torque values should be compared with that for 3% slip motoring, i.e. 613.6 Nm. Calculate also that I_m is now 50.3 A—increased from 11.7 A.

(b) For the alternative strategy of maintaining the flux constant instead of I_1, it is more convenient to use the alternative equation for I_2' since E_1 is now known—234 V, from Example 4.2.

Rotor current $I_2' = \dfrac{SE_1}{R_2' + Sx_2'} = 69.4$ A when $S = 0.97$

hence: $69.4^2 = \dfrac{(0.97 \times 234)^2}{(R + 0.1)^2 + (0.97 \times 0.5)^2}$

from which the extra resistance $R = \sqrt{10.46} - 0.1 = \underline{3.134 \ \Omega}$ (ref. to stator).

Reverting to the parallel-circuit relationship for the calculation of the initial stator current:

$$69.4^2 = I_1' \times \frac{20^2}{(3.234/0.97)^2 + (20.5)^2}$$

giving $I_1 = 72.1$ A; $I_{dc} = 72.1 \times 1.225 = \underline{88.3 \text{ A}}$ and d.c. voltage $= 88.3 \times 0.2 = \underline{17.7 \text{ V}}$.

The initial torque on changeover

$$= \frac{3}{2\pi \times 50/4} \times 69.4^2 \times \frac{3.234}{0.97} = \underline{613.4 \text{ Nm}}$$

which is virtually the same as the motoring torque before changeover. The flux and the current are the same, but the rotor power-factor, which is related to the induction machine load angle,[1] is slightly different. The power factor is nearly unity as distinct from part (a) where the power factor and torque are very low, though flux and rotor current are nearly the same.

For maximum torque, since

$$T_e = \frac{3}{2\pi \times 50/4} \times \frac{E_1^2}{(R'/S)^2 + X^2} \times \frac{R'}{S}$$

and E_1 is fixed, then $\hat{S}$ occurs when $R'/\hat{S} = X$. Hence $\hat{S} = 3.234/0.5 = 6.47$.

This means that the speed for maximum torque is impractically high above synchronous speed and therefore 613.4 Nm is the highest torque encountered in running down to zero speed.

The value of the maximum torque is:

$$\frac{3}{2\pi \times 50/4} \times \frac{234^2}{0.5^2 + 0.5^2} \times \frac{3.234}{6.47} = \underline{2091 \text{ Nm}}$$

(c) The changeover now corresponds to a reversal of n_s and slip becomes:

$$s = \frac{n_s - n}{n_s} = \frac{-750 - 727.5}{-750} = 1.97$$

Using the torque equation for constant voltage, since the only change from motoring is the phase sequence and slip:

$$T_e = \frac{3}{2\pi \times 50/4} \times \frac{(440/\sqrt{3})^2}{(0.1 + 0.1/1.97)^2 + 1^2} \times \frac{0.1}{1.97}$$

$$= \frac{1}{26.18} \times 251.2^2 \times 0.05076 = \underline{122.3 \text{ Nm}}$$

Note that although the current is nearly four times that for dynamic braking, the torque is very much less, because of the poor rotor-circuit power factor, the frequency being nearly 100 Hz initially. The various speed/torque curves are sketched on Fig. E.4.16.

EXAMPLE 4.17

A 3-phase, double-cage-rotor, 6-pole, 50-Hz, star-connected induction motor has the following equivalent-circuit parameters per phase:

$z_1 = 0.1 + j0.4 \,\Omega$; $z_2' = 0.3 + j0.4 \,\Omega$; $z_3' = 0.1 + j1.2 \,\Omega$—all at standstill.

Find, in terms of the line voltage V_1, the torque at 980 rev/min:

(a) including the outer-cage impedance;

(b) neglecting the outer-cage impedance.

What is the starting torque?

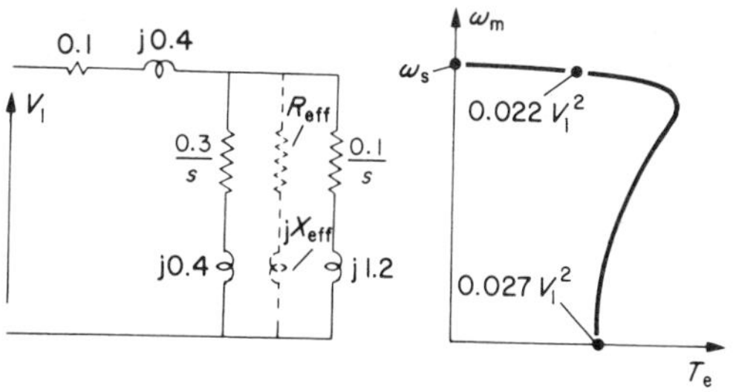

FIG. E.4.17.

The equivalent circuit is shown on the figure, the magnetising branch being neglected. The circuit assumes that both rotor windings embrace the same flux and that they only have leakage with respect to the primary winding. The calculation of torque is then virtually the same as for the single-cage rotor except that the two cages combine to an equivalent impedance $R_{eff} + jX_{eff}$. This impedance includes the effect of slip and is a function of slip. The high-resistance cage is nearer to the surface and therefore has the lower leakage reactance. It is responsible for most of the starting torque because of its lower impedance $\mathbf{z}_2'$ at standstill. $\mathbf{z}_3'$ represents the inner cage in which most of the working torque at low slip is produced, because of its lower resistance, reactances being very low at normal slip frequencies.

For a 6-pole, 50-Hz machine, $N_s = 1000$ rev/min so $s = (1000 - 980)/1000 = 0.02$.

(a) $$\mathbf{Z}_{rotor} = \frac{1}{\dfrac{1}{0.1/0.02 + j1.2} + \dfrac{1}{0.3/0.02 + j0.4}}$$

$$= \frac{1}{0.1891 - j0.04539 + 0.06661 - j0.00178}$$

$$R_{eff} + jX_{eff} = 3.78 + j0.698$$

Adding $\mathbf{z}_1$: $0.1 \ + j0.4$

gives $\mathbf{Z}_{in} = 3.88 + j1.098 = 4.032\ \Omega$

Hence:

$$T_e = \frac{3}{2\pi \times 50/3} \times \frac{(V\surd\surd 3)^2}{4.032^2} \times 3.78 = \underline{0.00222\ V_1^{\ 2}}$$

(b) Neglecting Z_2' and adding $z_1 + Z_3' = 5.1 + j1.6 = 5.3451\ \Omega$

then:

$$T_e = \frac{3}{2\pi \times 50/3} \times \frac{(V\sqrt{}\sqrt{3})^2}{5.3451^2} \times \frac{0.1}{0.02} = \underline{0.00167\ V_1^2}$$

which shows that the outer cage does contribute about 25% of the rated torque

For starting torque, $s = 1$

$$Z_{rotor} = \frac{1}{\dfrac{1}{0.1 + j1.2} + \dfrac{1}{0.3 + j0.4}}$$

$R_{eff} + jX_{eff}$ $= 0.169 + j0.324$

Adding z_1: $0.1\ \ \ + j0.4$

gives Z_{in} $= 0.269 + j0.724 = 0.772\ \Omega$

Hence:

$$T_e = \frac{3}{2\pi \times 50/3} \times \frac{(V\sqrt{}\sqrt{3})^2}{0.772^2} \times 0.169 = \underline{0.00271\ V_1^2}$$

The starting torque is a little higher than the full-load torque indicating the desired effect of the double-cage construction in improving the normally-low, single-cage starting torque; see figure

4.4 SINGLE-PHASE OPERATION

The vast majority of motors operate from single-phase supplies and are less than 1 kW in rating. Many special designs of very small machines have been developed. Theory and calculating procedures tend to be less accurate and more complex than for balanced polyphase and d.c. supplies so that the topic becomes almost a separate and specialised study. For example, the very popular universal a.c./d.c. commutator machine is basically a d.c series motor, but the a.c. supply brings deterioration in performance in terms of efficiency and commutation behaviour, inevitably complicating the theory. In practice of course these effects are alleviated by laminating the field iron and adding compensating windings. The normal single-phase induction motor will produce only a pulsating field so there is no starting torque. Steps have to be taken to add a winding in quadrature with the main winding and to apply phase-splitting circuits, thus producing an approximation to a 2-phase machine. However, once the motor is started, a net torque is developed even with the single winding alone.

The pulsations of the single-phase m.m.f. can be resolved into synchronous-speed forward-rotating and reverse-rotating m.m.f.s, each of half magnitude and considered to act separately on the rotor with slips of s and $2-s$ respectively, see Tutorial Example T.4.19. The second, reverse component gives a braking torque like the tail-end of the balanced polyphase-machine speed/torque characteristic and is much smaller than the forward torque. The performance can be calculated assuming each component has an equivalent circuit equal to half the short-circuit impedance between the terminals. These are connected in series, with the appropriate values of slip modifying the effective rotor resistance. If we consider the case of a 3-phase machine with one line opened—a fault condition called single-phasing which does sometimes occur—then the values of these two configurations are those of one phase of the normal 3-phase equivalent circuit. The magnetising reactance is much smaller however due to interference with the flux by the backwards rotating-field component. The equivalent circuit is shown on Fig. 4.3. Since the two circuits discussed above are in series, the two halves of the s.c. impedance between the line terminals can be combined to give $R_1 + jx_1$ for the stator and the total, referred rotor-impedance is left in two halves, $(R_2' + jx_2')/2$, with the appropriate slip dividing $R_2'/2$ to cover the general case of rotation when they are no longer equal. The total magnetising impedance must also be halved as shown. The voltages across the two sections will be quite different at working speeds and I_b somewhat greater than I_f. Neglecting the magnetising impedance when calculating the torque is a more drastic approximation than for the balanced polyphase machine since I_b will then be equal to I_f. However, $R_2'/(2-s)$ is so small at normal speeds that the error is tolerable for the purpose of comparing single-phase and 3-phase performance as in the next example.

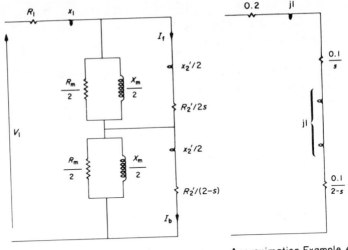

(a) Exact equivalent circuit   Approximation, Example 4.18

FIG. 4.3. Single-phase induction motor.

EXAMPLE 4.18

The 3-phase machine having the equivalent circuit used in Examples 4.1 and 4.2 is operating on no load when a fuse in one line blows to give a single-phasing condition. Determine the torque when the machine is now loaded and the speed falls to give the rated slip of 3%. The approximate equivalent circuit can be used. In order to make a general comparison of single-phase and 3-phase performance, even though this machine is of much higher rating than the normal maximum for single-phase (1–5 kW), calculate also the maximum torque as a 3-phase machine and the torque at slips of 7% and 10%, which will cover the maximum torque as a single-phase machine.

If the approximate circuit is used, Z_m need not be included in calculations of torque. For the 3-phase machine, the impedance required to calculate performance is:

$$0.1 + j0.5 + j0.5 + 0.1/s = (0.1 + 0.1/s) + j1 \ \Omega \text{ per phase.}$$

For the single-phase machine the impedance required is:

$$0.2 + j1 + j1 + \frac{0.1}{s} + \frac{0.1}{2-s} = \left(0.2 + \frac{0.1}{s} + \frac{0.1}{2-s}\right) + j2 \ \Omega$$

For the 3-phase machine

116

$$I_2' = \frac{440//3}{\sqrt{(0.1 + 0.1/s)^2 + 1}}$$

For the 1-phase machine

$$I_f = I_b = \frac{440}{\sqrt{[0.2 + 0.1/s + 0.1/(2 - s)]^2 + 2^2}}$$

For the maximum torque on the 3-phase machine,

$$\hat{s} = \frac{R_2'}{\sqrt{R_1^2 + (x_1 + x_2')^2}} = \frac{0.2}{\sqrt{0.01 + 1}} = 0.0995$$

Hence

$$T_{max} = \frac{3}{78.54} \times \frac{(440/\sqrt{3})^2}{(0.1 + 0.1/0.0995)^2 + 1^2} \times \frac{0.1}{0.0995} = \underline{1115 \text{ Nm}}$$

$$T_e \text{ at } s = 0.03 \text{ from Example 4.2} \qquad = \underline{642 \text{ Nm}}$$

For the single-phase machine:

Slip	=	0.03	0.07	0.1
$0.1/s$	=	3.3333	1.4285	1
$0.1/(2 - s)$	=	0.0508	0.0518	0.0526
$R = 0.2 +$ rotor resis.	=	3.584	1.68	1.253
$Z = \sqrt{R^2 + 2^2}$	=	4.104	2.612	2.36
$I_f = I_b$	=	107.2	168.5	186.4
$I_f^2\left(\dfrac{0.1}{s} - \dfrac{0.1}{2 - s}\right)$	=	37 722	39 088	32 883
$T_e -$ divide by ω_s	=	480	498	419

The maximum torque will be just over 500 Nm which is less than rated torque as a 3-phase machine for which the full-load current is less than 80 A, from Example 4.2. The deterioration for 1-phase operation is thus considerable, the maximum torque being rather less than 50% and the currents being much higher, when compared with the 3-phase motor. See also Tutorial Example T.4.19.

4.5 SPEED CONTROL BY SLIP-POWER RECOVERY

This method of speed control involves the application to the secondary terminals, of a voltage V_3 from an active source, which may provide or accept power. It must automatically adjust itself to slip frequency and this can be done with commutator machines or by power-electronic switching circuits. An external resistor, carrying the slip-frequency current, is the simplest device for automatic adjustment of its voltage to slip frequency since $V_3 = I_2R_3$. The slip power, $P_3 = V_3I_2 \cos \varphi_3$, can be fed back to the supply so that power changes with speed giving approximate constant-torque characteristics. If the slip-power is fed to a suitable machine on the main shaft, a "constant"-power drive is formed. Independently of the method, the speed variation can be calculated by applying $V_3'/$ to the rotor terminals on the equivalent circuit, V_3 having been transformed for turns ratio and for frequency, as for all the other rotor-circuit parameters.

The rotor current becomes:

$$I_2' = \frac{|V_1 - V_3'/s|}{\sqrt{(R_1 + R_2'/s)^2 + (x_1 + x_2')}} \tag{4.19}$$

and the rotor-circuit power per phase:

$$sP_g = sE_1I_2' \cos \varphi_2 = I_2^2R_2 + P_3.$$

The torque

$$T_e = \frac{3P_g}{\omega_s} = \frac{3}{\omega_s} \times \frac{(I_2'^2R_2' + V_3I_2' \cos \varphi_3)}{s}.$$

V_3 can be used to change the slip and/or the power factor.

EXAMPLE 4.19

A 3-phase, 440-V, star-connected shunt commutator-motor has the following equivalent-circuit parameters per phase:

$$R_1 = 0.2\,\Omega; \quad x_1 = 0.8\,\Omega; \quad R_2 = 0.06\,\Omega; \quad x_2 = 0.25\,\Omega.$$

The magnetising branch may be neglected and the stator/rotor turns ratio is $2:1$. With the commutator brushes short circuited, the motor develops full load torque at 3% slip.

(a) Determine the voltage, in phase with supply, which applied to the commutator brushes will cause the motor to develop full-load torque at 25% slip.
(b) What voltage in lagging quadrature with the supply is required to give unity

118

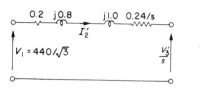

Part (a)

FIG. E.4.19.

(secondary) power-factor at the full-load slip? What effect will this have on the torque?

The shunt-commutator machine is an induction motor with a built-in frequency changer formed by commutator and brushes, to which variable supply-frequency-voltages are applied and automatically transformed to slip frequency for the rotor (commutator) winding.[1] The approximate equivalent circuit is shown on the figure. The rotor impedance has been referred to the stator winding; i.e. $R_2' = 2^2 \times 0.06 = 0.24 \Omega$; $x_2' = 4 \times 0.25 = 1 \Omega$.

(a) With brushes short circuited:

$$I_2'^2 = \frac{(440/\sqrt{3})^2}{(0.2 + 0.24/0.03)^2 + (0.8 + 1)^2} = 915.6 \text{ A}^2$$

With applied voltage V_3 at 25% slip:

$$I_2'^2 = \frac{(440/\sqrt{3} - V_3'/0.25)^2}{(0.2 + 0.24/0.25)^2 + 1.8^2}$$

$$= (118.63 - 1.868 V_3')^2$$

The rotor-circuit impedance is $\sqrt{1.16^2 + 1.8^2} = 2.1414 \Omega$

and since V_3 is in phase with V_1, power factor $\cos \varphi_2 = \dfrac{1.16}{2.414} = \cos \varphi_3$.

This last expression for I_2' and for $\cos \varphi_3$ is now substituted in the torque equation above and equated to the full-load torque for short-circuited brushes.

With V_3 applied: $I_2'^2 R_2 = (14\,073 - 443.2 V_3' + 3.489 V_3'^2) \times 0.24$

and $V_3' I_2' \cos \varphi_3 = V_3'(118.63 - 1.868 V_3') \times 1.16/2.1414$

$\dfrac{\text{Total rotor-circuit power}}{0.25} = -0698 V_3'^2 - 168.5 V_3' + 13\,510$ after some simplification.

This is equated to:

$$\frac{\text{Normal rotor-circuit power}}{s} = \frac{915.6 \times 0.24}{0.03} = 7324.8 \text{ watts/phase}$$

119

Again, after some simplification, this yields the expression $V_3'^2 + 241.4 V_3' - 8861.3 = 0$ and the quadratic solution gives, as the only positive value, $V_3' = 32.4$ V.

Allowing for the 2/1 turns ratio: $\underline{V_3 = 16.2 \text{ V}}$, in phase with V_1 will reduce speed to $0.75 N_s$ while delivering full-load torque.

(b) With V_3' lagging V_1 by 90° and at full-load slip of 3%:

$$I_2' = \frac{440/\sqrt{3} - (-j V_3'/0.03)}{(0.2 + 0.24/0.03) + j1.8} = \frac{254 + j33.3 V_3'}{8.2 + j1.8}$$

For unity power factor, this expression must be "real". This in turn means that the "real" and "imaginary" parts of numerator and denominator must be in the same ratio.

Hence:

$$\frac{254}{33.3 V_3'} = \frac{8.2}{1.8} \text{ from which } V_3' = 1.673 \text{ V and } \underline{V_3 = 0.836 \text{ V}}$$

Although this voltage is very low, it must be remembered that the rotor e.m.f. at this small slip is also low.

Substituting the value of V_3':

$$I_2' = \frac{254 + j33.3 \times 1.673}{8.2 + j1.8} = 33.1\underline{/+11°35}$$

and since V_3' is lagging V_1, the total angle of lead $\varphi_3 = 11°35 + 90 = 101°35$

The power P_3 is therefore $V_3' I_2' \quad \cos \varphi_3 = 1.673 \times 33.1 \quad \cos 101°35 = -21.8$ watts/phase

Hence: $T_e = \dfrac{3 P_g}{\omega_s} = \dfrac{3}{\omega_s} \dfrac{(33.1^2 \times 0.24 - 21.8)}{0.03} = \dfrac{3}{\omega_s} \times 8038$ Nm

This compares with the full-load torque of $(3\omega_s) \times 7324.8$ Nm so there would be a tendency for speed to rise with the additional torque and V_3 would have to be modified slightly to give a speed-reducing component. This tendency can also be understood from the sign of P_3 which is negative, indicating a power input to the rotor, increasing the speed. The phase angle of I_2' with respect to V_3 is greater than 90°. The exact calculations of V_3 for a given speed and power factor are more complex than the above.[1]

EXAMPLE 4.20

The induced voltage across one pole pitch of a 50-Hz, 6-pole Schrâge motor commutator is 36 V r.m.s. The stator (secondary) winding can be arranged either in parallel or series to give an induced voltage (E_2) at standstill of 30 V or 60 V. Find in each case the speed range on no load. For the paralleled stator winding find also the angular separation of the brushgear to give speeds of 1800, 400, and −100 rev/min.

The Schrâge motor is also a self-contained, variable speed induction motor, generating its own voltage V_3 by commutator action.[1] The primary winding is on the rotor this time, with the commutator, but unlike the shunt commutator-motor, a power-electronic replacement for the frequency-changing action would not be worth considering. Two sets of contra-rotating brushes pick up the voltage V_3 at variable angular separation of θ electrical degrees to give $V_3 = \hat{V}_3 \sin \theta/2$ as the injected voltage per phase. $\hat{V}_3$ is the maximum voltage available with angular separation of 180° (elec.). For the no-load condition, the secondary impedance drop is zero and so V_3 must be in balance with the induced secondary e.m.f. sE_2. Hence:

$$s = \frac{V_3}{E_2} \text{ and speed} = N_s(1-s) = \frac{50 \times 60}{3}\left(1 - \frac{V_3}{E_2}\right) = 1000\left(1 - \frac{36 \sin \theta/2}{E_2}\right)$$

with maximum brush separation 180°:

$$\text{speed range} = 1000\left(1 \pm \frac{36}{30}\right) = \underline{2200/-220 \text{ rev/min}}$$

$$\text{or } 1000\left(1 \pm \frac{36}{60}\right) = \underline{1600/400 \text{ rev/min}}$$

For the various speeds specified: since Rev/min $= 1000\left(1 - \frac{36}{30} \sin \theta/2\right)$

then θ_m in mechanical degrees $= \dfrac{\theta}{p} = \dfrac{2}{6/2} \sin^{-1} \dfrac{(1-(\text{rev/min})/1000)}{36/30}$

By substitution: for 1800 rev/min $\theta_m = \underline{-27°8}$ mechanical

for 400 rev/min $\theta_m = \underline{+20°}$ mechanical

for 1100 rev/min $\theta_m = \underline{+44°3}$ mechanical

Note that for 1800 rev/min, the speed is supersynchronous and V_3 must be negative; the positive sign in the equations developed assumed that P_3 was a power sink. For supersynchronous speeds, the power level in the secondary must have a tendency to rise, due to the action of P_3 as a power source.

EXAMPLE 4.21

A 6-pole, 50-Hz, wound-rotor induction motor drives a load requiring a torque of 2000 Nm at synchronous speed. It is required to have speed variation down to 50% of synchronous speed by slip-power control. Determine the maximum kW rating of the injected power source, (a) assuming $T_m \propto \omega_m^2$, and (b) assuming $T_m \propto \omega_m$. Neglect all the machine losses.

In this case, a standard induction motor is provided with an external slip-power source, which could be a commutator machine, or more usually nowadays, a power-electronic circuit to give frequency conversion from supply frequency to slip frequency.[1]

Since rotor copper loss is being neglected, the question is asking for the maximum rotor-circuit power $3sP_g = 3P_3$, as speed is reduced by slip-power control down to half synchronous-speed. The mechanical output $3(1 - s)P_g$, see Fig. 4.1b, also varies with speed and the nature of this variation governs the magnitude of P_3.

At synchronous speed, the mechanical power $3\hat{P}_m = 2000 \times 2\pi \times 50/3 = 209.4 \text{ kW}$

At any other speed $\omega_m = \omega_s(1 - s)$: $P_m/\hat{P}_m = (1 - s)^x$

Since mechanical power is $\omega_m T_m$, the index 'x' is either 3 for (a) or 2 for (b).

Equating expressions for power $3(1 - s)P_g = 3\hat{P}_m(1 - s)^x$

from which: $\qquad\qquad\qquad\qquad P_g = \hat{P}_m(1 - s)^{(x-1)}$

and $\qquad\qquad\qquad\qquad\qquad P_3 = sP_g = s\hat{P}_m(1 - s)^{(x-1)}$

differentiating: $\dfrac{\mathrm{d}P_3}{\mathrm{d}s} = \hat{P}_m[(1 - s)^{(x-1)} + (-1) \times s \times (x - 1)(1 - s)^{(x-2)}]$

This is zero when: $\qquad (1 - s)^{(x-1)} = s(x - 1)(1 - s)^{(x-2)}$

i.e. when $\qquad\qquad\qquad\qquad s = 1/x$

Substituting this value of s gives $P_3 = \dfrac{1}{x} \times P_m \times \left[\dfrac{x - 1}{x}\right]^{(x-1)} = \hat{P}_m\dfrac{(x -)^{(x-1)}}{x^x}$

Hence for $T_m \propto \omega_m^2$, $x = 3$ and $3P_3 = 209.4 \times \dfrac{2^2}{3^3} = \underline{31 \text{ kW}}$

and for $T_m \propto \omega_m$, $x = 2$ and $3P_3 = 209.4 \times \dfrac{1^1}{2^2} = \underline{52.4 \text{ kW}}$

The variations of P_3 with speed, for different values of x, see Fig. E.4.21, show that the above figures are maximum values occurring over the speed range. It can be seen too, that the higher the value

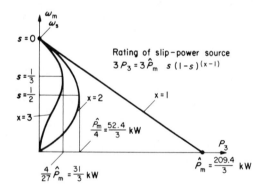

FIG. E.4.21.

122

of x, the more attractive is this method of speed control because the P_3 rating is reduced. Hence this slip-power system finds use in fan and pump drives, where T_m falls considerably as speed reduces.

This chapter has surveyed the more usual methods of controlling induction motors. But there are other ways of doing this, e.g. using unbalanced networks, for which Reference 3 should be consulted. Discussion of power-electronic control will be deferred till Chapter 7.

CHAPTER 5

SYNCHRONOUS MACHINES

ELECTRICAL power is generated almost entirely by synchronous machines, of individual ratings up to and beyond a million kW (1 GW). Consequently, problems of power-system generation, transmission, distribution, fault calculations and protection figure very largely in synchronous-machine studies and these receive more attention for example in Reference 4. The purpose of this present text is to place more emphasis on electrical drives, though some generator problems are given, e.g. determination of equivalent circuit from generating tests, calculation of excitation, simple multi-machine circuits and operating charts. Synchronous motors are the fewest in actual numbers but they are used up to the highest ratings. The facility for power-factor control is an important decisive element, if constant speed is suitable and in addition, synchronous machines have the highest efficiencies. With the advent of static variable-frequency supplies, variable-speed synchronous motors are gaining wider application, having a set speed as accurate as the frequency control. For steady-state operation, the equivalent circuit is simpler than for the induction machine and there is the additional, straightforward control facility—the excitation. Since the dominating magnetising reactance carries the total armature current, its variation with different air-gap flux and saturation levels should be allowed for. Although most synchronous motors are of salient-pole construction for which the equations are less simple than for the round-rotor equivalent circuit of Fig. 1.12c, this latter circuit still gives a fairly accurate answer to the general operating principles for steady state. A few examples with salient-pole equations are worked out at the end of this chapter.

5.1 SUMMARY OF EQUATIONS

Figure 1.12c shows all the parameters on the equivalent circuit. R_a is usually much less than the synchronous reactance $X_s = x_{al} + X_m$ and is often neglected in circuit calculations. It becomes important in efficiency calculations of course and also when operating at fairly low frequencies when reactances have fallen appreciably. The earlier problems in this chapter will include the resistance, the equations being quoted directly from Reference 1 when they are not developed in the text. The equivalent circuit is normally derived from tests at very low power-factor and this is not difficult to achieve, except for very small machines where R_a becomes relatively high. For such tests, the reactance voltage drops are virtually in phase with all the other voltages and can be combined therewith algebraically, to derive and separate the leakage and magnetising components of the synchronous reactance. Examples 5.1–5.3 will help in understanding the following terms and equations which relate to both the time-vectors for voltages and the interconnection with the space-vectors of m.m.f. The conversion is made through the magnetising-curve sensitivity in volts, per unit of m.m.f. Note that the m.m.f.s are all expressed in terms of field turns through which they are measured. The average sensitivity varies from the unsaturated value on the air gap line (k_f volts/At) to k_{fs}, that of the mean slope through the operating point determined by the air-gap e.m.f. E. The equations use motor conventions but can be used as they stand for a generator if this is considered as a "negative" motor, the I_a phasor being at an angle greater than 90° from the reference terminal voltage V.

Circuit equations:
$$E = V - R_a I_a - j x_{al} I_a \quad (5.1)$$
$$E_f = E - j X_m I_a \quad (5.2)$$

M.M.F. equation:
$$F_r = F_f + F_a \quad (5.3)$$

multiplied by k_{fs} volts/At:
$$k_{fs} F_r = k_{fs} F_f + k_{fs} F_a \quad (5.4)$$

gives voltage components:
$$E = E_f + j X_{ms} I_a \quad (5.5)$$

corresponding to flux component equation: $\quad \phi_m = \phi_f + \phi_a \quad$ (5.6)

Mag. curve gives general relationship: $\qquad E = f(F) \qquad$ (5.7)

At zero power factor, eqns (5.1)–(5.6) become algebraic. For zero leading as a motor, or zero lagging as a generator; V, I_a, F_{f1}, F_{f2} and k_f having been measured:

	Short-circuit test $(V = 0)$	Zero p.f. test $(V = 0; I_a = I_{asc})$
Circuit equations are:	$E_1 = x_{al}I_{asc}$ (5.1a)	$E_2 = V + x_{al}I_a$ (5.1b)
M.M.F. equations are:	$F_{f1} = F_a + F_{r1}$ (5.3a)	$F_{f2} = F_a + F_{r2}$ (5.3b)
Magnetisation curve gives:	$E_1 = k_fF_{r1}$ (5.7a)	$E_2 = f(F_{r2})$ (5.7b)

From these two tests and the six equations, a solution for one unknown will yield all the other five. It is only really necessary to solve for x_{al} though sometimes the armature m.m.f. F_a is required if the complete phasor diagram is to be drawn. Eliminating all unknowns apart from E_2 and F_{r2} leaves eqn (5.7b) and:

$$E_2 = V - k_f(F_{f2} - F_{f1}) + k_fF_{r2} \qquad (5.8)$$

The intersection of the straight line (5.8) with the curve (5.7b) yields E_2 and F_{r2}; hence x_{al} from (5.1b) and F_a from (5.3b); see Example 5.1.

The short-circuit test and the o.c. curve (5.7) also yield the unsaturated synchronous reactance;

since on o.c.; $I_a = 0$ $\therefore$ $V = E = E_f$;

and on s.c.; $V = 0$ $\therefore$ $E = x_{al}I_a$ and $E_f = (x_{al} + X_{mu})I_a = X_sI_a$.

The unsaturated value of the synchronous reactance X_{su} and of magnetising reactance X_{mu} are thus derived from the air-gap line, x_{al} having been found previously.

In using this equivalent-circuit information to determine the excitation for any specified terminal voltage, current and power factor, the air-gap e.m.f. E is first found from eqn (5.1). This gives the operating point and the appropriate value of k_{fs}. Hence the correct saturated value of magnetising reactance is $X_{mu}k_{fs}/k_f$ and completing the eqn (5.2) gives the value of E_f, the e.m.f. behind synchronous reactance. The required excitation is E_f/k_{fs}; see Examples 5.1–5.3.

Electromechanical Equations

Considerable insight is gained into the essential aspects of synchronous machine control and behaviour if the machine losses are neglected. The approximate circuit and the phasor diagram for this condition are shown on Fig. 5.1. We have the equation:

$$V\underline{/0} = E_f\underline{/\delta} + jX_sI_a\underline{/\varphi} \quad (5.9) \quad \text{and} \quad I_a\underline{/\varphi} = \frac{V\underline{/0}}{jX_s} - \frac{E_f\underline{/\delta}}{jX_s} \quad (5.9a)$$

Equation (5.9) shows the terminal voltage with its two components. Equation (5.9a) which is a rearrangement of eqn (5.9) shows the terminal current as the sum of two components, each lagging 90°

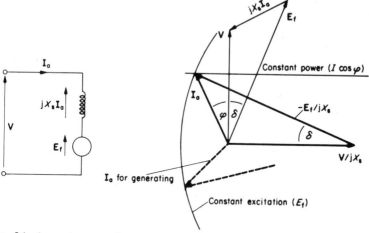

FIG. 5.1. Approximate equivalent circuit per phase and phasor diagram (motor conventions).

127

behind its corresponding voltage. Both equations are shown on the phasor diagram and power (which is the same for input and output since losses are being neglected) can be obtained from either equation, I_a being resolved along V directly, or in its two components. Note that V/jX_s resolves to zero.

Hence, for a 3-phase machine:

$$\text{Power} = 3VI_a \cos \varphi \qquad (5.10)$$

$$\text{or} = -3V \frac{E_f}{X_s} \sin \delta \qquad (5.10a)$$

The negative sign is explained by the choice of motor conventions. The load angle δ is negative (rotor falling back) when motoring, and power will then be positive. For a generator, as indicated, the sign of δ reverses and the I_a phasor falls in the lower part of the diagram, the real part of I_a being negative. Should generator conventions be desired, then it is only necessary to reverse the I_a phasor which will then clearly indicate whether the power-factor angle is leading or lagging on V. Note that at constant frequency, synchronous speed is constant, and torque is obtained on dividing either power expression by ω_s;

$$T_e = \text{Power}/\omega_s \qquad (5.10b)$$

The phasor diagram shows two particular conditions of interest. If power is maintained constant, then $I_a \cos \varphi$ is constant and the I_a phasor must follow a horizontal locus. This shows the variation of power factor and load angle as excitation is varied. A high value of E_f means that a motor *receives* power with current at a leading power-factor and a generator *delivers* power with current at a lagging power-factor; δ is small and there is a large overload capacity before $\sin \delta$ reaches unity. A low excitation leads to the opposite behaviour. If instead the power is allowed to vary but the excitation is constant, then I_a must follow a circular locus determined by the end of the E_f/jX_s phasor. Now, power, power-factor load angle and function can change. There is another important condition where the current phasor follows a horizontal locus along

128

the zero power axis; i.e. on no load as a "motor", I_a is completely leading V (at high values of E_f) or completely lagging V (at low values of excitation). This is operation as a synchronous compensator: similar to a capacitor when overexcited and to a lagging reactor when underexcited.

Generated-e.m.f. Equation

This is little different from the average voltage for the d.c. machine eqn (3.1), except that it is the r.m.s. value which is required so must be multiplied by 1.11. Further, the number of conductors in series z_s must refer to one phase of the winding. The distribution of the coils round the machine periphery is carried out in many different ways and there is inevitably a loss of total phase e.m.f. because the individual conductor voltages are slightly out of phase with one another. So the whole equation must be multiplied by a winding factor, typically about 0.9 for the fundamental voltage. It is different for the harmonic voltages and the winding is deliberately designed to suppress these. The overall effect is that the expression for the fundamental r.m.s. voltage per phase is almost the same as for the average voltage given by eqn (3.1). Alternatively, the transformer e.m.f. equation can be used for a.c. machines; i.e. induced r.m.s. e.m.f. $= 4.44 \times \hat{\phi} \times f \times N_s \times k_w$, where $\hat{\phi}$ is the maximum fundamental flux per pole, N_s the turns in series per phase and k_w the winding factor. No worked examples will be provided to illustrate this since a more detailed study of windings is really required, see Reference 1. It is sufficient to note that in the machine equations, the e.m.f. is proportional to the speed (or the frequency), and the flux component being considered.

5.2 SOLUTION OF EQUATIONS

A general plan for guidance on synchronous machine problems is now given.

Synchronous Machine Solution Programme

Input data from:

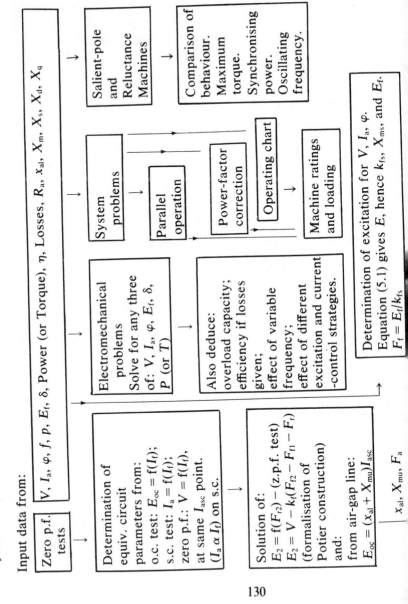

V, I_a, φ, f, p, E_f, δ, Power (or Torque), η, Losses, R_a, x_{al}, X_m, X_s, X_d, X_q

Zero p.f. tests →

Determination of equiv. circuit parameters from:
o.c. test: $E_{oc} = f(I_f)$;
s.c. test: $I_a = f(I_f)$;
zero p.f.: $V = f(I_f)$, at same I_{asc} point. $(I_a \propto I_f)$

Solution of:
$E_2 = f(F_{r2}) - (\text{z.p.f. test})$
$E_2 = V - k_f(F_{r2} - F_{fn1} - F_r)$
(formalisation of Potier construction)
and:
from air-gap line:
$E_{oc} = (x_{al} + X_{mu})I_{asc}$

x_{al}, X_{mu}, F_a

Electromechanical problems
Solve for any three of: V, I_a, φ, E_f, δ, P (or T)
→

Also deduce:
overload capacity;
efficiency if losses given;
effect of variable frequency;
effect of different excitation and current -control strategies.

System problems →

Parallel operation

Power-factor correction

Operating chart

→

Machine ratings and loading

Salient-pole and Reluctance Machines →

Comparison of behaviour. Maximum torque. Synchronising power. Oscillating frequency.

Determination of excitation for V, I_a, φ.
Equation (5.1) gives E, hence k_{fs}, X_{ms}, and E_f.
$F_f = E_f / k_{fs}$

130

EXAMPLE 5.1

The test results on a 5 MVA, 6.6 kV, 3-phase, star-connected synchronous generator are as follows:

Open-circuit test

Generated (line) e.m.f.	3	5	6	7	7.5	7.9	8.4	8.6	8.8	kV
Field current		25	42	57	78	94	117	145	162	181	A

Short-circuit test, at rated armature current required 62 field amperes.
Zero power-factor lagging test, at 6.6 kV and rated current required 210 field amperes.

If the field resistance is $1.2 \, \Omega$ cold, $1.47 \, \Omega$ hot, calculate for normal machine voltage, the range of exciter voltage and current required to provide the excitation from no load up to full load at 0.8 p.f. lagging. The armature resistance is $0.25 \, \Omega$ per phase.

$$\text{Rated armature current } I_{aR} = \frac{500}{\sqrt{3} \times 6.6} = 437.4 \text{ A}$$

The o.c. magnetisation curve is plotted on Fig. E.5.1 and the z.p.f. data ($F_{f1} = 62$ A and $F_{f2} = 210$ A) permit the line $E_2 = V - k_f(F_{f2} - F_{f1}) + k_f F_{f2}$, eqn (5.8) to be plotted. k_f, the unsaturated slope of the magnetisation curve, is $6000/50 = 120$ line V/A. Hence:

$$E_2 = 6.6 - 0.12(210 - 62) + 0.12 F_{f2} = -11.16 + 0.12 F_{f2} \text{ kV (line)}$$

Note, although the equivalent circuit parameters are per-phase values, it is merely a matter of convenience to use the given kV line voltages, but the scaling factor involved must be allowed for as below. Phase volts could of course be used to avoid the faintest possibility of error.

The intersection of the above line with the $E = f(F)$ curve gives simultaneous solution of the two equations at $E_2 = 8.6$ kV. F_{f2} is not usually required. Hence

$$\sqrt{3} x_{al} I_a = E_2 - V \text{ (line)} = 8.6 - 6.6 = 2 \text{ kV} \therefore x_{al} = \frac{2000}{\sqrt{3} \times 437.4} = \underline{2.64 \, \Omega}.$$

For total (unsaturated) synchronous reactance consider point on o.c. and s.c. at $F = 62$ A

$$X_{su} = \frac{7400/\sqrt{3}}{437.4} = 9.78 \, \Omega \text{ giving}$$

$$X_{mu} = 9.78 - 2.64 = 7.14 \, \Omega = \text{unsaturated magnetising reactance}$$

The equivalent circuit per phase is also shown on the figure.

The construction carried out is virtually the same as the Potier construction also described in Reference 1, but put into a more direct mathematical form. The armature m.m.f. F_a at rated current from the Potier triangle is equivalent to $210 - 164 = 46$ A times field turns.

131

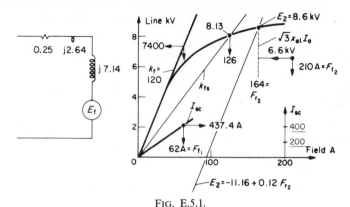

FIG. E.5.1.

Excitation Calculations

On no load, when the machine is cold, and the terminal voltage is the same as the air-gap e.m.f., the required field current from the o.c. curve is 69 A, requiring $69 \times 1.2 = 83 \text{ V}$ from the exciter.

On load, with $I_a = 437.4 (0.8 - j0.6) = 350 - j262$ A

the air-gap e.m.f. from the generator equation $\mathbf{E} = \mathbf{V} + z\mathbf{I}$ is:

$$\mathbf{E}(\text{phase}) = \frac{6600}{\sqrt{3}} + (0.25 + j2.64)(350 - j262)$$

$$= 3810.5 + 779 + j989.5$$

$$= 4589.5 + j989.5 = 8.132 \text{ kV (line)}$$

From the o.c. curve this gives a saturated volts/field A of:

$$k_{fs} = \frac{8132}{126} = 64.5 \text{ compared with } k_f = 120 \text{ line V/field A}$$

Hence saturated magnetising reactance $= 7.14 \times 64.5/120 = 3.84 \ \Omega$ and

$$\mathbf{E}_f = \mathbf{E} + jX_{ms}\mathbf{I}_a = 4589.5 + j989.5 + j3.84(340 - j262)$$

$$= 5595 + j2333 = 10.5 \text{ kV (line)}$$

$$\therefore F_f = \frac{E_f}{k_{fs}} = \frac{10.5}{64.5} = 163 \text{ A}$$

This will be for the "hot" condition so required exciter voltage is:

$$163 \times 1.47 = 239 \text{ V}$$

132

EXAMPLE 5.2

A 3 phase, 500 kVA, 3.3 kV, star-connected synchronous generator has a resistance per phase of 0.3 Ω and a leakage reactance per phase of 2.5 Ω. When running at full load, 0.8 p.f. lagging, the field excitation is 72 A. The o.c. curve at normal speed is:

Line voltage	2080	3100	3730	4090	4310	V
Field current	25	40	55	70	90	A

Estimate the value of the full-load armature ampere-turns per pole in terms of the field turns and hence calculate the range of field current required if the machine has to operate as a synchronous motor at full kVA from 0.2 leading to 0.8 lagging p.f.

In this example, as an alternative to the previous circuit approach, the phasor diagrams will be drawn for both time-vectors and m.m.f. space-vectors. On full load, F_f is given and by constructing $V + R_aI_a + jx_{al}I_a$ to get the gap e.m.f. E, the value of F_r can be read from the o.c. curve. It is shown as a space-vector lagging E by 90°. The vector F_a is known in direction, being in antiphase with I_a for a generator[1], and must intersect with an arc drawn for $F_f = 72$ A as shown. Hence its length is determined and the angle between F_f and F_r, which is also the angle between E and E_f, is available if it is desired to draw in the E_f phasor and the closing $jX_{ms}I_a$ phasor. An analytical solution based on the voltage equations is left as an exercise; it leads to a quadratic in X_{ms} for which the value on load is 12.3 Ω. The unsaturated value on allowance for k_f and k_{fs} is 14.3 Ω.

$$\text{Rated armature current} = \frac{500}{\sqrt{3} \times 3.3} = 87.47 \text{ A}$$

E phasor constructed from V, R_aI_a, $x_{al}I_a = \dfrac{3300}{\sqrt{3}}$, 0.3×87.47, 2.5×87.47

$$= 1905, \qquad 26, \qquad 219$$

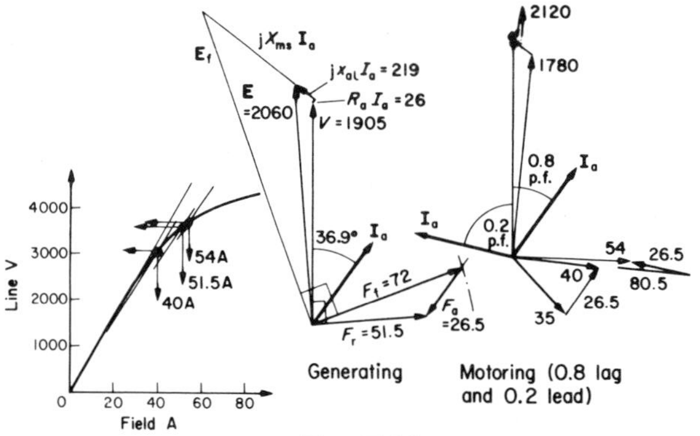

FIG. E.5.2.

133

The problem will now be solved entirely by the use of phasor diagrams. Accuracy will not of course be as good as by analysis. The first phasor diagram is for the loaded, generating condition giving first the value of E as 2060 volts/phase from which a resultant m.m.f. $F_r = 51.5$ A is read off from the o.c. curve. The m.m.f. diagram follows as explained above and F_a by measurement is 26.5 A. The E_f phasor is sketched in lightly at right angles to F_f and the closing vector is $jX_{ms}I_a$.

The procedure for finding the motoring excitation for the two specified power factors is not very different. The armature current and m.m.f. are the same throughout, but unless treated as a "negative" generator, the motor equation must be used. This gives E lagging instead of leading V as in the generator case. F_a is now drawn in phase with I_a for the motor and F_f is therefore found in each case from $F_f = F_r - F_a$. The values for the two different power factors are, by measurement:

$$E = 1780 \text{ V/phase (0.8 p.f.)} \quad E = 2120 \text{ V/phase (0.2 p.f.)}$$

$$F_r \text{ from o.c. curve} = 40 \text{ A (0.8 p.f.)} \qquad F_r = 54 \text{ A (0.2 p.f.)}$$

$$F_f = 35 \text{ A (0.8 p.f.)} \qquad F_f = 80.5 \text{ A (0.2 p.f.)}$$

The final answers could also be obtained by the same analytical method as in Example 5.1.

EXAMPLE 5.3

A 3-phase, 5 kVA, 1000 V, star-connected synchronous machine has $R_a = 4\,\Omega$ and $x_{al} = 12\,\Omega$ per phase. The o.c. curve is as follows:

Field current	4	6	8	10	12	14	16 A
Armature line voltage	490	735	900	990	1070	1115	1160 V at rated speed.

On a short-circuit test, 7 A was required in the field to circulate rated armature current.

Determine the field current and voltage required for operation at constant terminal voltage of 1000 V and (a) no load current; (b) rated current as a generator at 0.8 p.f. lagging; (c) rated current as a motor at unity power factor.

(d) The machine is going to be considered for operation as a synchronous capacitor. Plot a curve of reactive VAr in this mode against the required field current, up to about rated current, and hence determine the permissible rating of the machine, if the field current can be increased up to the generating value of part (c) above. Resistance may be neglected for this part (d).

$$\text{Rated armature current } I_{aR} = \frac{5000}{\sqrt{3 \times 1000}} = 2.89 \text{ A.}$$

From o.c. curve at $I_f = 7$ A:

$$X_{su} = \frac{\text{e.m.f. on air-gap line}}{I_{sc} (2.89 \text{ A})} = \frac{870/\sqrt{3}}{2.89} = 174\,\Omega \text{ per phase}$$

Hence

$$X_{mu} = 174 - 12 = 162 \ \Omega \text{ per phase}$$
$$k_f = 870/7 \quad = 124.3 \text{ line V/fld A}$$

Mode	(a) No load	(b) Generating	(c) Motoring
$\mathbf{I_a}$	0	$2.89(0.8 - j0.6)$ $2.31 - j1.73$	$2.89(1 + j0)$ $2.89 + j0$
$\mathbf{E} = \mathbf{V} \pm \mathbf{z}\mathbf{I_a}$ E r.m.s. line V	$1000/\sqrt{3}$ 577.4 1000	$577.4 + (4 + j12)(2.31 - j1.73)$ $607.3 + j20.8$ 1052.5	$577.4 - (4 + j12)(2.89)$ $565.7 - j34.7$ 981.7
k_{fs} line V/fld A	99	$1052.5/11.5 = 91.5$	$981.7/9.7 = 101.2$
$X_{ms} = 162 \times \dfrac{k_{fs}}{k_f}$		119.25	131.9
$jX_{ms}\mathbf{I_a}$		$206.3 + j275.5$	$j381.1$
$\mathbf{E_f} = \mathbf{E} \pm jX_{ms}\mathbf{I_a}$ E_f line V	577.4 1000	$813.6 + j296.27$ 1500	$565.7 - j415.8$ 1216
$F_f = E_f/k_{fs}$	10.1	16.4	12

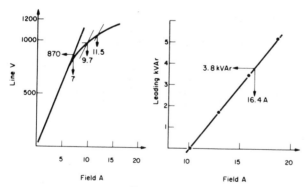

FIG. E.5.3.

135

(d) Calculations for excitation are similar, but for various currents, all of them leading voltage by 90°, up to j3 A and with R_a neglected. $jx_{al}I_a = -12I_a$.

I_a	0	j1	j2	j3
$E = V - zI_a$ E r.m.s. line V	577.4 1000	577.4 + 12 1021	577.4 + 24 1042	577.4 + 36 1062
k_{fs}	99	96.2	92.6	89.6
X_{ms}		125.4	120.7	116.8
$jX_{ms}I_a$		− 125.4	− 241.4	− 350.4
$E_f = E - jX_{ms}I_a$ E_f line V	577.4 1000	589.4 + 125.4 1239	601.4 + 241.4 1460	614.4 + 350.4 1669
$F_f = E_f/k_{fs}$	10.1	12.88	15.8	18.6
$kVA_r = \sqrt{3} \times 1 \times I_a$	0	1.73	3.46	5.2

The curve of kVAr against field current is plotted and although saturation has been allowed for, it is virtually a straight line. At the generating field current of 16.4 A, the kVA$_r$ is 3.8, which is therefore the permissible rating as a synchronous capacitor.

5.3 *PER-UNIT* NOTATION

For synchronous machines this notation is very commonly used and is perhaps the most straightforward in application, especially for the normal, constant-voltage and constant-frequency arrangement. Rated voltage, current and therefore rated kVA are taken as base quantities, plus the constant, synchronous speed. Rated electrical terminal power will therefore be cos φ_R in *per unit*. 1 *per-unit* impedance will be rated-voltage-per-phase/rated-current-per-phase and the synchronous reactance is typically of this order, approaching 2 *per unit* for large turbo generators and rather less than 1 *per unit* for motors with large overload capacity. The next example uses *per-unit* notation for convenience and is meant to illustrate in a simple manner, the essential aspects of synchronous machine behaviour; conventions, load angle, motoring, generating and synchronous-compensator operation. This will be achieved by calculating the current from specified voltage, e.m.f., load angle and reactance. A motor convention will be used and the synchronous reactance X_s assumed to be 1 *per unit*.

From eqn (5.9):

$$\mathbf{V} = \mathbf{E}_f + jX_s\mathbf{I}_a \quad \text{neglecting resistance;}$$

at rated voltage: $\quad 1 = E_f\underline{/\delta} + jI_a\underline{/\varphi}$

from which: $\quad I_a\underline{/\varphi} = \dfrac{1 - E_f\underline{/\delta}}{j} = -j(1 - E_f\underline{/\delta})$ per unit.

The solution for $\mathbf{I}_a$ will yield the mode; real-part positive means motoring, real-part negative means generating and real-part zero means operation as a synchronous compensator. The real part also represents the *per-unit* power and the *per-unit* torque, since losses are being neglected. The solution also gives the power factor, though for a generator this is best detected for lagging or leading by reversing the current phasor, as shown on the phasor diagrams in the next example.

EXAMPLE 5.4

A synchronous machine has $X_s = 1$ *per unit* and operates at rated voltage $V = 1$ *per unit*. Determine the *per-unit* values of current, power, torque, and the power factor and state the machine function when the e.m.f. due to field current (E_f in *per unit*) and the load angle δ have the following values: (a) $0.5\underline{/0°}$; (b) $1\underline{/0°}$; (c) $1.5\underline{/0°}$; (d) $0.5\underline{/-30°}$; (e) $1\underline{/-30°}$; (f) $1.5\underline{/-30°}$; (g) $0.5\underline{/+30°}$; (h) $1\underline{/+30°}$; (i) $1.5\underline{/+30°}$.

The expression for calculating $\mathbf{I}_a$ has just been developed as: $-j(1 - E_f\underline{/\delta})$ and it is only a matter of substituting the values above as in the table on pp. 138 and 139.

E_f	$\delta°$	I_a	Mode	Phasor diagrams
(a) 0.5	0	$-j(1-0.5) = -j0.5$ $= 0.5$ A	Synchronous reactor	$E_f = 1.5$ $E_f = 1.0$ $V = 1$ $E_f = 0.5$ I_a $+j0.5$ $-j0.5$
(b) 1.0	0	$-j(1-1.0) = 0$ $= 0$ A	Zero current	
(c) 1.5	0	$-j(1-1.5) = +j0.5$ $= 0.5$ A	Synchronous capacitor	
(d) 0.5	-30	$-j[1-0.5(\cos-30+j\sin-30)]$ $= 0.25 - j0.567 = 0.62$ A	Motoring 0.4 lagging	E_f $-30°$ (e) (d) V (f) I_a
(e) 1.0	-30	$-j[1-1.0(0.866-j0.5)]$ $= 0.5 - j0.134 = 0.52$ A	Motoring 0.96 lagging	
(f) 1.5	-30	$-j[1-1.5(0.866-j0.5)]$ $= 0.75 + j0.3 = 0.81$ A	Motoring 0.93 leading	

(g) 0.5	+30	$-j[1 - 0.5(\cos + 30 + j \sin + 30)]$ $= -0.25 - j0.567 = 0.62$ A	Generating 0.4 leading
(h) 1.0	+30	$-j[1 - 1.0(0.866 + j0.5)]$ $= -0.5 - j0.134 = 0.52$ A	Generating 0.96 leading
(i) 1.5	+30	$-j[1 - 1.5(0.866 + j0.5)]$ $= -0.75 + j0.3 \quad = 0.81$ A	Generating 0.93 lagging

The above example is a very simple application of the *per-unit* system but if it still causes a difficulty, take V as say, 1000 V per phase and E_f will then be 500, 1000, 1500 V. If X_s is taken as 10 Ω for 1 *per unit*, then I_{aR} must be 100 A. All the currents in the above table will be multiplied by 100.

139

5.4 ELECTROMECHANICAL PROBLEMS

In the circuit of Fig. 1.12c, it will be assumed that the synchronous impedance $R_a + jX_s$ is given, though R_a may be neglected as for Fig. 5.1. The excitation will be left in terms of E_f, knowing that the calculation of field current will require the techniques used in Examples 5.1–5.3. Apart from frequency and the related synchronous speed, there are six quantities of special interest; V, I_a, φ, E_f, δ, and total power P (or torque). The circuit equation, using motor conventions is:

$$V + j0 = E_f(\cos \delta + j \sin \delta) + (R_a + jX_s) \times I_a \times (\cos \varphi + j \sin \varphi)$$

or:

$$V = E_f + (R_a + jX_s) \times I_a; \text{ omitting the specification of } V \text{ as reference.}$$

Since there are real and imaginary parts, the equation will solve for two unknowns. The power equations, either $P_{elec} = 3VI_a \cos \varphi$ or Mech. power $= \omega_s T_e$, will solve for only one unknown. Both of these powers can be expressed in terms of the load angle δ, which is advanced (positive for a generator) or retarded (negative for a motor). They are[1]:

$$P_e \text{ (per phase } = VI_a \cos \varphi = \frac{-VE_f}{Z_s} \sin (\delta + \alpha) + \frac{V^2 R_a}{Z_s} \quad (5.11)$$

and: P_g (per phase) $= P_m$ for synchronous machine

$$= -\frac{VE_f}{Z_s} \sin (\delta - \alpha) - \frac{E_f^2 R_a}{Z_s^2} \quad (5.12)$$

where $\alpha = \sin^{-1} R_a/Z_s$.

If the electrical loss is neglected, both of these equations reduce to:

$$P_e = P_g = P_m = \frac{-VE_f}{X_s} \sin \delta$$

as also deduced from the phasor diagram of Fig. 5.1 as eqn (5.10a). With resistance neglected, the approximate-circuit equations become as (5.9) and (5.9a):

$$V = E_f + jX_sI_a \quad \text{and} \quad I_a = \frac{V}{jX_s} - \frac{E_f}{jX_s}.$$

There is enough information in the equations above to solve for any three of the six quantities, given the other three. Although V is commonly constant, the equations are not restricted to this condition. There are other possibilities which are briefly touched on in some of the later examples. Typical problem types are outlined below.

(A) Given V, P, E_f Vary P, with constant E_f to find I_a, φ, δ variation up to pull-out at δ_{max}. Or vary E_f with constant P, to find the same quantities.

(B) Given $V, \varphi,$ Power-factor control. Excitation required
$\quad\quad P$ (or I_a)   for specified power factor and for a given power (or current). Compensator.

(C) Given $V, I_{aR},$ Pull-out torque (or power) is really speci-
$\quad$ Pull-out torque   fying the rated load angle δ_R, to permit this overload at maximum angle. Solution yields required excitation, power at full load and power factor.

(D) Given $V, I_a,$ Find required excitation and power
$\quad\quad \varphi$ (or P)   developed (or power factor), load angle and hence overload capacity.

(E) Given I_a, P, φ Find V required $[P/(I_a \cos \varphi)]$ and excitation. Constant current drive.

(F) Given I_a, P, δ Find V required and excitation. Constant current with δ control.

(G) Given V, P, φ Fixed power factor (by excitation control) changes Power/δ characteristic. Data for required excitation control yielded.

Items (E), (F) and (G) would require special power-electronic control, possibly with microprocessor supervision. They are included here to show that the fundamental performance is still governed by the normal machine equations. Examples will be given later and there will be a brief discussion on power-electronic control in Chapter 7.

In the examples illustrating this section, to help understanding, the label from the nearest problem-type is quoted from the list just described; see below.

EXAMPLE 5.5

A 3-phase, 8-pole, 50 Hz, 6600 V, star-connected synchronous motor has a synchronous impedance of $0.66 + j6.6 \, \Omega$ per phase. When excited to give a generated e.m.f. of 4500 V per phase, it takes an input of 2500 kW.

(a) Calculate the electromagnetic torque, the input current, power factor and load angle.

(b) If the motor were to be operating at an input current of 180 A at unity power-factor, what would then be the value of E_f? Under these conditions, calculate also the mechanical output and efficiency if mechanical, excitation and iron losses total 50 kW.

$$Z_s = \sqrt{0.66^2 + 6.6^2} = 6.63 \, \Omega \text{ and } \alpha = \sin^{-1} 0.66/6.63 = 5.7$$

(a) *Type* (A). Substituting values in eqn (5.11) for electrical input:

$$\frac{2500 \; 000}{3} = -\frac{(6600/\sqrt{3} \times 4500)}{6.63} \sin(\delta + 5.7) + \frac{6600^2}{(\sqrt{3})^2} \times \frac{0.66}{6.63^2}$$

from which $\sin(\delta + 5.7) = -0.238$, so $(\delta + 5.7) = -13.76$; $\delta = -19.46$.
Substituting in eqn (5.12) for mechanical output per phase:

$$P_m = -\frac{(6600/\sqrt{3} \times 4500)}{6.63} \sin(-19.46 - 5.7) - 4500^2 \times \frac{0.66}{6.63^2}$$

$$= \qquad 1099.6 \text{ kW} \qquad -304 \text{ kW} \qquad = 795.6 \text{ kW}$$

Total air-gap power $= 3P_m = 3 \times 795.6 \text{ kW} = 2387 \text{ kW}$.

Hence electromagnetic torque $= T_e = 3P_m/\omega_s = \dfrac{2387 \times 1000}{2\pi \times 50/4} = \underline{30390 \text{ Nm}}$

$$I_a = \frac{V - E_f}{Z_s} = \frac{6600/\sqrt{3} - 4500(\cos - 19.46 + j\sin - 19.46)}{0.66 + j6.6} = \frac{-432.4 + j1499}{0.66 + j6.6}$$

$$= 218.7 + j87.3 = \underline{235.5/21.8 \text{ A}} \quad \cos\varphi = \underline{0.93 \text{ leading}}$$

Check input $= \sqrt{3} \times 6600 \times 218.7 = 2500 \text{ kW}$

(b) *Type (B)*

$$E_f = V - Z_s I_a = \frac{6600}{\sqrt{3}} - (0.66 + j6.6)(180 + j0)$$

$$= 3691.7 - j1188 = 3878\underline{/-17°8}$$

$$Output = 3P_m - \text{``fixed'' loss} = 3\left[\frac{-6600/\sqrt{3} \times 3878}{6.63}\sin(-17°8 - 5°7)\right.$$

$$\left. - \frac{3878^2 \times 0.66}{6.63^2}\right] - 50000$$

$$= 2666.2 \qquad -677.4 \qquad -50\,\text{kW}$$

$$= \underline{1938.7\,\text{kW}}$$

$$\text{Efficiency} = \frac{1938.7}{\sqrt{3} \times 6.6 \times 180} = \underline{94.2\%}$$

As an exercise, the above figures, apart from efficiency, can be checked using the approximate circuit. It will be found that the load angles are with 1° accuracy, with similar small errors for the other quantities.

EXAMPLE 5.6

A 3300 V, 3-phase, 50 Hz, star-connected synchronous motor has a synchronous impedance of $2 + j15\,\Omega$ per phase. Operating with an line e.m.f. of 2500 V, it just falls out of step at full load. To what open-circuit e.m.f. will it have to be excited so that it will just remain in synchronism at 50% above rated torque. With this e.m.f., what will then be the input power, current and power factor at full load?

$$Z_s = \sqrt{2^2 + 15^2} = 15.1\,\Omega \quad \alpha = \sin^{-1} 2/15.1 = 7°6$$

Type (C) problem, with pull-out torque equal to rated value; $\sin(\delta - \alpha) = -1$.

Hence, rated air-gap power $= 3P_m =$

$$3\left[\frac{-3300 \times 2500}{\sqrt{3} \times \sqrt{3} \times 15.1} \times (-1) - \frac{2500^2}{(\sqrt{3})^2} \times \frac{2}{15.1^2}\right] \times 10^3\,\text{kW}$$

$$= 546.4 \qquad\qquad -54.8$$

$$= 491.6\,\text{kW}$$

Since electromagnetic torque is proportional to this power, the new requirement is that pull-out should occur at 1.5 times this value; i.e. at 737.4 kW. Substituting again in eqn (5.12), but this time with E_f as the unknown:

$$737\,400 = \frac{3300 \times E_f\,(\text{line})}{15.1} - E_f^2 \times \frac{2}{15.1^2}$$

from which

$$E_f^2 - 24915 E_f + 84067287 = 0$$

$$\therefore E_f = \frac{24915 \pm \sqrt{24915^2 - 4 \times 84067287}}{2}$$

$$= 20890\,\text{V or } \underline{4024\,\text{V}}; \text{ the lower value being feasible.}$$

Substituting again in the output equation, this time set to full load:

$$491\ 600 = \frac{-3300 \times 4024}{15.1} \sin(\delta - 7.6) - 4024^2 \times \frac{2}{15.1^2}$$

gives $\sin(\delta - 7.6) = -0.7205 = -46°1$. Hence $\delta = -38°5$

$$\mathbf{I}_a = \frac{\mathbf{V} - \mathbf{E}_f}{\mathbf{Z}_s} = \frac{3300/\sqrt{3} - 4024/\sqrt{3}(\cos - 38.5 + j\sin - 38.5)}{2 + j15}$$

$$= \frac{(87 + j1446) \times (2 - j15)}{2^2 + 15^2} = 95.5 + j6.9\ \text{A} = 95.7\underline{/+3°7}$$

$\therefore$ input power $= \sqrt{3} \times 3300 \times 95.5 \times 10^{-3} = \underline{545.8\ \text{kW}}$ at $\cos\varphi = 0.998$ leading

If the above figures are checked using the approximate circuit, they will again be well within 10%, apart from the output power, since I^2R losses are neglected in the approximation.

EXAMPLE 5.7

A 3-phase, 4-pole, 400 V, 200 hp, star-connected synchronous motor has a synchronous reactance of 0.5 Ω per phase. Calculate the load angle in mechanical degrees and the input current and power factor when the machine is working at full load with the e.m.f. adjusted to 1 *per unit*. Neglect R_a but take the mechanical loss as 10 kW.

Type (A) problem. From eqn (5.10a) with e.m.f. the same as the terminal voltage:

$$\text{Power} = 200 \times 746 + 10000 = \frac{-3}{0.5} \times \left(\frac{400}{\sqrt{3}}\right)^2 \sin\delta$$

from which $\sin\delta = -0.4975$, $\delta = -29°8$(elec.), and since $p = 2$,

$$\delta_{mech} = -14°9$$

Rated current $\mathbf{I}_{aR} = \frac{\mathbf{V} - \mathbf{E}_f}{jX_s} = \frac{1}{\sqrt{3}}\left[\frac{400 - 400(\cos - 29.8 + j\sin - 29.8)}{j0.5}\right]$

$$= 229.8 - j61 = \underline{237.8\underline{/-14°9}} = 0.966\ \text{p.f. lagging}$$

EXAMPLE 5.8

A 6-pole, 3-phase, star-connected synchronous motor has an unsaturated synchronous reactance of 12.5 Ω per phase, 20% of this being due to leakage flux. The motor is supplied from 11 kV at 50 Hz and drives a total mechanical torque of 50×10^3 Nm. The field current is so adjusted that the e.m.f. E_f read off the air-gap line is equal to the rated terminal voltage. Calculate the load angle, input current and power factor and also the maximum output power with this excitation, before pulling out of step. Neglect resistance throughout and assume that E_f is unchanged when the power increases to the maximum. The calculations are to be conducted (a)

144

Full-load power $= \omega_s T_e = 2\pi \times 50/3 \times 50 \times 10^3 = 5\,236\,000$ watts $= 3\dfrac{VE_f}{X_s}\sin\delta$

	(a) Unsaturated	(b) Saturated
X_m	$10\ \Omega$	$6.67\ \Omega$
x_{al}	$2.5\ \Omega$	$2.5\ \Omega$
X_s	$12.5\ \Omega$	$9.17\ \Omega$
E_f	$11000/\sqrt{3}$ V $-3 \times \dfrac{11000^2}{(\sqrt{3})^2} \times \dfrac{\sin\delta}{12.5}$	$2/3 \times 11\,000/\sqrt{3}$ V $-3 \times \dfrac{11000^2}{(\sqrt{3})^2} \times \dfrac{2}{3} \times \dfrac{\sin\delta}{9.17}$
δ from $5\,236\,000 =$		
$\sin\delta =$	-0.5409	-0.5952
$\cos\delta =$	0.8411	0.8036
$\delta =$	$-32°7$	$-36°5$
$\mathbf{I_a}$ from eqn (5.9a): $\dfrac{1100}{\sqrt{3}} \times \left[\dfrac{1-(\cos\delta + j\sin\delta)}{jX_s}\right] =$	$\dfrac{11000}{\sqrt{3}} \times \left[\dfrac{1-(0.8411-j0.5409)}{j12.5}\right]$	$\dfrac{11000}{\sqrt{3}} \times \left[\dfrac{1-(0.8036-j0.5952)\times 2/3}{j9.17}\right]$
$=$	$274.9 - j80.7$	$274.8 - j321.5$
$=$	286.5 A	423 A
at $\cos\varphi =$	0.96 lagging	0.65 lagging
Maximum power; at $\sin\delta = 1$	$\dfrac{11000^2}{12.5} = 9680$ kW	$\dfrac{11000^2}{9.17} \times \dfrac{2}{3} = 8797$ kW
For unity power factor $\mathbf{E_f} =$	$11000 - j12.5 \times 286.5 \times \sqrt{3}$ $= 12.63$ line kV	$11000 - j9.17 \times 423 \times \sqrt{3}$ 12.89 line kV
giving an output $\sqrt{3}VI_a =$	$\sqrt{3} \times 11 \times 286.5 = 5459$ kW	$\sqrt{3} \times 11 \times 423 = 8059$ kW
For z.p.f. lead, $\mathbf{E_f} = \mathbf{V} - jX_s j I_a$	$11000 + 12.5 \times 286.5 \times \sqrt{3}$ $= 17.2$ line kV	$11000 + 9.17 \times 423 \times \sqrt{3}$ 17.72 line kV

145

assuming saturation can be neglected and (b) assuming that all components which would be affected would be reduced by a factor of 1/3 due to saturation.

With the current calculated as above, to what value would the excitation have to be adjusted, in terms of E_f, so that the power factor would be unity? What would then be the output?

Finally, to what value would E_f have to be adjusted so that the machine could operate as a synchronous capacitor at the same armature current?

This again is related to *problem types* (A) *and* (B) but the effect of allowing for and of neglecting saturation is included. 10 Ω of the total synchronous reactance is due to mutual flux and therefore will be reduced if saturation is allowed for. Further, the e.m.f. will have to be reduced by the same amount.

The calculations are shown in the table on p. 145. It can be seen that the most pronounced effects of allowing for saturation follow from the change of power-factor-angle φ, which is much increased because E_f is no longer equal to but is less than the terminal voltage. If the field current had been adjusted to correct for this, then the discrepancies would have appeared in the other quantities, like load angle and maximum power.

EXAMPLE 5.9

A 3-phase, 6-pole, 50 Hz, star-connected synchronous motor is rated at 500 kVA, 6600 V at unity power-factor. It has a synchronous impedance of j80 Ω per phase. Determine the mechanical torque for this rating neglecting all machine losses. If this torque can be assumed constant, what departure from rated armature current and excitation (in terms of $E_f\underline{/\delta}$) are necessary for operation at (a) 0.9 p.f. lag and (b) 0.9 pf lead? How will the maximum torque be affected in both cases?

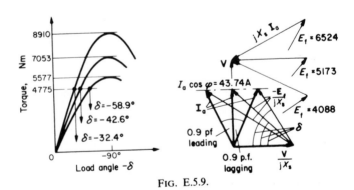

FIG. E.5.9.

146

Problem type (D) $\text{Torque} = \dfrac{\text{Power}}{\text{speed}} = \dfrac{500\,000}{2\pi \times 50/3} = \underline{4775\,\text{Nm}}$

Power component of current for this torque $= \dfrac{500\,000}{\sqrt{3} \times 6600} = 43.74\,\text{A}$

At 0.9 p.f., $(\sin \varphi = 0.436)\mathbf{I}_a = \dfrac{43.74}{0.9}(0.9 \pm j0.436) = 43.74 \pm j21.2$

Power factor	u.p.f.	0.9 lag	0.9 lead
$jX_s\mathbf{I}_a =$	$j80 \times (43.74 + j0)$	$j80 \times (43.74 - j21.2)$	$j80 \times (43.74 + j21.2)$
$=$	$j3499.2$	$1696 + j3499.2$	$-1696 + j3499.2$
$\mathbf{E}_f = \dfrac{6600}{\sqrt{3}} - jX_s\mathbf{I}_a =$	$3810.5 - j3499.2$	$2114.5 - j3499.2$	$5506.5 - j3499.2$
$=$	$5173\underline{/-42.6}$	$4088\underline{/-58.9}$	$6524\underline{/-32.4}$
$-90°/\sin \delta$	1.477	1.168	1.866
$\text{Max } T_e = 4775 \times \dfrac{\sin -90}{\sin \delta} =$	$7053\,\text{Nm}$	$5577\,\text{Nm}$	$8910\,\text{Nm}$

The last figures show that the higher excitations give higher overload capacities as well as the movement towards leading power factor. This is also indicated by the torque/load-angle and phasor diagrams which show the reduction of δ with increase of E_f.

EXAMPLE 5.10

A 1000 kVA, 6.6 kV, 50 Hz, 3-phase, 6-pole, star-connected synchronous machine is connected to an infinite system. The synchronous impedance per-phase can be taken as constant at $0 + j50\,\Omega$. The machine is operating as a motor at rated current and in such a manner, by excitation adjustment, that a 50% overload is possible before it pulls out of synchronism. What will be the necessary voltage E_f behind synchronous impedance to permit this overload margin? At what power and power factor will it be operating when the current is at the rated value? Neglect all machine losses.

If, with the same mechanical load, E_f was reduced by 30%, what would be the new status of the motor?

Type (C) $\text{Rated current} = \dfrac{1000}{\sqrt{3} \times 6.6} = 87.48\,\text{A}$

In order to permit a load increase of 1.5 times, the value of $\sin \delta$ at full load must be 2/3 so that a 50% increase will bring $\sin \delta$ to unity.

The easiest way to solve this problem is to draw the phasor diagram as shown.

147

Two sides of the current triangle are known, I_a and V/X_s, and the load angle δ_R is specified as $\sin^{-1} -2/3 = -41°8$. Either from the sine rule or resolving the two current components along E_f, the triangle can be solved. By the second method:

$$I_a \cos(\varphi + \delta_R) = \frac{V}{X_s} \sin \delta - \text{using positive } \delta \text{ for simplicity in this particular case,}$$

so: $\cos(\varphi + \delta_R) = \dfrac{6600/\sqrt{3}}{50} \times \dfrac{2/3}{87.48} = 0.5808$

giving: $(\varphi + \delta_R) = 54°49$ and hence $\varphi = 54.49 - 41.8 = 12°69$

$$\underline{\cos \varphi = 0.976}$$
$$\text{Power} = \sqrt{3} \times 6600 \times 87.48 \times 0.976 = 1000 \text{ kVA} \times 0.976 = \underline{976 \text{ kW}}$$

E_f follows from eqn (5.10a):

$$976\,000 = -3\left(\frac{6600}{\sqrt{3}} \times \frac{E_f}{50}\right) \times \left(\frac{-2}{3}\right) \text{ from which } E_f = \underline{6403 \text{ V/phase}}$$

If E_f is reduced to 70% of 6403 V = 4482 V

$$976\,000 = -3\left(\frac{6600}{\sqrt{3}} \times \frac{4482}{50}\right) \sin \delta$$

from which $\qquad \sin \delta = 0.952$ and $\delta = \underline{72°3}$. $\qquad \cos \delta = 0.306$

Maximum overload is now $\dfrac{\sin 90}{\sin 72.3} = \underline{1.05 \text{ i.e. 5% overload}}$

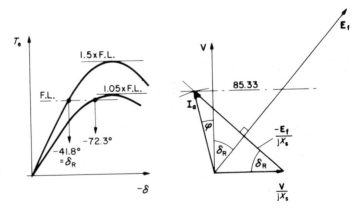

FIG. E.5.10.

148

he armature current at full load is

$$\frac{V - E_f}{jX_s} = \frac{6600/\sqrt{3} - 4482(0.306 - j0.952)}{j50}$$

$$= 85.33 - j48.8$$

$$= 98.3\underline{/29°8} \qquad \cos\varphi = 0.868 \text{ lagging}$$

he power component of the current, 85.33 A is the same as before (87.48 × 0.976), ince the load is unchanged. But the total current is greater at 98.3/87.48 = 1.12 *per nit*, the power factor is now 30° lagging and the load angle is greatly increased to 72°3 'hich leaves the overload margin very small at 5% before pull-out; see diagrams.

XAMPLE 5.11

A 3-phase, 6600 V, 6-pole, 50 Hz, star connected synchronous motor has a 'nchronous impedance of $0 + j30 \, \Omega$ per phase. At rated load the armature current is ·0 A at 0.9 p.f. leading. Neglecting losses:

) Determine the e.m.f. E_f, the load angle in mechanical degrees and the rated torque.

·) What increase of excitation will be required to sustain a torque overload of 25 000 Nm without falling out of step?

) With this new excitation, what would be the values of current, power factor and load angle at rated torque?

l) With this new excitation, what reduction of terminal voltage would be permissible so that the machine would just stay in synchronism at rated torque?

:) With this new excitation, and rated terminal voltage, what would be the value of current if the load was removed altogether?

his is a *Type* (D) *problem* with further variations.

) $E_f = V - jX_s I_a = \dfrac{6600}{\sqrt{3}} - j30 \times 100(0.9 + j0.436)$

$$5118.5 - j2700 = 5787\underline{/-27°8}$$

The load angle in mechanical degrees is $\delta/p = -27.8/3 = \underline{-9°3}$

Rated torque $= \dfrac{\sqrt{3} \times 6600 \times 100 \times 0.9}{2\pi \times 50/3} = \underline{9827 \text{ Nm}}$

·) For maximum torque of 25 000 Nm $= 3 \times \dfrac{6600}{\sqrt{3}} \times \dfrac{E_f}{30} \times \dfrac{1}{2\pi \times 50/3} \times \sin -90°$

$$E_f = \underline{6870 \text{ V}}$$

:) For new load angle: $\underline{9827 \text{ Nm}} = -3 \times \dfrac{6600}{\sqrt{3}} \times \dfrac{6870}{30} \times \dfrac{\sin\delta}{2\pi \times 50/3}$

from which $\qquad$ $\sin \delta = -0.393;$ $\quad \underline{\delta = -23°1}$ elec.

For new current: $\qquad I_a = \dfrac{6600/\sqrt{3} - 6870(0.92 - j0.393)}{j30}$

$$= 90 + j83.7 = 122.9\underline{/42°9} \quad \cos \varphi = 0.732 \text{ lead}$$

(d) For rated torque at reduced voltage:

$$9827\,\text{Nm} = 3 \times \frac{V}{\sqrt{3}} \times \frac{6870}{30} \times \frac{\sin 90°}{2\pi \times 50/3}$$

from which: $\qquad V = 2594\,\text{V} = 0.393\ per\ unit;$ $\quad 60.7\%$ reduction

(e) For zero load, $\delta = 0$, $\sin \delta = 0$ and $\cos \delta = 1$

$$I_a = \frac{V - E_f(1 + j0)}{jX_s} = \frac{6600/\sqrt{3} - 6870}{j30} = \underline{j102}\ \text{A zero leading p.f.}$$

EXAMPLE 5.12

If the excitation of a synchronous motor is so controlled that the power factor always unity, show that the power is proportional to the tangent of the load angle. Neglect all machine losses.

Type (G) *problem.* Referring to the phasor diagram and taking **V** as reference, the

$$I_a \text{ will always be } I_a + j0.$$

From $E_f = V - jX_sI_a$ it can be seen that the load angle is:

$$\delta = \tan^{-1}\frac{-X_sI_a}{V}$$

But power is proportional to VI_a so $I_a = \dfrac{kP}{V}$

Hence $\tan \delta = \dfrac{-X_s kP}{V^2}$ and with V constant; $\underline{\tan \delta \text{ proportional to } P}$

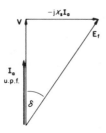

FIG. E.5.12.

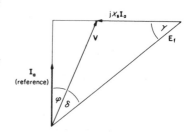

FIG. E.5.13.

EXAMPLE 5.13

If for a synchronous motor the r.m.s. armature current is maintained constant by varying the terminal voltage V, develop the relationships comparable to those for constant voltage, which will yield solutions for three unknowns given three values out of V, I_a, φ, E_f, δ, and P (or T). Neglect machine losses.

Type (E) problem, again solved more easily by referring to the phasor diagram, this time with I_a as the reference phasor instead of V. Take δ as +ve for simplicity.

$$P_e = P_g = P_m = I_a V \cos \varphi = I_a E_f \cos(\varphi + \delta) \text{ per phase}$$

and:

$$\mathbf{V} = \mathbf{E_f} + jX_s\mathbf{I_a}$$

$$V(\cos \varphi - j \sin \varphi) = E_f[\cos(\varphi + \delta) + j \sin(\varphi + \delta)] + jX_s\mathbf{I_a}$$

Hence for example, given I_a, P and φ $\quad V = \dfrac{P}{I_a \cos \varphi}$

and $\quad \mathbf{E_f} = V(\cos \varphi - j \sin \varphi) - jX_s\mathbf{I_a} = E_f/(\delta + \varphi$, hence δ

or; given I_a, P and δ; obtain V as before and:

$$\frac{X_s I_a}{\sin \delta} = \frac{V}{\sin \gamma}$$

Hence γ, and $180° - \gamma - \delta = 180° - (90° - \varphi)$

$$\therefore \varphi = 90 - \gamma - \delta \text{ and } \mathbf{E_f} = \mathbf{V} - jX_s\mathbf{I_a} = E_f/(\delta + \varphi)$$

Effect of Supply Voltage/Frequency Changes

This is best illustrated by an example.

EXAMPLE 5.14

If the supply frequency and voltage applied to a synchronous motor are both reduced to fractions kf and kV, what will be the effect on the values of maximum torque and on maximum power? Take V, f, E_f, ω_s and X_s as the normal parameter values.

If f becomes kf then the synchronous speed becomes $k\omega_s$ and therefore the induced e.m.f. E_f will become kE_f if the flux is maintained constant. The reactance too is proportional to frequency so X_s becomes kX_s. Substituting in the power equation (5.10a)

$$\text{Maximum power} = -3 \times \frac{kV \times kE_f}{kX_s} \times \sin(-90°) = \frac{3VE_f}{X_s} \sin 90 \times k$$

$$\text{Maximum } T_e = \frac{\text{power}}{\text{speed}} = \frac{3VE_f \sin 90 \times k}{k\omega_s X_s} = \frac{3VE_f}{\omega_s X_s}$$

151

The maximum torque is unchanged from the normal condition as might be expected since the flux and load angle are unchanged. Further, the voltages and the impedance are affected equally, by the terms of the question, so the current would be unchanged. The maximum power will be reduced by k from the normal value since although the torque is constant, the speed has been reduced by this k factor.

All the above reasoning neglects the effect of resistance. The equations are different if this is allowed for. Only the induced voltage terms are affected by the reduction in frequency (apart from the small resistance skin-effects), so the resistance assumes a more important role and at very low frequencies will dominate the current calculation. Expanding eqn (5.12) the electromagnetic torque is:

$$T_e = \frac{3P_g}{\omega_s} = \frac{3}{\omega_s}\left[\frac{-VE_f}{Z_s}(\sin\delta\cos\alpha - \cos\delta\sin\alpha) - \frac{E_f^2 R_a}{Z_s^2}\right]$$

Substituting $\sin\alpha = R_a/Z_s$ and $\cos\alpha = X_s/Z_s$, from the definition of α:

$$T_e = \frac{-3E_f}{\omega_s Z_s^2}(VX_s\sin\delta - VR_a\cos\delta + E_f R_a). \tag{5.13}$$

At any reduced frequency kf; E_f, ω_s and X_s are reduced in the same proportion and Z_s^2 becomes $R_a^2 + (kX_s)^2$. For the maximum torque it is more convenient to revert to the original expression of eqn (5.12), where for motoring, the angle $(\delta - \alpha)$ must be $-90°$ for maximum value. Hence, at any frequency kf:

$$\text{Max } T_e = \frac{-3}{k\omega_s}\left[\frac{VkE_f}{Z_s}(-1) + \frac{(kE_f)^2 R_a}{Z_s^2}\right] = \frac{3E_f}{\omega_s}\left[\frac{V}{\sqrt{R_a^2 + (kX_s)^2}} - \frac{kE_f R_a}{R_a^2 + (kX_s)^2}\right] \tag{5.14}$$

which, with resistance neglected, reduces to the maximum-torque expression deduced previously, if the applied voltage too is reduced by the same fraction k.

5.5 CONSTANT-CURRENT OPERATION

This mode was discussed in Section 4.3 for the induction motor. For the synchronous motor also, it is associated with variable frequency and special applications. Indeed, when the induction machine is in the dynamic-braking mode with a d.c. current-source for one winding, it is really operating as a synchronous generator, of variable frequency if the speed is changing. The power factor is always lagging, however, since it has a passive R.L. load.

Traditional approaches to electrical-machine theory have tended to assume nominally constant-voltage sources in deriving the various equations since this is the normal steady-state running condition. If, instead, currents are specified and controlled, with the voltages adjusted automatically to suit this condition, a different performance results. This is especially important when considering maximum-torque capability. The equivalent-circuit parameters are unchanged—apart from the greater likelihood of parameter changes due to saturation effects—but the viewpoint is different. For example, primary impedance does not come into the calculation for the required supply voltage until the performance is deduced from the specified currents. Variable frequency and changes of speed are the normal situation.

It is helpful as an introduction to return to the induction-motor phasor diagram which is shown on Fig. 5.2a. The emphasis will be on the current phasors, which can also represent the m.m.f. space vectors to which they are proportional, being expressed in terms of the stator winding turns. I_1 is for the stator (primary); I_2' is for the rotor (secondary) and I_m, the magnetising current, represents the resultant m.m.f. The general expression for torque, eqn (4.4):

$$T_e = \frac{3}{\omega_s} \times \frac{I_2'^2 R_2'}{s} \quad \text{can be rearranged as:}$$

$$\frac{3}{\omega/\text{pole pairs}} \times X_m \times \frac{E_1}{X_m} \times \frac{E_1}{Z_2'} \times \frac{R_2'/s}{Z_2'},$$

$$\text{where } Z_2' = \frac{R_2'}{s} + jx_2'$$

$$\left. \begin{aligned} &= 3 \times \text{pole pairs} \times M \times I_m \times I_2' \times \cos \varphi_2 \\ &= 3 \times \text{pole pairs,} \times M \times I_m \times I_2' \times \sin(\varphi_m - \varphi_2) \end{aligned} \right\} \quad (5.15)$$

where the angles have been measured from E_1 for convenience. Basically this equation has been obtained by dividing the air-gap power by the synchronous speed, $3P_g/\omega_s$, but it now expresses the torque as a product of the mutual inductance, the r.m.s. currents referred to the same side of the air gap and the sine of the angle between the rotor and resultant m.m.f.s represented by I_2' and I_m. For a.c. machines, this angle is closest to the conventional load angle δ, between air-gap flux and rotor m.m.f.

From the geometry of the triangle, using the sine rule, it is readily shown that the same torque will be given by using the currents I_1 and I_2' or I_1 and I_m, with the appropriate correction for angular difference substituted; e.g.

$$T_e = 3 \times \text{pole pairs} \times MI_1I_2' \sin(\varphi_1 - \varphi_2) \qquad (5.16)$$

as proved by an alternative approach in Reference 1. The angle here is the torque angle, between the stator and rotor m.m.f.s, as on the d.c. machine, between field and brush axes.

Turning now to the synchronous machine, the corresponding m.m.f. diagram (Fig. 5.2b) is obtained on dividing the $\mathbf{E}$, $\mathbf{E_f}$, $jX_m\mathbf{I_a}$ voltage triangle by jX_m which gives currents referred to the armature turns. E/X_m, in phase with the mutual air-gap flux ϕ_m is really the equivalent magnetising current I_m like the induction motor and producing the air-gap e.m.f. E. The current E_f/X_m is really the equivalent field current I_f' in armature winding terms, producing E_f and is readily converted back to I_f if the coefficient relating E_f to I_f is known from the magnetising characteristic, i.e. k_f for unsaturated conditions; see Section 5.1. The torque is given by:

$$T_e = \frac{\text{Air-gap power}}{\omega_s} = \frac{3EI_a \cos(\varphi + \gamma)}{\omega_s}$$

$$= 3 \times \frac{X_m}{\omega/\text{pole pairs}} \times \frac{E}{X_m} \times I_a \times \sin[90 - (\varphi + \gamma)]$$

$$= 3 \times \text{pole pairs}, \times M \times I_m \times I_a \times \sin \varphi_{ma} \qquad (5.17)$$

which really corresponds to the third equation which could be derived from Fig. 5.2a, using $\mathbf{I_1}$ and $\mathbf{I_m}$. The angle φ_{ma} is that between $\mathbf{I_m}$ and $\mathbf{I_a}$, but any of the three angles, with the corresponding currents, could be used.

For constant-voltage constant-frequency drives, the air-gap flux is approximately constant since $V/f(\simeq E/f)$ is constant, therefore one value of M is usually adequate for calculations. For current-fed drives, as already discovered with Examples 4.12–4.16, the flux may vary considerably and saturation changes which affect X_m have to be allowed for. Given the magnetising curve, which

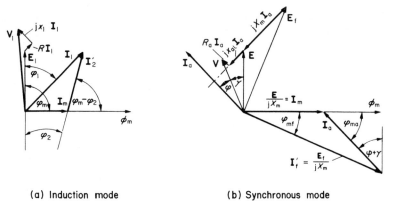

(a) Induction mode   (b) Synchronous mode

FIG. 5.2. Torque from phasor diagrams.

relates I_m (or I'_m) to E, at a particular frequency, this can be included since $X_m = E/I_m$. An iterative procedure may be necessary to match calculated values with the correct value of X_m and M.

It is now appropriate and instructive to compare the induction machine and the synchronous machine in terms of their m.m.f. diagrams. Note that positive I'_2, the rotor m.m.f., is conventionally taken to be magnetising in the opposite sense to positive I_1, unlike the rotor m.m.f. I'_f (F_f), which is taken to be magnetising in the same sense as I_a (F_a) when both are positive. Reversing the phasor I'_2 would bring Fig. 5.2a into the same convention as Fig. 5.2b. The important thing to realise is that the torque is a function of the m.m.f.s and angles, for either synchronous or induction machines and regardless of the speed (though the condition must be steady state, with the m.m.f.s in synchronism). Synchronous and induction machines can thus have a common basis when considering the torque produced and its control. If the three current magnitudes are predetermined, then the geometry of the triangle constrains the angles to certain values in accordance with the cosine rule. Alternatively, if two of the current magnitudes are specified and the

155

angle of one current with respect to another, then again the geometry determines the remaining current and angles.

This last statement is important when considering the maximum-torque conditions. Clearly, from the equations derived, for a fixed M and for any two specified currents, maximum torque occurs when the angle between them is 90°. For the induction motor, Fig. 5.2a, this cannot occur with an uncontrolled (cage) rotor, since I_2' must always lag behind E_1. The torque can only be obtained with an angle $(\varphi_m - \varphi_2)$ less than 90°; or considering the angle between I_m and $-I_2'$, an angle greater than 90° which in fact has the same sine.

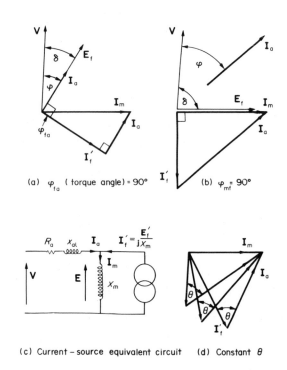

(a) φ_{fa} (torque angle) = 90°   (b) $\varphi_{mf} = 90°$

(c) Current – source equivalent circuit   (d) Constant θ

FIG. 5.3. Maximum-torque conditions for synchronous machine.

156

This is a consequence of the induction mode, with the rotor current dependent on induction from the stator currents. For the d.c. machine, a torque angle of 90° is the normal condition, with field and armature m.m.f.s maintained in quadrature by the angluar-position switching of brushes and commutator.

For the synchronous machine, the angles are functions of load, voltage, field current and frequency. But supposing a position detector was incorporated, so that specified stator and rotor m.m.f.s could be held at a fixed relative angle, this could be made 90° and again the maximum torque could be obtained (Fig. 5.3a). In practice, however, this would mean that the flux would have to adapt as the dependent variable, and saturation effects on the value of M would have to be allowed for. Maximum torque then occurs at a torque angle greater than 90° as will be seen. The normal, voltage-fed machine, with flux per pole approximately constant ($\phi \propto E/f \doteq V/f$), and with a particular field m.m.f., will have maximum torque when the load angle δ between $\mathbf{V}$ and $\mathbf{E_f}$ is virtually 90°, δ being the same as the angle between $\mathbf{I_m}$ and $\mathbf{I_f'}$ neglecting leakage impedance; see Fig. 5.3b. With this as the constraint, I_a is the dependent variable and will be higher in terms of its m.m.f. than either I_m or I_f'. The third possibility is to specify the flux level (I_m) and the armature current I_a, with an angle of 90° between them for maximum torque. $\mathbf{I_a}$ would then be vertical on Fig. 5.3b and I_f' would have to be the highest in terms of its m.m.f. This might be the most appropriate option since the field power is very much less than the armature power and would therefore be cheaper to control.

The current-source equivalent circuit for the synchronous machine is shown on Fig. 5.3c. It follows from Fig. 5.2b, though the current source due to the field could also be obtained from standard circuit techniques which would convert a voltage source E_f behind an impedance jX_m to a current source I_f' (E_f/jX_m), at an angle which is known only with respect to $\mathbf{V}$ as ($\delta - 90°$). But V itself is not specified if I_a is to be predetermined and controlled. V awaits the solution of performance from the current diagram. The angles of the other currents are also unknown, though it is usually convenient to take $\mathbf{I}_a$ as the reference phasor, Example (5.13), and $\mathbf{I}_m$ is known to lag $\mathbf{E}$, $(X_m I_m)$, by $90°$.

If current-controlled sources are to be used, it has already been found when discussing the induction motor, Section 4.3, that saturation effects become very important. Consider Fig. 5.3d. This shows a particular $\mathbf{I}_m$ and flux, which may or may not result in pronounced saturation effects, and the two currents $\mathbf{I}_f'$ and $\mathbf{I}_a$ with an angle θ which is actually equal to $(180 -$ the torque angle $\varphi_{fa})$. A few simple drawings will quickly demonstrate that maximum torque occurs when $\mathbf{I}_f'$ and $\mathbf{I}_a$ are equal[5]. Actually this follows from eqn (5.17) which has the same form as the area-of-a-triangle formula, $\frac{1}{2}a \times b \sin C$, and maximum area occurs for the condition stated. A comparison of control strategies could as a first approximation consider the criterion of torque per ampere of <u>total</u> current, which based on eqn (5.17) would be:

$$T/A = \frac{3 \times \text{pole pairs} \times M I_a I_f' \sin \theta}{I_a + I_f'} \; \alpha \frac{M I^2 \sin \theta}{2I} \; \alpha \frac{M I \sin \theta}{2I} \quad (5.18)$$

if $I_a = I_f' = I$. For optimum torque angle $\varphi_{fa}(= 180 - \theta) = 90°$, then $\theta = 90°$ and the maximum torque per ampere would be directly proportional to I. However, this assumes that M is unaffected by the value of I, which is only a reasonable assumption for a low-flux, unsaturated state. But if I was the rated value and $\theta = 90°$, I_m would be $\sqrt{2}I$ and M would therefore be appreciably lower than its unsaturated value. Suppose now that θ is reduced from $90°$; I_m will be less and so M will increase. If this increase is greater than the decrease of $\sin \theta$, the torque will actually rise. What this means is that in the saturated state the maximum torque occurs at a torque angle greater than $90°$[5], though the effect is not very marked until the magnetising current is approaching 1.5 per unit or more, and costs of excessive currents must be taken into account.

In the next example, a simplification will be made by expressing all the relevant equations in *per-unit*, with rated kVA, rated voltage and the synchronous speed at rated frequency, as base values. The equations are unchanged apart from the omission of constants like

"3", $\omega_{s(base)}$ and pole pairs. The conversion is simple; for example, base torque is: (rated $kVA \times 10^3)/\omega_{s(base)}$ and on dividing the torque expressions by this, the voltages V and E_f by V_{base} and remembering that $Z_{base} = (V_{base})^2/Power_{base}$ (see Example 4.2d), the following equations result:

For the voltage equation at any frequency $k \times f_{base}$:

$$V = kE_f + R_aI_a + jkX_sI_a \qquad (5.19)$$

For eqn (5.12):

$$T_e = \frac{-VE_f}{Z_s} \sin(\delta - \alpha) - \frac{E_f^2 R_a}{Z_s^2} \text{ which is unchanged in form.}$$

For eqn (5.14):

$$T_e = E_f\left[\frac{V}{\sqrt{R_a^2 + (kX_s)^2}} - \frac{kE_fR_a}{R_a^2 + (kX_s)^2}\right] \qquad (5.20)$$

For eqn (5.17)

$$T_e = X_m I_f' I_a \sin\theta \qquad (5.21)$$

now expressed in terms of I_f' and I_a.

EXAMPLE 5.15

A polyphase, cylindrical-rotor synchronous machine has a *per-unit* synchronous impedance $Z_s = 1$. The resistance when allowed for can be taken as 0.05. The leakage impedance can be taken as zero ($X_s = X_m$). Determine:

(a) the *per-unit* E_f for operation as a motor at unity power-factor and rated armature current and voltage;

(b) the *per-unit* torque at this rated condition calculated from (i) $VI_a \cos\varphi - I_a^2 R_a$, (ii) eqn (5.12) and (iii) eqn (5.21);

(c) the maximum torque with rated voltage and the same value of E_f;

(d) the armature current at condition (c);

(e) the air-gap e.m.f. E at condition (c);

(f) I_m and I_f' at condition (c);

(g) the phasor diagram for condition (c), checking all the angles of the m.m.f. triangle by the cosine rule on the current magnitudes;

(h) the voltage and frequency required to sustain condition (c) at a speed of 0.1 *per unit*;

(i) the answers to (a)–(h) if resistance is neglected;

(j) the values of torque and torque per ampere in *per unit*, for the following

159

conditions when supplied from current sources giving $I_a = I_f = 2$. (i) $I_m = 1$; (ii) $I_m = 2$; (iii) $I_m = 3$. Neglect the armature resistance and use the approximation to the magnetisation curve employed in Example (4.15) for determining the reduction in per-unit mutual inductance $- X_m = 1$ at $I_m = 1$. (M per unit $= \omega_{base} M I_{base} / V_{base} = X_m / Z_{base}$.)

If $R_a = 0.05$, then $X_s = \sqrt{1^2 - 0.05^2} = 0.9987$ and $\alpha = \tan^{-1} R_a / X_s = 2°87$

(a) $E_f = V - I_a(R_a + jX_s) = 1 - (1 + j0)(0.05 + j0.9987) = \underline{1.3784 / -46°43}$

(b) (i) $T_e = 1 \times 1 \times 1 - 1^2 \times 0.05 = \dfrac{}{} \qquad \underline{0.95}$

$\quad$ (ii) $T_e = \dfrac{-1 \times 1.3784}{1} \sin(-46.43 - 2.87) - \dfrac{1.3784^2 \times 0.05}{1^2} = \underline{0.95}$

$\quad$ (iii) $I_f = \dfrac{E_f}{jX_m} = \dfrac{1.3784 / -46.43}{0.9987 / 90} = \underline{1.38 / -136.43}$

$\quad$ so $T_e = X_m I_f I_a \sin \varphi_{fa} = 0.9987 \times 1.38 \times 1 \times \sin 136°43 \qquad = \underline{0.95}$

(c) $T_{e(max)}$, from eqn (5.12) with $(\delta - \alpha) = -90°$

$$= \dfrac{-1 \times 1.3784}{1} \times (-1) - \dfrac{1.3784^2 \times 0.05}{1^2} = \underline{1.283}$$

(d) $I_a = \dfrac{V - E_f / -(90 - \alpha)}{Z_s / 90 - \alpha} = \dfrac{1 - 1.3784(0.05 - j0.9987)}{0.05 - j0.9987} \qquad = \underline{1.662 / -31°2}$

(e) $E = V - I_a R_a = 1 - 1.662 / -31.2 \times 0.05 \qquad\qquad = \underline{0.93 / 2°65}$

(f) $I_f = \dfrac{E_f / -90 + 2.87}{0.9987 / 90} \qquad\qquad\qquad\qquad = \underline{1.38 / -177°13}$

$\quad I_m = \dfrac{E}{jX_m} = \dfrac{0.93 / 2.65}{0.9987 / 90°} \qquad\qquad\qquad = \underline{0.931 / -87°35}$

The angle between I_f and I_m is thus $-177.13 - (-87.35) = 89°78$ which is very nearly at the optimum value of 90°, even though it is the result of a maximum-torque condition deduced from the voltage-source equations. These equations allow for impedance drop and maximise the air-gap power rather than considering the optimum angle as for the current-source approach. In fact, if the leakage reactance had been allowed for, this angle would have progressively reduced from 90° as a larger share of X_s was ascribed to leakage reactance. The maximum torque would have been unchanged since the value depends on the total synchronous impedance. This will be verified if the calculations are repeated with x_{al} typically 0.1 per unit, leaving X_m as 0.8987 per unit.

(g) The phasor diagram has been constructed from the above information and is shown on the first figure. The check on the angles from the calculated current magnitudes is left as an exercise to familiarise the calculation procedure when the currents are specified, as indeed they are in the next question and part (j).

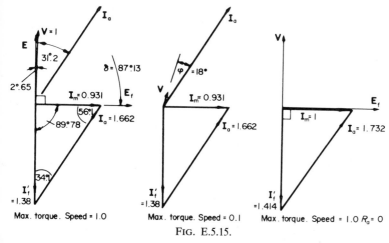

FIG. E.5.15.

(h) The condition here is a speed and frequency of 0.1 per unit which means that k in the variable-frequency expressions of eqns (5.19) and (5.20) is 0.1. The m.m.f. diagram is to be the same, to give the same torque – which is not quite the maximum for this particular flux (I_m) and field current, since the angle between them is slightly less than 90°. It is convenient to take I_a as a reference phasor; it will be $1.662 + j0$. Hence, from eqn (5.19): and the phasor diagram from which the angles can be deduced:

$$V = kE_f + R_aI_a + jkX_sI_a = kI'_fX_m + R_aI_a + jkX_sI_a$$
$$= 0.1 \times 1.38\underline{/-145.93} \times 0.9987\underline{/90} \quad + \quad 0.05 \times 1.662 \quad + \quad j0.1 \times 0.9987 \times 1.662$$
$$= 0.1378\underline{/-55.93} \quad\quad\quad\quad + \quad 0.0831 \quad\quad + \quad j0.166$$
$$= 0.16 + j0.052 = \underline{0.168\underline{/+18°}}$$

Note that in the above calculations, cartesian and polar forms have been used as convenient but care must be taken in combining them finally. The second figure shows the phasor diagram, the current I_a being at a slightly lagging power-factor of 0.95.

The calculations neglecting resistance are much simpler and will now be outlined in the same sequence as previously.

(a) $E_f = 1 - 1 \times j1 = 1 - j1 = \underline{1.414/-45}$

(b) (i) $\quad T_e = 1 \times 1 \times 1 \quad\quad\quad\quad = \underline{1}$

(ii) $\quad T_e = \dfrac{-1 \times 1.414 \times \sin(-45°)}{1} \quad = \underline{1}$

(iii) $\quad T_e = 1 \times \dfrac{1.414}{1} \times 1 \times \sin 45 \quad = \underline{1}$

161

(c) $T_{e(max)} = \dfrac{-1 \times 1.414}{1}(-1) = \underline{1.414}$

(d) $I_a = \dfrac{1 - 1.414\underline{/-90}}{j1} = 1.414 - j1 = \underline{1.732\underline{/-35.3}}$

(e) $E = V = 1$

(f) $I_f = \dfrac{1.414\underline{/-90}}{j1} = \underline{-1.414} \qquad I_m = \dfrac{1}{j1} = \underline{-j1}$

(g) The phasor diagram is shown on the 3rd figure and should be compared with th
one including resistance. The differences are about 5% but note that the angle i
now exactly 90°.

(h) With I_a as the reference phasor, I_f is $1.414\underline{/-180} - 35.3 = 1.414\underline{/-144.7}$
So $V = kI_f X_m + jkX_s I_a$

$= 0.1 \times 1.414\underline{/-144.7} \times 1\underline{/90} + j0.1 \times 1 \times 1.732$

$= 0.1414(0.578 - j0.816) \qquad + j0.1732$

$= 0.082 + j0.058 = \underline{0.1\underline{/+35.3}}$

This result, which shows that V is proportional to k when resistance is neglected
has already been illustrated in Example 5.14, but is now confirmed. A much highe
voltage is required to provide for the increasingly dominating effect of resistance a
low frequencies as shown in the first part of this question.

(j) Allowance for saturation of mutual inductance is now to be made and curren
sources $I_a = I_f = 2$ are to be supplied at different phase angles to permit I_m t
vary from rated value of 1, to 3 per unit. The empirical expression relating flu:
and magnetising current is, from Example 4.15:

$$I_m = \frac{0.6\phi_m}{1 - 0.4\phi_m} \text{ from which } \phi_m = \frac{I_m}{0.6 + 0.4I_m}$$

The average slope of the flux/I_m curve is proportional to the mutual inductance
When $I_m = 1$, $\phi_m = 1$ and the slope is proportional to 1. For $I_m = 2$, $\phi_m = 2/1.4$ an
for $I_m = 3$, $\phi_m = 3/1.8$. The average slopes for the last two are $1/1.4$ and $1/1.$
respectively. These are the coefficients by which M must be reduced. The angle
between I_a and I_f used on Fig. 5.3d is obtained from the cosine rule as:

$$\cos^{-1}\theta = \frac{I_f^2 + I_a^2 - I_m^2}{2I_f I_a}$$

and the torque expression of eqn. (5.21) will complete the calculation. The result
are tabulated below:

	(i)	(ii)	(iii)
M	1	1/1.4	1/1.8
θ	29°	60°	97°
$T_e = 4M \sin\theta$	1.93	2.47	2.2
Torque/amp $T_e/4$	0.48	0.62	0.55

A few more calculations will show that the maximum torque occurs at an angle θ rather less than 90° which means that the torque angle between stator and rotor m.m.f.s is rather greater than the unsaturated value of 90°. The load angle between I_m and I_f is still less than 90°. The maximum torque per ampere is somewhat less than the unsaturated value given by eqn. (5.18) which is $I/2$, equal to 1 in this case.

5.6 OPERATING CHARTS

Under certain circumstances the phasor diagrams for a.c. circuits under variable conditions give rise to phasor loci which are circular. Such circle diagrams are useful visual aids and assist in rapid calculations. They are less important nowadays with improved calculating facilities which can operate directly on the equations, which are really the basis on which the diagrams are constructed. No examples of induction machine circle diagrams have been given in this book though they are dealt with in Reference 1. However, for synchronous machines they are still of general interest because they delineate the various regions of operation in a manner especially useful for power-systems studies. One example will therefore be given here, as a simple extension of the phasor loci shown on Fig. 5.1.

EXAMPLE 5.16

A 3-phase synchronous machine has a synchronous reactance $X_s = 1.25$ *per unit* and on full load as a generator it operates at 0.9 power-factor lagging. The machine losses may be neglected.

(a) Determine the rated excitation in *per unit* to sustain this condition.

(b) What excitation would be required to operate at full-load current but 0.707 p.f. lagging?

(c) With this maximum excitation, what would be the maximum motoring torque in *per unit*—expressed in terms of full-load torque?

(d) What *per-unit* current would be drawn for condition (c)?

(e) What power can be developed as a motor when running at 0.8 power-factor leading, without exceeding rated excitation?

(f) With the maximum excitation of condition (c) what will be the kVAr rating as a synchronous capacitor?

163

(g) What will be the maximum kVAr rating as a synchronous reactor with the excitation reduced to a minimum of 1/3 of the rated value?

The problem can be solved using the approximate circuit as in the previous examples. With the circle diagrams, the solution is much quicker though less accurate.

(a) The two current phasors; $V/jX_s = 1/j1.25$, lagging 90° behind V, and $I_a = 1$ *per unit* at $\cos \varphi = 0.9$ lagging as a generator, are first drawn. With a motor convention, the I_a phasor is reversed at angle 25°.8 lagging $-V$. The closing phasor of the triangle is the rated excitation divided by jX_s, which by measurement is 1.52 *per unit*. Hence rated $E_f = 1.52 \times 1.25 = \underline{1.9\ per\ unit}$.

(b) More excitation will be required to operate at rated current and a lower power-factor. Drawing an arc from the origin at $I_a = 1$ *per unit* to angle 45° for 0.707 power factor identifies the end of the E_f/jX_s phasor which by measurement is 1.64 *per unit*. Hence $E_f = 1.64 \times 1.25 = \underline{2.05\ per\ unit}$.

(c) An arc drawn at this new E_f/jX_s radius into the motoring region until E_f/jX_s makes an angle $\delta = 90°$ with the V/jX_s phasor defines the point of maximum torque. The rated torque corresponds to rated $I_a \cos \varphi = 0.9$ *per unit* and so the maximum torque is 1.64/0.9 = 1.82 *per unit*.

(d) A current phasor drawn from the origin to the point of maximum torque has a value of $\underline{1.85\ per\ unit}$, at angle $\varphi = 25°.8$ lagging; $\cos \varphi = 0.9$.

(e) A motoring-current phasor drawn at $\varphi = \cos^{-1} 0.8$ leading = 36°.9 intersects the rated excitation circle at $I_a = 0.9$ *per unit*, and $I_a \cos \varphi = \underline{0.72\ per\ unit}$ is the power and torque for this condition.

(f) For a "motor" at zero p.f. leading, the maximum excitation circle intersects the zero-power axis at $I_a = j0.83$ *per unit*, so kVAr as a synchronous capacitor is $\underline{0.83}$ *per unit*.

(g) For zero power-factor lagging, the excitation circle drawn at 1/3 of the rated $E_f/jX_s = 1/3 \times 1.52 = 0.507$ intersects the zero-power axis at $-j0.3$, so kVAr as a synchronous reactor would be $\underline{0.3\ per\ unit}$. This rating is always less than as a capacitor because of stability considerations at low excitation.

Boundaries are shown on Fig. E.5.16 indicating the operating limits for the various modes. *Per-unit* notation is especially useful for the portrayal of so many operating modes and conditions. Resistance can be incorporated quite simply by drawing the excitation circles from a V/Z_s phasor, which will be at an angle less than 90° behind V, and the radii will then be $|E_f/Z_s|$.

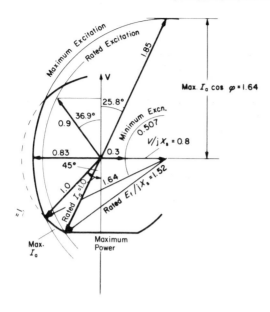

FIG. E.5.16.

5.7 MULTI-MACHINE PROBLEMS

This area of study for synchronous machines is very important for power systems. Only a few simple examples will be given here to illustrate parallel operation of generators and the use of synchronous motors to improve an industrial-system power factor. Examples up to now have assumed that the supply-system has zero impedance, giving constant terminal voltage V; and infinite inertia, giving constant frequency. These are the characteristics of the so-called "infinite" busbar system. For two paralleled generators, the interaction of the individual machine impedances and e.m.f.s on the sharing of kW and kVAr is instructive as an introduction to the power-flow problem.

165

EXAMPLE 5.17

Two 3-phase, 3.3 kV, star-connected alternators are connected in parallel to supply a load of 800 kW at 0.8 power factor lagging. The prime movers are so set that one machine delivers twice as much power as the other. The more heavily loaded machine has a synchronous reactance of 10 Ω per phase and its excitation is so adjusted that it operates at 0.75 p.f. lagging. The synchronous reactance of the other machine is 16 Ω per phase.

Calculate the current, e.m.f., power factor and load angle of each machine. The internal resistances may be neglected.

$$\text{Total kVA} = \frac{800}{0.8} = 1000 \text{ kVA.}$$

$$\text{Total current} = \frac{1000}{\sqrt{3} \times 3.3} \times (0.8 - j0.6) \qquad = I = 140 - j105 \text{ A}$$

For the heavier loaded machine (Machine A say)

$$I_A \cos \varphi_A = \frac{2}{3} \times 140 = 93.3 \text{ A}$$

and
$$I_A \sin \varphi_A = I_A \cos \varphi_A \times \tan \varphi_A = 93.3 \times 0.882$$
$$= 82.3 \text{ A.}$$
$$\therefore I_A = 93.3 - j82.3.$$
$$\therefore I_B = I - I_A = 46.7 - j22.7.$$

$$\therefore I_A = \underline{124.4 \text{ A}} \text{ at } \cos \varphi_A = \underline{0.75}.$$
$$I_B = \underline{51.9 \text{ A}} \text{ at } \cos \varphi_B = \underline{0.9}.$$

$$E_A = V + jX_A I_A = \frac{3300}{\sqrt{3}} + j10(93.3 - j82.3) = 2728 + j933 = \underline{2888 / 18°0}.$$

$$E_B = V + jX_B I_B = \frac{3300}{\sqrt{3}} + j16(46.7 - j22.7) = 2268 + j747 = \underline{2388 / 18°2}.$$

EXAMPLE 5.18

Two star-connected, non salient-pole, synchronous generators of identical rating operate in parallel to deliver 25 000 kW, 0.9 power-factor lagging-current at 11 kV. The line induced e.m.f. of Machine A is 15 kV and the machine delivers 10 MW, the remaining power being supplied by Machine B. Determine for each machine:

(a) the load angle in electrical degrees

(b) the current and power factor

(c) the kVA

Find also the induced e.m.f. of Machine B. Take the synchronous reactance for each machine as 4.8 Ω per phase and neglect all machine losses.

166

Total kVA $= \dfrac{25\,000}{0.9}$ $= 27\,777$ kVA.

Total current $= \dfrac{27\,777}{\sqrt{3} \times 11}(0.9 - j0.436)$ $= 1312 - j635.7.$

Load angle δ_A from 10 MW $= \dfrac{3 \times 11\,\text{kV} \times 15\,\text{kV}}{4.8 \times \sqrt{3} \times \sqrt{3}} \sin \delta_A$

from which: $\sin \delta_A = 0.291$; $\delta_A = \underline{16°9}$; $\cos \delta_A = 0.957.$

Hence $I_A = \dfrac{E_f - V}{jX_s} = \dfrac{1000}{\sqrt{3}} \times \dfrac{15(0.957 + j0.291) - 11}{j4.8}$ $= \underline{525 - j403.5.}$

Hence $I_B = I - I_A = \underline{787 - j232.2.}$

$E_B = V + jX_s I_B = 11\,000 + \sqrt{3} \times j4.8(787 - j232.2)$ $= 12.93 + j6.54$ Line kV
       $= 14.49\underline{/26°8.}$

From above:

(a) $\delta_A = \underline{16°9}.$ $\delta_B = \underline{26°8}.$

(b) $I_a = \underline{662\,A}$ at $\cos \varphi_A = \underline{0.793.}$ $I_B = \underline{820.5\,A}$ at $\cos \varphi_B = \underline{0.959.}$

(c) $\text{kVA}_A = \sqrt{3} \times 11 \times 662 = \underline{12\,600.}$ $\text{kVA}_B = \sqrt{3} \times 11 \times 820.5 = \underline{15\,630.}$

Induced e.m.f. for Machine B $= \underline{14.49}$ Line kV.

EXAMPLE 5.19

A 6.6 kV industrial plant has the following two induction motor drives and a main transformer for the other plant

	Ind. Mtr A	Int. Mtr B	Transformer
Rated output (kW)	100	200	300
Full-load efficiency	94%	95%	99%
Full-load power factor	0.91	0.93	0.98 lagging

A star-connected synchronous machine rated at 250 kVA is to be installed and so controlled that when all the equipment is working at full rating, the overall power-factor will be unity. At the same time, the synchronous machine is to draw rated current and deliver as much mechanical power as possible within its current rating. If its efficiency can be taken as 96% and its synchronous impedance $0 + j100\,\Omega$, calculate the required e.m.f. behind synchronous impedance to sustain this condition.

As an alternative strategy, consider what rating of synchronous machine, operating the same motoring load, would be required to bring the overall works power-factor to 0.95 leading.

First, the total works load can be calculated by summing

$$I = \sum \dfrac{\text{Power}}{\eta \times \sqrt{3} \times V \times \text{p.f.}}(\cos \varphi + j \sin \varphi)$$

Ind. Mtr A. $I_A = \dfrac{100}{0.94 \times \sqrt{3} \times 6.6 \times 0.9}(0.91 - j0.4146) \quad = 9.306 - j4.24$

Ind. Mtr B. $I_B = \dfrac{200}{0.95 \times \sqrt{3} \times 6.6 \times 0.93}(0.93 - j0.3676) \quad = 18.42 - j7.28$

Transformer. $I_T = \dfrac{300}{0.99 \times \sqrt{3} \times 6.6 \times 0.98}(0.98 - j0.199) \quad = \underline{26.51 - j5.38}$

Total current $= I_P - jI_Q$ $\qquad\qquad\qquad\qquad\qquad\qquad = \underline{54.24 - j16.9}$

Rated synchronous machine current $= \dfrac{250}{\sqrt{3} \times 6.6} = 21.87$ A

Reactive component of current must be j16.9 to bring p.f. to unity.

$\therefore$ active component of current $= \sqrt{21.87^2 - 16.9^2} = 13.88$ A.
 So synchronous motor output power $= \sqrt{3} \times 6.6 \times 13.88 \times 0.96 = \underline{152.3\ kW} = \underline{204\ hp}.$

$\mathbf{E_f} = \mathbf{V} - jX_s\mathbf{I_a} = \dfrac{6600}{\sqrt{3}} - j100(13.88 + j16.9) = 5500.5 - j1388 = \underline{5673\ V} = \underline{1.49\ p.u.}$

For a power factor of 0.95 leading, and with the same power component of synchronous–motor current, the phasor diagram shows that the following relationship holds:

$$\tan \varphi = \frac{I_{QS} - I_Q}{I_{PS} + I_P} = \frac{I_{QS} - 16.9}{13.88 + 54.24},$$

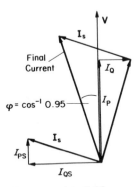

Improvement to 0.95

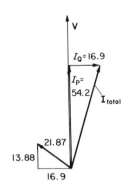

Improvement to u.p.f.

FIG. E.5.19.

168

and since $\tan \varphi = \tan(\cos^{-1} 0.95) = 0.3286 = (I_{QS} - 16.9)/68.12$,

$$I_{QS} = 39.29 \text{ A}.$$

Hence required synchronous machine rating $= \sqrt{3} \times 6.6\sqrt{(39.29^2 + 13.88^2)} =$ 476 kVA, requiring a machine of nearly twice the previous size.

5.8 SALIENT-POLE AND RELUCTANCE-TYPE MACHINES. SYNCHRONISING POWER

All the examples so far posed have been solved using round-rotor or cylindrical-rotor theory; viz. assuming that synchronous machines are built like induction machines with uniform air gap such that a sinusoidal m.m.f. distribution will produce a sinusoidal flux distribution. The majority of synchronous machines do not have such a symmetrical magnetic geometry though the high-power turbo-generators are close to this. Most synchronous-motor drives have salient-pole rotors giving two axes of symmetry per pole pair; the direct axis, along the main field winding, and the axis in quadrature, between the poles. Consequently, the magnetic permeance and the synchronous reactances as measured on the two axes, X_d and X_q, are very different. In spite of this, the steady-state behaviour is not vastly different from that calculated by assuming $X_s = X_d$ in round-rotor theory. This is not true for transient behaviour however, when considering the likelihood of instability, oscillatory behaviour or loss of synchronism, since the power/load-angle characteristic is much more helpful in these circumstances. In addition, the salient-pole synchronous motor will operate without excitation, due to the reluctance effect of the non-uniform air gap.

Transient stability studies are largely outside the scope of this book but the oscillatory frequency can be approximated by ignoring damping. From the general expression in dynamics:

$$\text{Natural frequency} = \sqrt{(\text{stiffness/inertia})} \text{ rad/s}.$$

For a synchronous machine, the stiffness is the rate of change of

169

torque per mechanical radian, obtained by differentiating the torque/load-angle curve at the operating point. Sometimes the term "synchronising power" is used to define the power ΔP, brought into play on a change of angle $\Delta\delta$, and this in turn is obtained by differentiating the power/load-angle curve to get $dP/d\delta$.

EXAMPLE 5.20

A 3-phase, 5000 kVA, 11 kV, 50 Hz, 1000 rev/min, star-connected synchronous motor operates at full load, 0.8 p.f. leading. The synchronous reactance is 0.6 *per unit* and the resistance may be neglected. Calculate for these conditions, the synchronising power per mechanical degree of angular displacement. The air gap may be assumed to be uniform around the periphery.

Working in *per unit*; $E_f = 1 - jX_sI_a = 1 - j0.6 \times 1(0.8 + j0.6)$

$$= 1.36 - j0.48 = 1.44\underline{/19°44}.$$

Power/angle equation $P = \dfrac{VE}{X_s}\sin\delta = \dfrac{1 \times 1.44}{0.6}\sin\delta = 2.4\sin\delta.$

Hence, synchronising power from $dP/d\delta = 2.4\cos\delta = 2.4\cos 19.44 = 2.263$ *p.u.*/radian

$$1\ per\text{-}unit\ \text{torque} = \frac{5\,000\,000}{2\pi \times 1000/60} = 47746\ \text{Nm}.$$

$\therefore$ 2.263 *per unit* $= 2.263 \times 47746 \times \dfrac{\pi}{180} \times 3 = \underline{5657\ \text{Nm/mechanical degree}}$

since there must be 6 poles, if the synchronous speed is 1000 rev/min at 50 Hz.

EXAMPLE 5.21

A salient-pole synchronous motor has $X_d = 0.9$ and $X_q = 0.6$ *per unit* and is supplied from rated voltage and frequency. Calculate the current, power factor and power for a load angle of $-30°$ (motoring) and for excitation e.m.f.s (E_f) of 1.5, 1.0, 0.5 and 0 *per unit*, the latter case being the reluctance motor (zero excitation). What would be the new values if, as a reluctance motor, the rotor was redesigned to give $X_d = 0.75$ and $X_q = 0.25$? What would then be the maximum torque? Armature resistance may be neglected throughout.

The phasor diagram of Fig. 5.4a is shown for the overexcited condition as a motor. The equation is similar to that for the round-rotor machine but the resolution of the armature m.m.f. F_a into direct-axis (F_{ad}) and quadrature axis (F_{aq}) components is reflected in the two component currents I_d and I_q of the armature

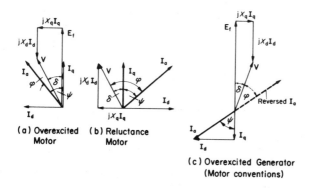

(a) Overexcited Motor

(b) Reluctance Motor

(c) Overexcited Generator (Motor conventions)

FIG. 5.4. Salient-pole synchronous machines.

current I_a. The equation is:

$$V = E_f + jX_qI_q + jX_dI_d \quad \text{(see reference 1).}$$

Remembering that δ is negative for a motor, the angle between I_a and I_q, which is in phase with E_f is:

$$\psi = \varphi - \delta$$

From the geometry of the diagram:

$$X_qI_q = - V \sin \delta \qquad \therefore I_q = \frac{- V \sin \delta}{X_q},$$

$$X_dI_d = E_f - V \cos \delta \qquad \therefore I_d = \frac{E_f - V \cos \delta}{X_d}$$

and $I_a = \sqrt{I_d^2 + I_q^2}$ $\cos \psi = I_q/I_a$ and $\sin \psi = I_d/I_a$.

Power = (torque in *per unit*)

$$= VI_a \cos \varphi = V(I_q \cos \delta - I_d \sin \delta)$$

$$= V\left[\frac{- V \sin \delta}{X_q} \cos \delta - \frac{(E_f - V \cos \delta)}{X_d} \sin \delta\right]$$

$$= \frac{-V}{X_d}\left[E_f \sin \delta + \frac{V}{2}\left(\frac{X_d}{X_q} - 1\right) \sin 2\delta\right].$$

171

In the problem, $\delta = -30°$ so $\sin \delta = -0.5$, $\cos \delta = 0.866$ and $\sin 2\delta = -0.866$

	D.C. excited salient-pole motor, $X_d = 0.9$, $X_q = 0.6$				Reluctance motor	
E_f	1.5	1.0	0.5	0	$X_d = 0.75$, $\delta = -30°$	$X_q = 0.25$, $\delta = -45°$
$I_q = \dfrac{-V \sin \delta}{X_q}$	$\dfrac{0.5}{0.6} = 0.833$	0.833	0.833	0.833	2	2.83
$I_d = \dfrac{E_f - V \cos \delta}{X_d}$	$\dfrac{1.5 - 0.866}{0.9} = 0.704$	0.149	-0.406	-0.96	-1.155	-0.943
$I_a = \sqrt{I_d^2 + I_q^2}$	1.091	0.846	0.927	1.271	2.309	2.98
$\psi = \sin^{-1} I_d/I_a$	$40°.2$	$10°.1$	$-25°.9$	$-49°$	$-30°$	$-18°.4$
$\varphi = \psi + \delta$	$10°.2$	$-19°.9$	$-55°.9$	$-79°$	$-60°$	$-63°.4$
$\cos \varphi$	0.98 lead	0.94 lag	0.56 lag	0.19 lag	0.5 lag	0.45 lag
$VI_a \cos \varphi$	1.073	0.795	0.52	0.242	1.155	1.334
$\dfrac{V}{X_d} E_f \sin \delta +$	0.833	0.555	0.277	0	0	0
$\dfrac{V^2}{2X_d}\left(\dfrac{V_d}{X_q} - 1\right) \sin 2\delta$	0.241	0.241	0.241	0.241	1.155	1.333
= Total power (check)	1.07	0.796	0.518	0.241	1.155	1.333

For the reluctance motor, terms in E_f become zero and I_d becomes negative as shown on Fig. 5.4b. Its maximum torque, by differentiation, will occur at $\delta = -45°$. For a generator, the same equations apply (as a negative motor), but δ becomes positive, and for the overexcited condition as shown on Fig. 5.4c, ψ and φ are both negative. Reversing the current phasor brings back the generator convention and enables the power-factor angle to be seen as less than 90°.

The adjacent table of results gives a very comprehensive comparison of performance. With the excited salient-pole machine of course the power factor can be controlled from lagging to leading. As excitation is reduced step by step to zero, the power factor falls drastically as does the power and torque. The output as a reluctance motor is very small. However, with a higher X_d/X_q ratio, the performance is much improved, at the expense of higher currents. This is due to the fact that the magnetising current must now come from the a.c. supply as for an induction machine. The table also shows the value and simplicity of the *per-unit* system in making these kinds of comparisons. As an exercise, the maximum torque for the excited machine could be worked out for further comparisons. The next example provides the maximum torque expression.

EXAMPLE 5.22

A 6.6 kV, 5 MVA, 6-pole, 50 Hz, star-connected synchronous generator has $X_d = 8.7\,\Omega$ per phase and $X_q = 4.35\,\Omega$ per phase. Resistance may be neglected. If the excitation is so adjusted that $E_f = 11$ kV (line), and the load angle is 30° (elec.), determine:

(a) the power factor, output current and power in *per unit*;

(b) the load angle at maximum torque;

(c) the ratio between maximum torque and that occurring with $\delta = 30°$;

(d) the stiffness in newton metres per mechanical radian for a load angle of 30°;

(e) the frequency of small undamped oscillations if the total coupled inertia is 8200 kg m², the mean load angle being 30°;

(f) the inertia constant.

Rated armature current $I_a = \dfrac{5{,}000}{\sqrt{3} \times 6.6} = 437.4\text{A} = 1$ *per unit* current.

(a) $I_q = \dfrac{-V \sin \delta}{X_q} = \dfrac{-6600/\sqrt{3} \times \sin 30°}{4.35} = -438$ A.

$I_d = \dfrac{E_f - V \cos \delta}{X_d} = \dfrac{1100 - 6600 \cos 30°}{\sqrt{3} \times 8.7} = 350.7$ A.

$I_a = \sqrt{I_d^2 + I_q^2} = \sqrt{438^2 + 350.7^2} = \underline{561.1\ \text{A}} = 1.283\ per\ unit.$

Reversing the current to give a generator convention, to determine the power-factor angle as less than 90° we have:

$$\sin \psi = \dfrac{I_d}{I_a} = \dfrac{-350.7}{561.1} = -0.625. \quad \psi = -38°7$$

$$-38°7 = \varphi - \delta = \varphi - 30, \quad \text{so } \varphi = -8°7, \quad \cos \varphi = \underline{0.988 \text{ lagging.}}$$

Power $= VI_a \cos \varphi = 1 \times 1.283 \times 0.988 = \underline{1.268\ per\ unit.}$

(b) Torque $= \dfrac{-3}{\omega_s} \times \dfrac{V}{X_d} \times \left[E_f \sin \delta + \dfrac{V}{2}\left(\dfrac{X_d}{X_q} - 1\right) \sin 2\delta \right],$

$\dfrac{dT}{d\delta} = 0$ when $E_f \cos \delta = -V\left(\dfrac{X_d}{X_q} - 1\right) \cos 2\delta = -V\left(\dfrac{X_d}{X_q} - 1\right)(2\cos^2 \delta - 1).$

Forming the quadratic: $2\cos^2 \delta + \dfrac{E_f}{V}\left(\dfrac{X_q}{X_d - X_q}\right) \cos \delta - 1 = 0.$

From which: $\cos \delta = \dfrac{-E_f}{4V}\left(\dfrac{X_q}{X_d - X_q}\right) \pm \sqrt{\left(\dfrac{E_f}{4V}\right)^2 \left(\dfrac{X_q}{X_d - X_q}\right)^2 + \dfrac{1}{2}}.$

Substituting: $\cos \delta = \dfrac{-11}{4 \times 6.6}\left(\dfrac{4.35}{4.35}\right) \pm \sqrt{\dfrac{121}{26.4^2} + 0.5}$

$$= -0.4135 \qquad \pm 0.8207$$

$$= 0.4072 = \underline{\cos 66°}; \quad \sin \delta = 0.914 \quad \sin 2\delta = 0.743.$$

(c) The ratio of torques is obtained by substituting the appropriate values of $\sin \delta$ and $\sin 2\delta$ for $\delta = 30°$ *and* $\delta = 66°$ in the torque expression. Some constants cancel

$$\dfrac{T_{max}}{T_{rated}} = \dfrac{11 \times 0.914 + \dfrac{6.6}{2}(2-1) \times 0.743}{11 \times 0.5 + \dfrac{6.6}{2}(2-1) \times 0.866} = \underline{1.496.}$$

(d) Torque at angle $\delta = \dfrac{3}{2\pi \times 50/3} \times \dfrac{6600}{\sqrt{3} \times 8.7} \times \left[\dfrac{11000}{\sqrt{3}} \sin \delta + \dfrac{6600}{2 + \sqrt{3}} \times (2-1) \sin 2\delta \right]$

$\dfrac{dT_e}{d\delta} = \dfrac{3}{100\pi} \times \dfrac{6600}{8.7} \times (11\,000 \cos 30° + 6600 \times 1 \times \cos 60°)$

$$= 92915 \text{ Nm per electrical radian}$$

$$= 92915 \times 6/2 = \underline{2.78 \times 10^5 \text{ Nm/mechanical radian.}}$$

(e) Undamped natural frequency $= \sqrt{\dfrac{\text{stiffness}}{\text{inertia}}} = \sqrt{\dfrac{2.78 \times 10^5}{8200}} = \underline{5.82 \text{ rad/s}}$

$\qquad\qquad = \dfrac{1}{2\pi} \times 5.82 = \underline{0.927 \text{ Hz}}.$

(f) The inertia constant is defined as: $\dfrac{\text{Stored energy at rated speed}}{\text{Rated voltamperes}} = \dfrac{\frac{1}{2}J\omega_s^2}{\text{MVA} \times 10^6}$

$\qquad\qquad = \dfrac{\frac{1}{2} \times 8200 \times (100\pi/3)^2}{5\,000\,000} = \underline{9 \text{ seconds}}.$

CHAPTER 6

TRANSIENT BEHAVIOUR

So far, nearly all the examples have been concerned with steady-state behaviour. It is important however to introduce the ideas underlying the equally significant behaviour which occurs during the approach to, or the retreat from a particular steady state. The transient state is a very interesting field for mathematical and computer experts, but it is still possible to study many practical aspects of machine transients without going much beyond the theory of the first-order differential equation. Thermal, electrical and mechanical transients are all partly covered by such simple equations, though clearly these will have to become more complex as more elements and control circuits are included in the system of which the machine may be only the main power unit. Usually the machine has a much larger time-constant than the control and power-electronic time-constants, so has a dominant effect and will be the area of study in this chapter as a simple introduction to the topic. Even for the machine itself, the mechanical time-constant is usually much greater than the electrical time-constants and so the electrical and mechanical responses can often be studied separately. The meaning of this is that the electrical-system changes take place at virtually constant speed and the mechanical changes take place after the electrical system has virtually reached its steady state. This particular problem will be discussed in illustrative examples but of course in the space available, the coverage of the transient state can only be limited and selective.

6.1 TRANSIENT EQUATIONS

First-order Equation

If a system has a variable θ, and an equation which can be expressed in the form:

$$\tau \frac{d\theta}{dt} + \theta = \theta_f, \tag{6.1}$$

where τ is a constant and θ_f the value of θ when the steady state is reached $(d\theta/dt = 0)$, the solution to a suddenly applied, or step function (to which θ_f is related) is most conveniently expressed as[1]:

$$\theta = \theta_0 + (\theta_f - \theta_0)(1 - e^{-t/\tau}). \tag{6.2}$$

This is illustrated on Fig. 6.1a for the initial value θ_0 positive. For θ_f either positive and negative, the same equation holds. If the response was linear at the same rate as the initial slope of the curve, then θ_f would be reached in a time τ (in time units). Actually, the response is exponential and θ reaches only 0.632 of the change $(\theta_f - \theta_0)$. After another time τ, a further 0.632 of the remaining change is accomplished, to $0.864(\theta_f - \theta_0)$. For 3τ the figure is 0.95 and for 4τ the figure is 0.98, which is often taken as the effective response time. The coefficient τ is called the time-constant.

Non-linear Response

The solution just described refers to a linear first-order equation, with τ constant and also, the driving function θ_f is constant. There are many practical situations where these conditions do not hold but a solution can still be organised fairly simply using numerical or graphical techniques. As will be seen in the following examples it is possible to express $d\theta/dt$ as a function of θ. So for various values of θ, and for a small change $\Delta\theta$ about these points we can

177

write:

$$\frac{\Delta\theta}{\Delta t} \simeq \frac{d\theta}{dt} = f(\theta). \tag{6.3}$$

Hence the time required to change by $\Delta\theta$ is equal to:

$$\Delta t = \frac{\Delta\theta}{d\theta/dt} = \frac{\Delta\theta}{f(\theta)}.$$

The method could be applied to the linear equation but of course there is no point in doing this since an analytical solution is available here.

Second-order Equation

The next stage of complexity to be described is the situation where there are two energy stores in the system. For the first-order equation there is only one, like the magnetic energy in an inductor or the electrostatic energy in a capacitor. If both these elements are in circuit, or any other two such stores, then the second differential coefficient comes into the system equation. Depending on the system parameters, the response can have rather similar characteristics (if heavily damped), or can be quite different in that the response can be oscillatory. The second case is of more general interest and occurs when the two roots of the quadratic equation are imaginary. The general form of the system equation in this case is expressed in terms of the undamped natural frequency of oscillation ω_0, and the damping ratio ζ:

$$\omega_0^{-2}\frac{d^2\theta}{dt^2} + 2\zeta\omega_0^{-1}\frac{d\theta}{dt} + \theta = \theta_f. \tag{6.4}$$

Again considering a suddenly applied driving function θ_f, the solution is:

$$\theta = \theta_f\left[1 - \frac{e^{-\zeta\omega_0 t}}{\sqrt{(1-\zeta^2)}} \sin\{\omega_0\sqrt{(1-\zeta^2)} \cdot t - \psi\}\right] \tag{6.5}$$

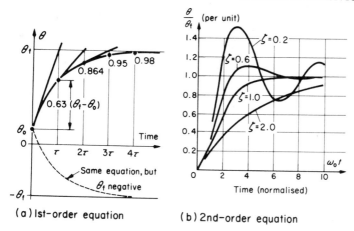

(a) Ist-order equation   (b) 2nd-order equation

FIG. 6.1. Transient response.

and is shown graphically on Fig. 6.1b for different damping ratios. When ζ, the damping ratio, is unity, the system is just not oscillatory. It is critically damped, and at a time equal to the coefficient of the first-order differential term, the variable θ reaches nearly 60% of the final value θ_f, which is close to the first-order equation solution. θ_0 could be included as for this solution, but is left here as zero. As the damping ratio falls below unity, the oscillatory condition exists, but the time response is speeded up. In practice, a ratio of about $\zeta = 0.6$ might be acceptable to gain this advantage without too much overshoot. More complex systems with third-order and higher-order terms can sometimes be approximated by this quadratic form to give a general idea of system performance. The overshoot can be controlled by appropriate external techniques to get fast response without instability or excessive oscillation. The natural frequency of oscillation in the damped state is given by: $\omega_n = \omega_0\sqrt{(1-\zeta^2)}$. Should the damping be zero, we have $\omega_n = \omega_0$ and the equation would be that of simple harmonic-motion with a zero first-order term and an oscillation between 0 and $2\theta_f$.

179

Transfer Functions

In studying complex systems, it is convenient to represent each element in the system by a relationship which relates its output to its input in both steady and transient states. This relationship is called the transfer function, defined as:

$$\text{T.F.} = \frac{\text{Output}}{\text{Input}}$$

and hence: Output = T.F. × Input.

It is a simple matter to interconnect the various elements by combining their transfer functions to give a mathematical expression for the overall system equation. For example, if two elements having transfer functions A and B are in cascade (series connected), then the overall transfer function is A × B. If the two elements are in parallel, with B as the transfer function of the negative feedback loop around A, then the overall transfer function is[1]:

$$\frac{A}{1 + A \times B}.$$

Example 6.14 will apply these relationships but it must be appreciated that it represents only a simplified use of basic concepts in control theory.

As an illustration of the transfer function consider eqn (6.1). Suppose that it refers to a series *L.R.* circuit having a time constant L/R. The equation would be:

$$\frac{L}{R}\frac{di}{dt} + i = \frac{V}{R}(= I_f).$$

Replacing d/dt by the operator p and rearranging:

$$(1 + \tau p)i = V/R$$

and: $\qquad \dfrac{\text{Output}}{\text{Input}} = \dfrac{i}{V/R} = \left(\dfrac{1}{1+\tau p}\right)$ which is the transfer function.

o the differential equation for this element can be formed from he transfer function by cross-multiplication and this applies also vhen all system elements are combined in the overall transfer unction.

Frequency Response

The emphasis so far has been on the response to a suddenly pplied d.c. driving function, but the transfer function and related quation are quite general. In control theory, for example, the esponse of the system to sinusoidal stimuli, at particular frequenies, is very important to the prediction of behaviour under all onditions. The transfer function can be used for this purpose. uppose that the *L.R.* circuit is the field winding of a d.c. generaor. The output will be i_f and the input voltage v_f, the field-circuit esistance being R_f. The equation will be:

$$(1 + \tau_f p)i_f = v_f/R_f.$$

If the generated voltage at a particular speed can be expressed as $_{out} = k_f i_f$ where k_f has the units of volts per field amp, then the ransfer function of the generator will be:

$$\frac{v_{out}}{v_f} = \frac{k_f i_f}{(1 + \tau_f p)i_f R_f} = \frac{k_f/R_f}{(1 + \tau_f p)} = \frac{\text{Steady-state voltage gain}}{(1 + \tau_f p)}.$$

Now let v_f be an a.c. voltage of angular frequency ω. The quations become, with r.m.s. values of voltages and currents:

$$V_f = (R_f + j\omega L_f)I_f \quad \text{or} \quad (1 + j\omega\tau_f)I_f R_f$$

nd:

$$V_{out} = k_f I_f$$

ssuming that the d.c. generator gives a linear response to field urrent variations. Hence:

$$\frac{V_{out}}{V_f} = \frac{k_f I_f}{(1 + j\omega\tau_f)I_f R_f} = \frac{k_f/R_f}{(1 + j\omega\tau_f)},$$

181

which is the same expression as before but with p replaced by $j\omega$ in the transfer function.

This frequency response has both a magnitude ratio and a phase angle and these are easily shown by simple a.c. theory to be:

$$\text{Magnitude ratio} = \frac{k_f/R_f}{\sqrt{1 + \omega^2 \tau_f^2}} \text{ and phase angle} = -\tan^{-1} \frac{\omega L_f}{R_f}$$

$$= -\tan^{-1} \omega \tau_f.$$

Mechanical System

On the front cover of the book is shown a schematic diagram of a motor driving a mechanical load through a coupling shaft. The torque is transmitted because the shaft tends to twist and carry the load round in the same direction. The angle of twist at the motor end θ_{m1} on steady state will be greater than the angle of twist θ_{m2} at the load end, because of the shaft flexibility, or resilience. Within the elastic limit, the torque transmitted is proportional to the difference $(\theta_{m1} - \theta_{m2})$, the resulting angle of shaft twist. In the transient state, there is another (viscous) damping force exerted by the shaft due to rate of change of shaft twist-angle, $p(\theta_{m1} - \theta_{m2})$. The inertia of the motor, J_1 kg m^2 opposes the acceleration $d\omega_m/dt = p^2\theta_{m1}$. The electromagnetic torque T_e is therefore opposed by the loss torque, the inertia torque and the shaft torques giving the following equation, where C and K are the coefficients of proportionality:

$$T_e = T_{loss} + J_1 p^2 \theta_m + C p(\theta_{m1} - \theta_{m2}) + K(\theta_{m1} - \theta_{m2}).$$

At the load end, the shaft torques tending to turn the load in the same direction as the motor are opposed by the load inertia-torque and the load torque itself. Hence:

$$C p(\theta_{m1} - \theta_{m2}) + K(\theta_{m1} - \theta_{m2}) = J_2 p^2 \theta_{m2} + T_{load}.$$

These two second-order simultaneous equations can be solved for the two variables θ_{m1} and θ_{m2} and the possibility of oscillation is present, depending on the parameter values. The undamped natural frequency is $\omega_0 = \sqrt{(K/J_1) + (K/J_2)}$ rad/sec and clearly must have a value well away from any torque-pulsation frequency arising either in the load, e.g. if it is a compressor, or from the motor, if it is supplied through certain types of power-electronic circuit. These factors are of concern for the drives specialist. For present purposes, it will be assumed that the shaft is stiff enough to transmit the torque without twisting. This means that the combined inertia of the whole drive-system can be referred through to the motor as say J kg m^2, by summing the total stored energy in the moving parts, $\Sigma \frac{1}{2}(J\omega^2 + Mv^2)$, and dividing it by the corresponding motor-speed squared ($\frac{1}{2}\omega_m^2$). From the above two equations, substituting for the last two terms of the first one, the following equation is formed for the mechanical system:

$$T_e = T_{\text{loss}} + \frac{J}{dt}\frac{d\omega_m}{dt} + T_{\text{load}} = T_m + \frac{J}{dt}\frac{d\omega_m}{dt} \qquad (6.6)$$

since $p\theta_{m1} = \omega_m$. On steady state when the speed has settled down, T_e is balanced by the total mechanical torque $T_m = T_{\text{load}} + T_{\text{loss}}$. The electromagnetic torque T_e is a function of the motor currents or may be expressed as a function of speed through the speed/torque curve. If the $T_m(\omega_m)$ characteristic is of simple form, eqn (6.6) is of first order and easily solved. In any case:

$$J\frac{d\omega_m}{dt} = T_e - T_m \quad \text{so} \quad \frac{d\omega_m}{dt} = \frac{T_e - T_m}{J}.$$

If the torques are some known function of ω_m, the last expression is the f(θ) required for the solution of eqn (6.3).

Example of Electromechanical System in Transient State

Because the d.c. machine equations are relatively simple, this machine provides an easy introduction to the application of the mechanical equations just described. For the present, the armature inductance will be neglected so that the armature current at any instantaneous speed ω_m, and e.m.f. e, with supply voltage V, will be given by $(V - e)/R$ and e itself will be $k_\phi \omega_m$. Hence, during a speed transient, the electromagnetic torque will be:

$$k_\phi i_a = k_\phi \frac{(V - k_\phi \omega_m)}{R} = \frac{k_\phi V}{R} - \frac{k_\phi^2 \omega_m}{R}.$$

This must be balanced against $T_m + J \, d\omega_m/dt$ from eqn (6.6) giving

$$\frac{k_\phi V}{R} - \frac{k_\phi^2 \omega_m}{R} = T_m + J \frac{d\omega_m}{dt}.$$

To get this into the standard form of eqn (6.1), the coefficient of the variable must be brought to unity which means dividing throughout by k_ϕ^2/R and rearranging:

$$\frac{JR}{k_\phi^2} \frac{d\omega_m}{dt} + \omega_m = \frac{V}{k_\phi} - \frac{RT_m}{k_\phi^2} \ (= \omega_{mf}). \tag{6.7}$$

The solution given by eqn (6.2) can now be applied for sudden, step changes of V, R or T_m. Step changes of flux are not practicable because of the relatively-slow field time-constant. It is assumed that T_m is not a function of ω_m; i.e. is constant. Under these circumstances, the speed time-constant is JR/k_ϕ^2. Since this is a function of mechanical, electrical and magnetic parameters it is sometimes referred to as τ_m, the electromechanical time-constant. If T_m was a function of speed, say $T_m = k\omega_m$, then the value of τ_m would be $JR/(k_\phi^2 + kR)$, the proof of this being left as an exercise. Note that eqn (6.7) has only one more term than the general speed/torque equation for a d.c. machine. When steady-state speed has been reached, $d\omega_m/dt = 0$ and the equation is then identical with eqn (3.8).

Invoking the solution given by eqn (6.2), we can write:

$$\omega_m = \omega_{mo} + (\omega_{mf} - \omega_{mo})(1 - e^{-t/\tau})$$

and Fig. 6.2 shows three transients:

(a) Acceleration on no load, V change from 0 to V.

(b) Sudden application of load T_m after reaching no-load speed.

184

(c) Reversal of V, usually with extra limiting resistance. Note that beyond zero speed, T_m, if a passive load, would also become negative as well as V and the speed response would become slower. τ_m governs all response times, with the appropriate value of resistance inserted.

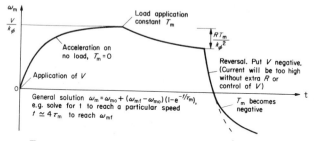

FIG. 6.2. Electromechanical transient on d.c. machine.

EXAMPLE 6.1

The temperature rise of a certain motor can be assumed to follow an exponential law of time-constant $\tau = 2$ hours. The machine operates on a duty cycle in which it is clutched to its load for 20 minutes and then declutched to run on no-load for 30 minutes. This cycle is repeated continually. The steady temperature rise when running on no-load continuously is 10°C and when operating the above duty cycle, the maximum temperature rise at the end of an ON period is 50°C. In the event of a timing failure, a thermostat is set at 60°C and shuts down the drive. Calculate:

(a) the minimum temperature rise above ambient when operating the above duty cycle;

(b) the maximum temperature rise if both the timing mechanism—which sets the ON period—and the thermostat fail to protect the system.

This example assumes that the thermal response is governed by a first-order equation so that the solution of eqn (6.2) can be invoked for the two different sections of the cycle. The figure shows the variation of temperature rise, which, with a repetitive duty-cycle will eventually settle down to a regular pattern between θ_1 and θ_2.

θ_2 has been given as 50°C. θ_{min} has been given as 10°C above ambient.
(a) asks for θ_1 and (b) asks for θ_{max}, the "runaway" temperature rise.

Considering the ON and OFF periods separately, θ_{max} is θ_f for the ON period and θ_{min} is θ_f, the final steady temperature rise for the OFF period. From eqn (6.2),

for the ON period: $\theta_2 = \theta_1 + (\theta_{max} - \theta_1)(1 - e^{-t_{ON}/\tau})$;

185

substituting: $\qquad 50 = \theta_1 + (\theta_{max} - \theta_1)(1 - e^{-1/6})$ ($t_{ON} = 1/3$ hour);

for the OFF period: $\theta_1 = \theta_2 + (\theta_{min} - \theta_2)(1 - e^{-t_{OFF}/\tau})$;

substituting: $\qquad \theta_1 = 50 + (10 - 50)(1 - e^{-1/4})$ ($t_{OFF} = 1/2$ hour).

(a) Solving the last equation: $\theta_1 = 50 - 40(1 - 0.7788) = \underline{41.15°C}$.

(b) Substituting in the ON equation: $50 = 41.15 + (\theta_{max} - 41.15)(1 - 0.8465)$

$$= 41.15 - 6.32 + 0.1535\theta_{max},$$

from which: $\underline{\theta_{max} = 98.8°C}$.

It is a very common requirement for equipment to work in this way, with varying load duties. The motor does not have to be rated for the full load continuously, since there is an OFF period. Thus the motor can be smaller than if it was rated for the full load. However, the specified duration of this load must not be exceeded or else the temperature too will be excessive as in (b). If we assume as an approximation that the temperature rise is proportional to the load, then the continuous rating of this motor would be about one-half of the 20-minute-ON, 30-minute-OFF, duty-cycle rating, in order not to exceed the normal 50°C maximum.

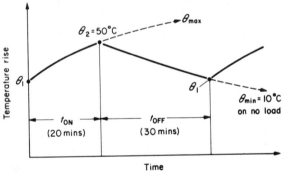

FIG. E.6.1.

EXAMPLE 6.2

The d.c. generator for which data were given in Example 3.2 has a shunt-field inductance of 23 henries (unsaturated). Derive the voltage transfer-function when run as a generator at 1000 rev/min on open circuit, and operating up to the limit of the linear part of the magnetising curve—represented by the first point on the curve.

If the field were to be excited instead from a sinusoidal voltage, at what frequency would the phase angle between output armature-voltage and input field-voltage be $-45°$? What would then be the voltage gain?

Referring back to Example 3.2, the lowest point on the o.c. curve, which is being taken as the limit of the linear range, is 71 volts generated at a field current of 0.25 A when running at 500 rev/min.

$\therefore$ at 1000 rev/min, generated volts = 142 and $k_f = 142/0.25 = 568$ V/A.

The field-circuit resistance required to give a current of 0.25 A from a supply voltage of 220 V is:

$$220/0.25 = 880 \ \Omega.$$

Hence, T.F. as a generator is:

$$\frac{k_f/R_f}{1 + \tau_f p} = \frac{568/880}{1 + p23/880} = \frac{0.645}{1 + 0.0261p}.$$

For $-\tan^{-1} \omega\tau_f$ to be $-45°$, $\omega\tau_f = 1$. Hence:

$$f = \frac{1}{\tau_f \times 2\pi} = \frac{1}{0.0261 \times 2\pi} = \underline{6.1 \ Hz}.$$

Voltage gain $= \dfrac{0.645}{\sqrt{1+1}} = \underline{0.456}$.

EXAMPLE 6.3

The same machine as in the last question and Examples 3.2 and 3.3 is to be started from a 220 V supply which is first connected directly across the field winding. The series winding is not in circuit. An external armature resistor is used to limit the maximum starting current to 80 A and is left in circuit while the motor runs against a torque T_m corresponding to this field flux and rated armature current. Calculate the expression for electromagnetic torque T_e as speed changes.

Develop the differential equation for speed when the total coupled inertia is 13.5 kg m^2. What is the electromechanical time-constant and the final steady-state speed in rev/min?

Referring back to the data of Examples 3.2 and 3.3, with 220 V across the field alone the current would be $220/110 = 2$ A and from the curve this gives $k_\phi = 4.43$.

Required total armature-circuit resistance to limit current to 80 A $= 220/80 = 2.75 \ \Omega$. At any speed during run up;

$$i_a = \frac{V - k_\phi\omega_m}{R} = \frac{220 - 4.43\omega_m}{2.75} = 80 - 1.61\omega_m.$$

Instantaneous torque $T_e = k_\phi i_a = 4.43(80 - 1.61 \ \omega_m) = \underline{354.4 - 7.14\omega_m \ Nm}$.

Mechanical torque corresponds to $k_\phi I_{aR} = 4.43 \times 40 = 177.2 \ Nm$.

From eqn (6.6) $\qquad\qquad T_e = T_m + J \ d\omega_m/dt$;

substituting: $345.4 - 7.14\omega_m = 177.2 + 13.5 \, d\omega_m/dt$;

rearranging: $1.89 \, d\omega_m/dt + \omega_m = 177.2/7.14 = 24.8 = \omega_{mf}$.

From eqn (6.2): $\omega_m = \omega_{mo} + (\omega_{mf} - \omega_{mo})(1 - e^{-t/\tau})$ is the solution for ω_m;

substituting: $= 0 + (24.8 - 0)(1 - e^{-t/1.89})$.

So the final balancing speed is $24.8 \times 60/2\pi = \underline{236.8 \, \text{rev/min}}$ and the electromechanical time-constant is $\underline{1.89 \, \text{seconds}}$.

The first part of Fig. 6.2 is relevant to this question.

EXAMPLE 6.4

A 500 V d.c. series motor drives a fan, the total mechanical load torque being given by the expression: $T_m = 10 + (\omega_m/4.2)^2$ Nm. An external resistor 7.5 Ω is added at starting to limit the current when full voltage is applied, and the motor is allowed to run up to the balancing speed corresponding to this circuit condition. The resistor is then cut out and again the speed is allowed to rise to the new balance condition in this single-step starting procedure.

(a) Calculate the starting current.

(b) Calculate the two balancing speeds, noting that the machine resistance itself is 0.8 Ω.

(c) Estimate the currents at the two balancing speeds, and on changeover.

(d) Estimate the time to accelerate from 0 to 100 rev/min if total inertia is 14.5 kg m^2.

A magnetisation curve at 550 rev/min gave the following information:

Field current	I_f	20	30	40	50	60	70	A
Generated e.m.f.	(E_{test})	309	406	468	509	534	560	V

Calculation of ω_m/T_e curves proceeds in a similar manner to Examples 3.15 and 3.16.

$k_\phi = E_{test}/(550 \times 2\pi/60)$	5.36	7.05	8.12	8.84	9.27	9.72 Nm/A
$T_e = k_\phi I_a = k_\phi I_f$	107.2	211.5	324.8	442	556.2	680.4 Nm
For high resis. $E = 500 - (0.8 + 7.5)I_f$	334	251	168	85	2	-81 V
$\omega_m = E/k_\phi$	62.3	35.6	20.7	9.6	0.2	-8.3 rad/s
For low resis. $E = 500 - 0.8I_f$	484	476	468	460	452	444 V
$\omega_m = E/k_\phi$	90.3	67.5	57.6	52	48.8	45.6 rad/s
T_m (use high resis. ω_m) $10 + \left(\dfrac{\omega_m}{4.2}\right)^2$	230	81.8	34.3	15.2	10	

(a) Starting current, $(\omega_m = 0) = 500/(0.8 + 7.5) = \underline{60.2 \, \text{A}}$.

(b) From the above tabular calculations the two ω_m/T_e curves and the ω_m/T_m curve are plotted on the figure. The two balancing speeds at the intersections are 50 and 64.5 rad/s = $\underline{477}$ and $\underline{616 \, \text{rev/min}}$.

188

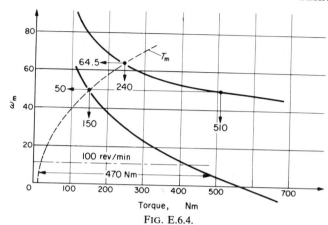

FIG. E.6.4.

(c) The corresponding torques are 150 and 240 Nm. Since $T_e = k_\phi I_f$ there is a unique relationship between torque and I_f and one can interpolate between the torque/I_f points in the table, to estimate the corresponding currents at 25 and 33 A. At changeover, the torque rises to 510 Nm and the current will be approximately 56 A, a little less than at the first step of starting.

(d) Between 0 and 100 rev/min (10.47 rad/s), the mean accelerating torque $T_e - T_m$, by measurement from the curve, is 470 Nm and since:

$$T_e - T_m = J\frac{\Delta\omega}{\Delta t}, \quad \Delta t = \frac{14.5 \times 10.47}{470} = 0.323 \text{ sec.}$$

EXAMPLE 6.5

A d.c. shunt motor has its supply voltage so controlled that it produces a speed/torque characteristic following the law:

$$\text{Rev/min} = 1000\sqrt{1 - (0.01 T_e)^2}$$

where T_e is in Nm. The total mechanical load, including machine loss-torque, has the following components: Coulomb friction 30 Nm; Viscous friction (α speed) 30 Nm at 1000 rev/min; and fan-load torque [α(speed)^2], 30 Nm at 1000 rev/min. The total coupled inertia is 4 kg m^2. Determine the balancing speed and also calculate the time to reach 98% of this speed, starting from rest.

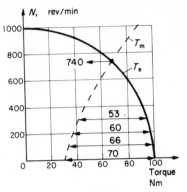

FIG. E.6.5.

From the given laws of the speed/torque relationships, the curves are calculated below and plotted on the figure.

$$N = 1000\sqrt{1 - (0.01T_e)^2}$$

T_e	20	40	60	70	80	90	100 Nm
	980	917	800	714	600	436	0 rev/min
N	200	400	500	600	700	800	900 1000 rev/min

$$T_m = 30\left[1 + \left(\frac{N}{1000}\right) + \left(\frac{N}{1000}\right)^2\right] \quad 37.2 \quad 46.8 \quad 52.5 \quad 58.8 \quad 65.7 \quad 73.2 \quad 81.3 \quad 90 \text{ Nm}$$

For speed/time calculations, we require the accelerating torque $T_e - T_m = J(\Delta\omega_m/\Delta t)$ over a series of intervals from zero to the top speed. Accuracy falls off when $T_e - T_m$ becomes small because Δt is inversely proportional to this Extra intervals are taken therefore near the final speed.

From the intersection of the curves, the balancing speed is <u>740 rev/min</u> and 98% of this is 725 rev/min. The following table is completed with the aid of readings from the graph.

N $T_{acc} = T_e - T_m$ ω_m	0 70 0	100 66 10.5	200 60 20.9	300 53 31.4	400 44.5 41.9	500 34 52.4	600 22 62.8	650 14.5 68.1	690 8 72.3	725 3 75.9
Mean T_{acc} $\Delta\omega_m$ $\Delta t = \dfrac{4\Delta\omega_m}{\text{mean } T_{acc}}$		68 10.5 0.62	63 10.5 0.66	56.5 10.5 0.74	48.8 10.5 0.86	39.3 10.5 1.07	28 10.5 1.5	18.3 5.3 1.14	11.3 4.2 1.48	5.5 3.6 2.67
$t = \Sigma\Delta t$	0	0.62	1.28	2.02	2.88	3.95	5.45	6.59	8.07	10.74

Speed/time coordinates can now be read from the above table and a curve plotted if desired. The time to 98% of the balancing speed is 10.74 seconds. Note that the longest times apply to the final build-up intervals and accuracy here is relatively poor.

EXAMPLE 6.6

The induction motor of Example 4.8 is to be braked to standstill by reversing the phase sequence of the supply to the stator. The mechanical load remains coupled and the total drive inertia is 0.05 kg m². An additional speed torque coordinate will be required to construct the reverse sequence characteristic and this may be taken as (∓1500 rev/min; ±3 Nm). Make an approximate estimate of the time to zero speed.

The reverse-sequence characteristic is a mirror image of the forward sequence characteristic but only the portion in the top left-hand quadrant is required. The figure shows the two ω_m/T_e curves over the required range and the load characteristic has determined the normal speed as 1420 rev/min. It is also seen to be approximately parallel to the "tail end" of the reverse characteristic and a mean value of the decelerating torque down to zero speed is measured as 9.5 Nm.

$\Delta\omega_m$, taking just one interval, is: $1420 \times 2\pi/60 = 149.75$ rad/s.

Hence $\Delta t = \dfrac{J\Delta\omega_m}{T_e - T_m} = \dfrac{0.05 \times 149.75}{9.5} = \underline{0.79 \text{ sec.}}$

Note: if the supply is not switched off at zero speed, the machine will run up in the reverse direction.

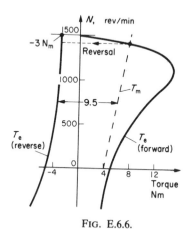

FIG. E.6.6.

191

EXAMPLE 6.7

A 500-V, 60-hp, 600-rev/min, d.c. shunt motor has a full-load efficiency of 90%. The field circuit resistance is 200 Ω and the armature resistance is 0.2 Ω. Calculate the rated armature current and hence find the speed under each of the following conditions at which the machine will develop rated electromagnetic torque.

(a) Regenerative braking; no limiting resistance;

(b) Plugging (reverse current) braking—external limiting resistor of 5.5 Ω inserted;

(c) Dynamic braking—external limiting resistor of 2.6 Ω inserted.

Rated field-current is maintained and armature reaction and brush drop may be neglected.

The machine is to be braked from full-load motoring using the circuit configurations of (b) and (c). What time would it take in each case to bring the machine to rest? The inertia of the machine and coupled load is 4.6 kg m² and the load, which is coulomb friction, is maintained.

Using the same equation as in Example 3.6:

$$\eta_R = \frac{60 \times 746}{500 \times I_{aR} + (500)^2/200} = \frac{90}{100}, \quad \text{from which } I_{aR} = \underline{97 \text{ A}}.$$

Rated flux $k_{\phi R} = \dfrac{500 - 0.2 \times 97}{600 \times 2\pi/60} = 7.65 \text{ Mn/A}$, which is maintained constant.

The braking-circuit calculations are similar to those for Example 3.19 and the basic equation is:

$$\omega_m = \frac{V}{k_\phi} - \frac{RT_e}{k_\phi^2}.$$

The value of rated torque is $k_{\phi R}I_{aR} = 7.65 \times 97 = 742 \text{ Nm}.$

(a) For regeneration, $T_e, = -742.$ $\quad \omega_m = \dfrac{500}{7.65} - \dfrac{0.2(-742)}{7.65^2} = 67.9 = \underline{648 \text{ rev/min}}.$

(b) For plugging, $T_e = -742,$

$V = -500$ and $R = 5.5 + 0.2.$ $\quad \omega_m = \dfrac{-500}{7.65} - \dfrac{5.7(-742)}{7.65^2} = 6.91 = \underline{66 \text{ rev/min}}.$

(c) For dynamic braking $T_e = -742,$

$V = 0$ and $R = 2.6 + 0.2.$ $\quad \omega_m = 0 - \dfrac{2.8(-742)}{7.65^2} = 35.5 = \underline{339 \text{ rev/min}}.$

To solve the final part of the question, eqn (6.7) could be used directly but instead will be built up from the data given. The electromagnetic torque $T_e = k_\phi i_a$ has to be balanced against $T_m + J \, d\omega_m/dt = 742 + 4.6 \, d\omega_m/dt$ and:

for (b): T_e at any speed $\omega_m = k_\phi \dfrac{(V - k_\phi \omega_m)}{R} = 7.65 \dfrac{(-500 - 7.65\omega_m)}{5.5 + 0.2}$

$$= -671 - 10.27\omega_m,$$

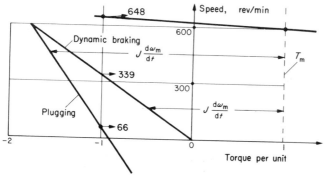

Fig. E.6.7.

for (c): T_e at any speed $\omega_m = k_\phi \dfrac{(-k_\phi \omega_m)}{R} = 7.65\dfrac{(-7.65\,\omega_m)}{2.6 + 0.2} = -20.9\,\omega_m,$

where the appropriate values of V and R have been inserted. In both cases, the initial speed starts off from the full-load value which is $600 \times 2\pi/60 = 62.8$ rad/s $= \omega_{mo}$, in the solution given by eqn (6.2), viz. $\omega_m = \omega_{mo} + (\omega_{mf} - \omega_{mo})(1 - e^{-t/\tau})$.

For (b) the differential equation is therefore: $-671 - 10.27\omega_m = 742 + 4.6\,d\omega_m/dt,$

which can be rearranged in standard form as: $0.448\,d\omega_m/dt + \omega_m = -137.6,$

and the standard solution is: $\omega_m = 62.8 + (-137.6 - 62.8)(1 - e^{-t/0.448}).$

The question asks for the stopping time; i.e. when $\omega_m = 0$. Substituting and rearranging:

$$\frac{-62.8}{-200.4} = 1 - e^{-t/0.488},$$

$$e^{t/0.448} = \frac{1}{1 - 62.8/200.4} = 1.456.$$

from which t the time to stop is $0.448 \times 0.376 = \underline{0.168 \text{ sec.}}$

For (c) the differential equation is: $-20.9\omega_m = 742 + 4.6\,d\omega_m/dt,$

which can be rearranged in standard form as: $0.22\,d\omega_m/dt + \omega_m = -35.5$

and the standard solution is: $\omega_m = 62.8 + (-35.5 - 62.8)(1 - e^{-t/0.22})$

For the stopping time, putting $\omega_m = 0$:

$$\frac{-62.8}{-98.3} = 1 - e^{-t/0.22},$$

$$e^{t/0.22} = \frac{1}{1 - 62.8/98.3} = 2.769,$$

from which the time t to stop is $0.22 \times 1.018 = \underline{0.224 \text{ sec.}}$

193

WORKED EXAMPLES IN ELECTRICAL MACHINES AND DRIVES

Dynamic braking gives a slower stopping time, even though the peak armature current is about the same in (b) and (c) (as could be checked); and the load torque, which in this case is a major braking force, is the same. A study of the figure will show why this is so. For plugging, (b), the machine will run up in reverse rotation after stopping unless it is switched off.

EXAMPLE 6.8

A 250 V d.c. shunt motor has an armature resistance of 0.15 Ω. It is permanently coupled to a constant-torque load of such magnitude that the motor takes an armature current of 120 A when running at rated speed of 600 rev/min. For emergency, provision must be made to stop the motor from this speed in a time not greater than 0.5 second. The peak braking current must be limited to twice the rated value and dynamic braking is to be employed with the field excited to give rated flux. Determine the maximum permissible inertia of the motor and its coupled load, which will allow braking to standstill in the specified time. Calculate also the number of revolutions made by the motor from the initiation of braking, down to standstill.

If after designing the drive as above, it was found that the stopping time was too long and had to be reduced to 0.4 second, determine the reduced value of resistance necessary to achieve this, and calculate the increased value of peak current.

At the rated condition, e.m.f. $E = 250 - 0.15 \times 120 = 232$ V. So:

$$k_{\phi R} = \frac{232}{600 \times 2\pi/60} = \frac{232}{62.8} = 3.69 \text{ Nm/A and } T_{eR} = 3.69 \times 120 = 443 \text{ Nm.}$$

The limiting resistance must keep the current to $2 \times 120 = 240$ A and since on dynamic braking the current is E/R in magnitude $= 232/R$ on changeover; $R = 232/240 = 0.967$ Ω, an extra $0.967 - 0.15 = \underline{0.817 \, \Omega}$.

As in the previous question, $T_e = k_\phi \dfrac{(-k_\phi \omega_m)}{R} = \dfrac{-3.69^2}{0.967} \omega_m = -14.1 \omega_m.$

Forming the mechanical balance equation: $T_e = T_m + J \, d\omega_m/dt$

$$-14.1 \, \omega_m = 443 + J \, d\omega_m/dt,$$

and rearranging:

$$\frac{J}{14.1} \frac{d\omega_m}{dt} + \omega_m = -31.4.$$

Standard solution is: $\omega_m = \omega_{mo} + (\omega_{mf} - \omega_{mo})(1 - e^{-t/\tau_m})$
$$= 62.8 + (-31.4 - 62.8)(1 - e^{-0.5 \times 14.1/J})$$
$$= -31.4 + 94.2 \, e^{-7.05/J},$$

194

from which: $e^{7.05/J} = \dfrac{1}{31.4/94.2}$ and $\underline{J = 6.42 \text{ kg m}^2}$.

Substituting this value of J gives the general expression for speed under these conditions:

$$\omega_m = 62.8 + (-31.4 - 62.8)(1 - e^{-t \times 14.1/6.42})$$
$$= -31.4 + 94.2 \, e^{-2.196t}.$$

To find the number of revolutions turned through we require to integrate

$$\int \frac{d\theta}{dt} \, dt = \int d\theta.$$

Hence $\theta = \displaystyle\int_0^{0.5} \omega_m \, dt = \left[-31.4t + \frac{94.2}{-2.196} e^{-2.196t} \right]_0^{0.5}$

$$= [-15.7 - 42.9(0.3335 - 1)] = 12.9 \text{ radians.}$$

$\therefore$ Number of revolutions to stop $= 12.9/2\pi = \underline{2.05}$.

If the stopping time is to be changed to 0.4 second and R is unknown,

$$T_e = \frac{-3.69^2}{R} \omega_m.$$

The mechanical balance equation is now:

$$\frac{-13.63}{R} \omega_m = 443 + 6.42 \, d\omega_m/dt.$$

Rearranging:

$$0.471 \frac{d\omega_m}{dt} + \omega_m = -32.5R.$$

The solution is: $\omega_m = 62.8 + (-32.5R - 62.8)(1 - e^{-t/0.471R})$.

With $t = 0.4$ second: $= -32.5R + (32.5R + 62.8) e^{-0.849/R}$,

$$1 = \left(1 + \frac{1.93}{R}\right) e^{-0.849/R}.$$

An explicit solution for R is not possible, but by trying a few values of R somewhat below the previous value of $0.967 \, \Omega$ a solution close to the correct answer is quickly found. For $R = 0.6 \, \Omega$ the R.H.S. of the equation is 1.02 so the additional series resistor must be reduced to about $0.6 - 0.15 = \underline{0.45 \, \Omega}$.

The peak current on changeover would be $232/0.6 = \underline{387 \text{ A}} = 3.22$ *per unit* which is a considerable increase on the previous value of 2 *per unit* for 0.5 second stopping time. The machine designer would have to be consulted to approve this increase.

EXAMPLE 6.9

A small permanent-magnet, 100-V d.c. motor drives a constant-torque load at 1000 rev/min and requires an input of 250 watts. The armature resistance is 10 Ω. The motor is to be reversed by a solid-state contactor which can be assumed to apply full reverse-voltage instantaneously. The inertia of the motor and drive is 0.05 kg m^2. Calculate the time:

(a) to reach zero speed
(b) to reach within 2% of the final reverse speed.

The armature inductance can be neglected, but assuming it is 1 henry, make an estimate of the actual peak current during reversal.

$$I_a = P/V = 250/100 = 2.5 \text{ A},$$

$$k_\phi = \frac{E}{\omega_m} = \frac{200 - 10 \times 2.5}{1000 \times 2\pi/60} = 0.7162 \text{ Nm/A}.$$

Rated torque = $k_\phi I_a = 0.7162 \times 2.5 = 1.79$ Nm.

(a) During the transient:

$$T_e = T_m + J \, d\omega_m/dt \text{ and } V = -100$$

$$0.7162 \left(\frac{-100 - 0.7162\omega_m}{10} \right) = 1.79 + 0.05 \, d\omega_m/dt.$$

Rearranging: $\quad\quad 0.9748 \, d\omega_m/dt + \omega_m = -174.5.$

Solution is: $\quad\quad\quad\quad \omega_m = \omega_{mo} + (\omega_{mf} - \omega_{mo})(1 - e^{-t/\tau_m}).$

Substituting $\omega_m = 0$: $\quad\quad 0 = 104.7 + (-174.5 - 104.7)(1 - e^{-t/0.9748})$

$$= -174.5 + 279.2 \, e^{-t/0.9748}.$$

from which: $\quad\quad$ time to stop, $t = 0.458$ sec.

Acceleration in the reverse direction will also be exponential of time-constant τ_m, and to 98% of final speed, time will be $4\tau_m = 3.9$ seconds. Total time = 4.36 seconds.

(b) If L is neglected, peak current on changeover = $\dfrac{-100 - 75}{10} = -17.5$ A,

$$\text{current at zero speed} \quad = \frac{-100}{10} = -10 \text{ A},$$

giving a current waveform as shown on Fig. E.6.9 over the period 0.458 second.

Electrical time-constant $\tau_e = L/R = 1/10 = 0.1$ second which is approximately 1/4 of stopping time. Dividing this part of the current wave into four intervals, an estimate of the current actually reached can be based on the exponential response of Fig. 6.1.

After 1st interval, current will be approximately $0.632 \times 15.7 = 9.9$ A.

196

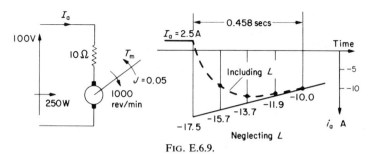

FIG. E.6.9.

After 2nd interval, current will be approximately $0.864 \times 13.7 = 11.8$ A.
After 3rd interval, current will be approximately $0.95 \times 11.9 = 11.3$ A.

So the actual current peak will be about 12 A, not the 17.5 A calculated with inductance neglected. See Example 6.14 for equations including effect of inductance.

EXAMPLE 6.10

An 8-pole, 50-Hz induction motor coupled to a flywheel drives a load which requires a torque $T_0 = 110$ Nm when running light. For an intermittent period of 8 seconds, a pulse load rising instantaneously to 550 Nm is to be supplied. What must be the combined inertia of the system to ensure that the peak motor torque does not exceed 400 Nm? The motor characteristic may be taken as linear and giving a torque of 350 Nm at a slip of 5%.

If the coupled inertia was to be changed to 200 kg m^2, what would then be the peak motor torque with the same duty?

Intermittent loads of this kind are not an uncommon requirement. To rate the motor for the full peak would be wasteful. Instead, the stored energy in the inertia, $\frac{1}{2}J\omega_m{}^2$, supplemented by a flywheel if necessary, is partly extracted during the pulse, by designing the motor with a steep enough speed-regulation to release the required amount. Figure E.6.10 shows the duty pulse and the motor characteristic from the given data. The law of the motor characteristic is linearised as

$$T_e = k\frac{(\omega_s - \omega_m)}{\omega_s} = k\, s.$$

Substituting the point given: $350 = k \times 0.05$ so $k = 7000$.

197

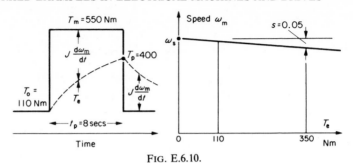

FIG. E.6.10.

It is not essential of course that the motor should be of the induction type and the characteristic is being simplified here by assuming it is a straight line.

From the mechanical balance equation: $T_e = T_m + J\, d\omega_m/dt$
$$= T_m + J\, d\omega_s(1 - s)/dt,$$

substituting: $\qquad\qquad\qquad\qquad = T_m - J\omega_s\, ds/dt,$

rearranging: $\qquad\qquad\qquad \dfrac{J\omega_s}{k}\dfrac{ds}{dt} + s = \dfrac{T_m}{k},$

which again is in standard form and the standard solution of eqn (6.2) can be invoked.

$$s = s_0 + \left(\frac{T_m}{k} - s_0\right)\left(1 - e^{-(t_p/J\omega_s/k)}\right),$$

multiply by k: $\; k_s = T_e = T_0 + (T_m - T_0)(1 - e^{-kt_p/J\omega_s}).$

There are five variables and the equation can be solved for any one of them, with all the others specified; i.e. minimum inertia (as in this question), maximum torque pulse, maximum pulse time t_p, steepness of speed regulation k and motor peak torque T_p (as in the second part of this question). Notice that the speed time-constant $\tau_m = J\omega_s/k$ is a different expression from those met in earlier examples in this chapter.

198

Substituting values:
$$\frac{J \times 2\pi \times 50/4}{7000}\frac{ds}{dt} + s = \frac{550}{7000},$$

$$\frac{J}{89.13}\frac{ds}{dt} + s = 0.07857.$$

In the solution at time t_p, motor torque $= T_p = 400 = 110 + (550 - 110)(1 - e^{-8/\tau_m})$

from which: $\tau_m = 7.434 = J/89.13$ so $\underline{J = 663 \text{ kg m}^2}$.

With $J = 200$: $T_p = 110 + (550 - 110)(1 - e^{-(8 \times 89.13)/200}) = \underline{538 \text{ Nm}}$,

which is almost the same as the pulse torque because the inertia is too small.

EXAMPLE 6.11

A high-power d.c. magnet of resistance $0.1\ \Omega$ is pulsed occasionally with 2000 A maintained constant for a period of 8 seconds. A 6-pole 50-Hz induction motor drives the supply generator, the speed regulation being set to give a speed of 800 rev/min at the end of the load pulse. The induction motor torque at 800 rev/min is 1500 Nm. For the purposes of estimating the required flywheel effect, make the following assumptions:

a) negligible light-load torque;

b) d.c. generator efficiency 92%;

c) induction motor torque proportional to slip;

d) the pulse is of rectangular shape having a magnitude corresponding to the generator coupling torque which occurs at the mean speed (900 rev/min).

Calculate this torque and the required flywheel effect of the motor-generator set. Estimate how frequently the pulse could be applied without exceeding the specified limit.

Generator input power = Magnet power/efficiency

$$= I^2 R/\eta = \frac{2000^2 \times 0.1}{0.92}$$

Coupling torque at mean speed

$$= \frac{P}{\omega_m} = \frac{2000^2 \times 0.1}{0.92 \times 900 \times 2\pi/60} = \underline{4613 \text{ Nm}}$$

For the motor characteristic; at 800 rev/min, slip $= (1000 - 800)/1000 = 0.2$

The peak value, $T_p(= T_e) = 1500 = ks = k \times 0.2$ from which $k = 7500$. Setting up the mechanical equation: $7500s = 4613 + J\ d\omega_m/dt = 4613 - J\omega_s\ ds/dt$. Rearranging and substituting $\omega_s = 2\pi \times 50/3 = 104.7$ rad/s

$$\frac{J \times 104.7}{7500}\frac{ds}{dt} + s = \frac{4613}{7500}$$

$$\frac{J}{71.63}\frac{ds}{dt} + s = 0.615 = s_f$$

The solution is:

$$T_e = T_o + (T_m - T_o)(1 - e^{-t_p/\tau_m})$$

Substituting at the end of the pulse:

$$1500 = 0 + (4613 - 0)(1 - e^{-8/\tau_m})$$

from which:

$$e^{8/\tau_m} = \frac{1}{1 - 1500/4613}$$

and:

$$\tau_m = 20.34 = J/71.63$$

hence required inertia

$$= \underline{1457 \text{ kg m}^2}$$

After the pulse has been removed, the motor speed will rise and recharge the inertia. The only change in the basic mechanical equation is that the load pulse will be replaced by the light-load torque which in this case is taken to be zero. The factors affecting the time-constant are not changed. Consequently, the slip will have returned to within 2% of its no-load value in a time equal to four time-constants.

Hence rest time must be at least $4\tau_m = 4 \times 20.34 = 81$ seconds.

The frequency of pulse application should not therefore exceed *one every* $1\frac{1}{2}$ *minutes*. If the frequency must be greater than this, then the analysis will have to be different since the minimum torque will no longer be T_o. The method used in Example 6.1 is applicable.

EXAMPLE 6.12

A d.c. rolling-mill motor operates on a speed-reversing duty cycle. For a particular duty, the field current is maintained constant and the speed is reversed linearly from $+100$ to -100 rev/min in a time of 3 seconds. During the constant-speed period, the first pass requires a steady rolling torque of 30 000 lbf ft for 6 seconds

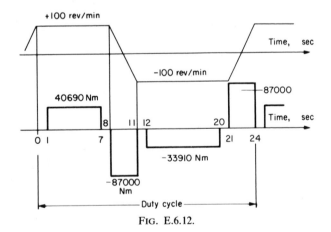

FIG. E.6.12.

and the second, reverse pass requires 25 000 lbf ft for 8 seconds. At the beginning and end of each pass there is a 1 second period of no-load running at full speed. If the total inertia J referred to the motor shaft is 12 500 kg m^2, find the r.m.s. torque, r.m.s. power and peak motor power.

This example, as an introduction to the effect of duty cycles on motor ratings, is somewhat simplified, but sufficiently realistic to illustrate the general method used when the duty cycle is not an intermittent pulse as in the previous two examples.

The figures are drawn from the data and should help to interpret these data. The torques are converted to Nm on multiplication by 746/550. During reversal, the inertia torque is far greater than any no-load torque, which has been neglected, giving:

$$\text{Reversing torque} = J \frac{d\omega_m}{dt} = 12\,500 \frac{[100 - (-100)] \times 2\pi/60}{3}$$

$$= 87\,000 \text{ Nm.}$$

Since the motor is on fixed field current, the torque is proportional to armature current. Therefore if the r.m.s. value of the torque duty-cycle is obtained, it will be proportional to the r.m.s. current of the motor, which determines the motor rating. Since the torque/time curves are all simple rectangles, the r.m.s. value is:

$$T_{rms} = 10^4 \sqrt{\frac{4.069^2 \times 6 + (8.7^2 \times 3) \times 2 + 3.391^2 \times 8}{24}} = \underline{51860 \text{ Nm.}}$$

Hence the motor power-rating =

$$\omega_m T_{rms} = \frac{2\pi \times 100}{60} \times 51860 = \underline{543 \text{ kW.}}$$

The motor must also be designed to withstand the peak torque and current corresponding to 87 000 Nm. The peak power is

$$\frac{2\pi \times 100}{60} \times 87\,000 = \underline{911 \text{ kW.}}$$

EXAMPLE 6.13

The motor coach on a 4-car suburban train weighs 50 tonnes (1 tonne = 1000 kg) and the remaining coaches with passengers weigh a further 100 tonnes. All four axles are driven by d.c. series motors supplied through a.c./d.c. rectifiers. If the maximum coefficient of friction before wheel-slip is 0.2, calculate the maximum possible acceleration on level track and also up a gradient of 1 in 120. Allow an extra 10% on the weight for the stored energy of the machinery in rotary motion.

For a particular duty, the train is on level track and travels under the following conditions:

Mean starting current per motor 400 A, maintained by tap changing on the rectifier transformer to increase the voltage uniformly to 750 V on each motor. Acceleration up to 50 km/hour, whereupon the power is shut off and coasting commences.

Braking is imposed at the rate of 3 km/hour/sec.

Resistance to motion is 4.5 kgf/tonne normally but is 6.5 kgf/tonne when coasting.

Calculate:

(a) distance travelled in 2 minutes;

(b) average speed;

(c) energy consumption in watt hours;

(d) specific energy consumption in watt hours/tonne/km.

The characteristics of each series motor are as follows, in terms of motor current, torque converted to kilogram force at the motor-coach couplings, and linear speed in km/hour.

Current	400	320	240	160	120	80	A
Force per motor	2500	1860	1270	650	390	180	kgf
Speed		29	31.5	36.9	44.6	53	72.4	km/h

In the case of linear motion, the force equation is $F = M \, dv/dt$ newtons, where M is the mass in kg and velocity v is in metres/sec. If acceleration α is in the usual units of km/h per second and the effective mass for both translational and rotational stored-energy is M_e tonnes:

$$F = (M_e \times 1000) \times \left(\alpha \times \frac{1000}{60^2} \right) \text{ newtons}$$

in kgf:

$$F = \frac{1}{9.81} \times \frac{10^6}{3600} \times M_e \alpha = \underline{28.3 \, M_e \alpha \text{ kgf}}. \tag{6.8}$$

In the example: $M_e = (50 + 100) \times 1.1 = 165$ tonnes.

Maximum force before slipping at the driving axles $= (50 \times 0.2) \times 1000 = 10\,000$ kgf.

Train resistance $= (50 + 100) \times 4.5 = 675$ kgf.

Downwards force due to gravity on a gradient of 1 in $120 = \dfrac{(50 + 100)}{120} \times 1000 = 1250$ kgf. The motor-torque-pulsations due to the rectifier supply will be neglected.

From equation (6.8), on level tract k: $\alpha = \dfrac{10\,000 - 675}{28.3 \times 165} = 2$ km/h/sec (1.25 mph/sec);

on gradient: $\alpha = \dfrac{10\,000 - 675 - 1250}{28.3 \times 165} = \underline{1.73 \text{ km/h/sec}}$.

Calculation of the speed/time curve will also use eqn (6.8) in the form:

202

Accelerating force = $28.3\, M_e \dfrac{\Delta v}{\Delta t}$ from which $\Delta t = \dfrac{28.3\, M_e \times \Delta v}{\text{Accel. force}}$

The method is similar to Example 6.5 for rotary motion.

The motor characteristics are repeated here in terms of the total force.

Current	400		320		240		160		120		80		A
Total force	10 000		7440		5080		2600		1560		720		kgf
Speed v	29		31.5		36.9		44.6		53		72.4		km/h
Accel. force (-675)	9325		6765		4405		1925		885		45		kgf
Mean acc. force	9325		8045		5385		3165		1405		465		kgf
v	29		2.5		5.4		7.7		8.4		19.4		km/h
$\Delta t = \dfrac{28.3\, M_e \Delta v}{\text{mean force}}$	14.5		1.45		4.5		11.36		27.9		194.8		sec
Time t from start	14.5		15.95		20.45		31.8		69.7		264.5		sec

(a) From these results, the speed/time and current/time curves can be plotted as on the figure. At 50 km/h, power is shut off and coasting commences at a decelerating rate of:

$$\frac{\text{Resistance force}}{28.3\, M_e} = \frac{6.5 \times 150}{28.3 \times 165} = 0.209 \text{ km/h/sec.}$$

From a time of 2 minutes, the braking line can be drawn in at the specified rate of 3 km/h/sec to complete the speed/time curve. The distance travelled is now the area under this curve from $v = dx/dt$ so $x = \int v\, dt$. By counting squares, or any other method, this area is 4700 km/h × seconds and dividing by 60^2 gives distance as 1.306 km (0.81 mile).

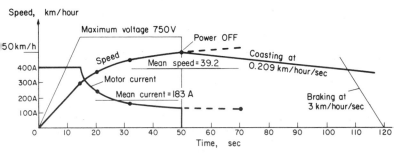

FIG. E.6.13.

203

(b) Mean speed $= \dfrac{1.306}{120/3600} = \underline{39.2 \text{ km/h}}$ (24.3 mph).

(c) Energy in first accelerating period is (mean voltage) $\times 400 \text{ A} \times \Delta t = \dfrac{750}{2} \times 400 \times 14.5$

and in the second period is: $750 \text{ V} \times$ (mean current) $\times \Delta t = 750 \times 183 \times (50 - 14.5)$.

For the four motors, in watt hours:

$$\text{energy consumed} = \frac{4}{3600}(375 \times 400 \times 14.5 + 750 \times 183 \times 35.5) = \underline{7830 \text{ watt hours}}$$

the mean current during the second period being obtained from the area under the current/time curve.

(d) This performance figure is $\dfrac{7830}{150 \times 1.306} = \underline{40 \text{ watt hours/tonne km}}$ (63.4 wh/ton mile).

EXAMPLE 6.14

Consider a d.c. separately excited motor and include the effect of armature-circuit inductance.

(a) Show how the response of current is affected by the electrical and electromechanical time constants and how, for a constant mechanical load T_m, the system itself exhibits a capacitance effect of J/k_ϕ^2 farads.

(b) Derive the transfer function ω_m/v for the motor, by considering it as a feedback system (the e.m.f. being fed in negatively with respect to v), and interlinking the various equations in terms of their individual "transfer functions". Consider first a pure inertia load, but by the same technique, examine the effect of load torque T_m, by superposition. Show that the speed response will be oscillatory if the electrical time constant $\tau_e > \tau_m/4$ and derive the frequency in terms of these time constants.

(c) If the motor is supplied from an electronic amplifier of linear gain K with a closed-loop speed control, show in general terms, the effect of this on the speed response and speed regulation. Use the same techniques as in (b).

(a) The motor circuit equation is: $v = Ri + Lpi + k_\phi \omega_m$,
and since $T_e = k_\phi i$:

$$\frac{d\omega_m}{dt} = \frac{T_e - T_m}{J} = \frac{k_\phi i - T_m}{J}.$$

Integrating this expression gives

$$k_\phi \omega_m = k_\phi \int \frac{k_\phi(i - T_m/k_\phi)\, dt}{J} = \frac{k_\phi^2}{J} \int (i - I_{ss})\, dt.$$

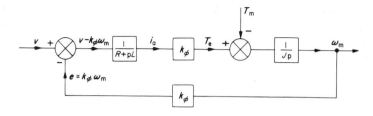

Substituting in the voltage equation and dividing throughout by R:

$$\frac{v}{R} = i\left[1 + \frac{L}{R}\frac{di}{dt} + \frac{1}{JR/k_\phi^2}\int (i - I_{ss})\,dt\right].$$

This is in the same form as the circuit equation for an LCR circuit, with C having a value of J/k_ϕ^2. The electrical time constant is $\tau_e = L/R$ and $\tau_m = {}^\prime C^\prime$ $R = JR/k_\phi^2$ is the electromechanical time constant. I_{ss} is the steady-state current T_m/k_ϕ.

b) The block diagram on the first figure shows how the net voltage $v - e = v - k_\phi\omega_m$ is applied to the armature-circuit impedance, $R + Lp$ to produce the armature current i_a which in turn produces T_e when acted upon by the torque "transfer function" k_ϕ. At the next mixing point, the mechanical torque is fed in negatively, opposing T_e, though this will first be neglected and superimposed afterwards. From the equation $J\,d\omega_m/dt = T_e - T_m$, the "transfer function" relating torque to speed is formed as:

$$\frac{\omega_m}{T_e - T_m} = \frac{1}{Jp}.$$

The output now is ω_m and on multiplying this by the speed/e.m.f. "transfer function" k_ϕ, the e.m.f. can be fed back negatively at the $v:e$ mixing point. We can now combine all these individual "transfer functions" to form the overall ω_m/v transfer function using the techniques explained under this heading in Section 6.1. First of all the forward elements are combined by simple multiplication to form

$$A = \frac{k_\phi}{(R + Lp)Jp}$$

and feedback transfer function $B = k_\phi$. A and B are now combined as explained in Section 6.1 with B in "parallel" with A.

$$\frac{\omega_m}{v} = \frac{A}{1 + AB} = \frac{1}{\dfrac{1}{A} + B} = \frac{1}{\dfrac{JLp^2 + JRp}{k_\phi} + k_\phi} = \frac{k_\phi}{JLp^2 + JRp + k_\phi^2}.$$

Multiplying the first term of the denominator by R/R and by some rearrangement:

$$\frac{\omega_m}{v} = \frac{1/k_\phi}{\dfrac{JR}{k_\phi^2}\dfrac{L}{R}p^2 + \dfrac{JR}{k_\phi^2}p + 1} = \frac{1/k_\phi}{\tau_m\tau_e p^2 + \tau_m p + 1}.$$

If we now consider the effect of load T_m alone, its forward transfer function to ω_m is $1/Jp$ and its parallel "feedback" loop is the product of the remaining elements $k_\phi^2/(R + Lp)$. Again applying the parallel combination formula:

$$\frac{\omega_m}{T_m} = \frac{1}{Jp + \dfrac{k_\phi^2}{R + Lp}} = \frac{1/k_\phi^2(R + Lp)}{\dfrac{JR}{k_\phi^2}\dfrac{L}{R}p^2 + \dfrac{JR}{k_\phi^2}p + 1}.$$

The denominator is the same as for the ω_m/v transfer function so the two equations for ω_m can be superimposed to give T.F.$_1 \times v - $ T.F.$_2 \times T_m$

i.e.
$$\omega_m = \frac{1}{k_\phi(\tau_m\tau_p p^2 + \tau_m p + 1)}\left[v - \frac{RT_m}{k_\phi} - \frac{L}{k_\phi}pT_m\right].$$

The final bracketed term consists of the voltage applied, the steady-state R drop since $T_m/k_\phi = I_{ss}$, and a zero term since $dT_m/dt = 0$. Hence for application of V:

$$\frac{V - RI_{ss}}{k_\phi} = (\tau_m\tau_e p^2 + \tau_m p + 1)\omega_m$$

and considering the quadratic in this differential equation, the solution will be imaginary (and oscillatory) if $\tau_m^2 < 4\tau_m\tau_e$ or $\tau_m/4 < \tau_e$.

The oscillatory solution can be obtained by comparing coefficients with the standard form of eqn (6.4); i.e.

$$\Omega(\text{s.s. speed}) = (\omega_0^{-2}p^2 + 2\zeta\omega_0^{-1}p + 1)\omega_m.$$

The standard solution from eqn (6.5) for a step change to Ω_m from whatever cause is:

$$\omega_m = \omega_{mo} + (\Omega_m - \omega_{mo})\left[1 - \frac{e^{-\zeta\omega_0 t}}{\sqrt{1 - \zeta^2}}\sin\{\omega_0\sqrt{(1 - \zeta^2)}t - \psi\}\right].$$

Comparing coefficients:

Undamped oscillation frequency $= \omega_0\sqrt{\dfrac{1}{\tau_m\tau_e}}$.

Damping ratio $\zeta = \dfrac{\omega_0\tau_m}{2} = \dfrac{1}{2}\sqrt{\dfrac{\tau_m}{\tau_e}}$.

Damping factor $\qquad \zeta\omega_0 = \dfrac{1}{2\tau_e} = \dfrac{R}{2L}$.

206

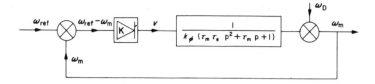

FIG. E.6.14(b).

Actual oscillation frequency $= \omega_o \sqrt{1 - \zeta^2} = \sqrt{\dfrac{1}{\tau_m \tau_e}\left(1 - \dfrac{\tau_m}{4\tau_e}\right)}$

$$= \sqrt{\dfrac{1}{\tau_m \tau_e} - \dfrac{1}{4\tau_e^2}}.$$

$$\psi = \tan^{-1}(\sqrt{1 - \zeta^2})/(-\zeta) = \tan^{-1}\sqrt{\dfrac{4\tau_e}{\tau_m} - 1}.$$

In practice, the response of a single motor to the sudden application of supply voltage does not give rise to oscillation. The small permanent-magnet d.c. motor of Example 6.9 has $\tau_m = 0.9748$ and $\tau_e = 0.1$ which is well clear of the oscillatory condition that $\tau_e > \tau_m/4$. However, on high-performance drives, for example multi-stand, metal-strip rolling mills, this phenomenon could occur and would cause non-uniform metal thicknesses and breakages unless properly damped.

(c) Taking the motor transfer function as just developed, it is now inserted in the forward loop of the block diagram in the second figure. It is preceded by the linear amplifier of gain K and the feedback loop is closed at the mixing point of the reference speed ω_{ref} and the actual speed ω_m. These are both converted to some convenient control voltage and the difference, proportional to $\omega_{ref} - \omega_m$ is the error and the control signal for the amplifier. A speed disturbance ω_D, due to the natural load regulation is inserted at the output to examine the effect of the speed-control loop on this quantity. By combining the transfer functions as before:

$$\frac{\omega_m}{\omega_{ref}} = \frac{1}{\dfrac{k_\phi(\tau_m\tau_e p^2 + \tau_m p + 1)}{K} + 1} \quad \text{noting that B is unity.}$$

$$\frac{\omega_m}{\omega_D} = \frac{1}{1 + \dfrac{K}{k_\phi(\tau_m\tau_e p^2 + \tau_m p + 1)}} \quad \text{noting that A is now unity.}$$

207

From these two equations, the two contributions to ω_m—from the control signal and from the load—can be obtained. It can be seen that the response to ω_{ref} will be speeded up due to the feedback action since the gain K, which will be greater than unity, reduces the magnitude of the time-constants governing the response. The normal steady-state regulation, ω_D, will also be reduced, by a factor of $1 + K/k_\phi$, and p terms becoming zero when the speed has settled down. Overall, then, the effect of feedback is beneficial in two clear ways. There is a price to pay in terms of the additional gain required and the likelihood of instability. But this is no problem with modern control methods which can readily introduce amplifying the stabilising circuits.

Note that this example is merely a simple introduction to the general effects of closed-loop feedback control on performance.

CHAPTER 7

POWER-ELECTRONIC/ELECTRICAL MACHINE DRIVES

ELECTRICAL machines have been controlled through power-electronic circuits since the early days of mercury-arc-type rectifiers. The development of compact power semi-conductors has increased such applications enormously. Only a limited amount of power can be dissipated by such a small device and so it must be operated as a switch, either open—rated at maximum circuit voltage and zero current; or closed—rated at maximum circuit current and the relatively small forward-voltage-drop. Power-electronic circuits therefore involve ON/OFF switching and waveforms which are neither pure d.c. nor pure sinusoidal a.c., but the average d.c. voltage or the average a.c. voltage and fundamental frequency can be controlled as desired. It is no longer possible to calculate the complete performance so simply as for the ideal waveforms, because of the harmonics introduced, but even if these are neglected the errors in the general electromechanical performance-calculations are not usually serious. Methods of dealing with more detailed calculations are introduced at the end of this chapter after some discussion and illustration of approximate solutions.

7.1   CHOPPER-CONTROLLED D.C. MACHINE

This is one of the simplest power-electronic/machine circuits and with a battery supply, it is the most common electric road-vehicle drive. The power is switched ON and OFF through a controlled rectifier (thyristor or power transistor), as indicated on Fig. 7.1a for the motoring condition. Across the motor is a free-wheel diode through which the machine inductance discharges in the OFF period, avoiding the switch-off transient and keeping the motor current flowing. The firing-control circuitry is not shown. For a fixed field-current, the speed is nearly proportional to the duty cycle ratio δ of ON-time to (ON + OFF)-time, since the average voltage is determined by this. At low ratios, the current would fall to zero in the OFF period so that the current pulses would be discontinuous. The terminal voltage would then rise to the value of the e.m.f. during this short part of the cycle.

The electrical-circuit transients are much faster than those of the mechanical system so there is no detectable change of speed due to the current and torque pulsations which are typically at 100+ Hz. For constant flux, the e.m.f. may be assumed constant during the cycle. If the motor is series excited, then the e.m.f. does vary and can be expressed as $k_{fs}i_a$ where k_{fs} is the mean slope of the magnetisation curve in volts per amp at the appropriate speed, and over the small current pulsation range from i_1 to i_2.

The volt drops of the semi-conductors can be included as constant voltages of say 1 V and the battery resistance R_B is in circuit during the ON period. The equations are:

	ON	OFF
	$E_B = E + (R_a + R_B)i_a + Lpi_a + 1$	$0 = E + R_ai_a + Lpi_a + 1$
Rearranging:	$\dfrac{L}{R}pi_a + i_a = \dfrac{E_B - E - 1}{R} = I_{max}$	$\dfrac{L}{R_a}pi_a + i_a = \dfrac{-E - 1}{R_a} = I_{min}$
	(7.1a)	(7.1b)
Solutions: [Eqn (6.2)]	$i_2 = i_1 + (I_{max} - i_1)(1 - e^{-t_{ON}/\tau})$	$i_1 = i_2 + (I_{min} - i_2)(1 - e^{-t_{ON}/0.06})$

Note in the above that E_B is the battery e.m.f., $R = (R_a + R_B)$ and the two time constants are different because in the OFF condition the resistance is just R_a.

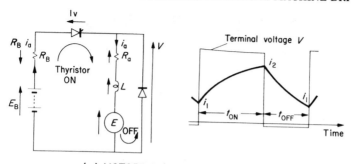

(a) MOTORING (Motoring conventions)

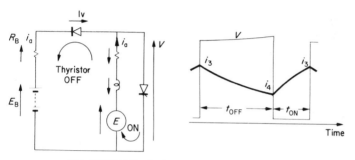

(b) GENERATING (Generating conventions)

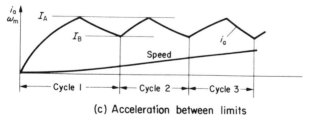

(c) Acceleration between limits

FIG. 7.1. Chopper-fed d.c. machine.

211

For the series motor, the e.m.f. $= k_{fs}i_a$ so the equations become:

	$E_B = k_{fs}i_a + Ri_a + Lpi_a + 1$	$0 = k_{fs}i_a + R_ai_a + Lpi_a + 1$
Rearranging:	$\dfrac{L}{R + k_{fs}}pi_a + i_a = \dfrac{E_B - 1}{R + k_{fs}}$ (7.2a)	$\dfrac{L}{R_a + k_{fs}}pi_a + i_a = \dfrac{-1}{R_a + k_{fs}}$ (7.2b)

The equations are still of first order but the values are different and the response faster as shown by the reduced time-constant. Increase of current causes increase of flux.

From the viewpoint of energy conservation, it is important to consider regenerative braking where possible and the chopper circuit lends itself simply to this. The arrangement is shown in Fig. 7.1b for the regenerative condition. The thyristor is effectively short-circuiting the machine and the current builds up rapidly to charge the inductance during the thyristor ON period. When switched OFF, the fall of current causes the inductive e.m.f. to supplement the machine e.m.f. and force current into the battery, thus recovering the energy (minus losses) given up by the mechanical system as the speed falls. The equations are:

	Thyristor ON	Thyristor OFF
	$0 = E - R_ai_a - Lpi_a - 1$	$E_B = E - (R_a + R_B)i_a - Lpi_a - 1$
Rearranging:	$\dfrac{L}{R_a}pi_a + i_a = \dfrac{E - 1}{R_a} = I_{max}$ (7.3a)	$\dfrac{L}{R}pi_a + i_a = \dfrac{E - E_B - 1}{R} = I_{min}$ (7.3b)
Solutions:	$i_3 = i_4 + (I_{max} - i_4)(1 - e^{-t_{ON}/\tau})$	$i_4 = i_3 + (I_{min} - i_3)(1 - e^{-t_{OFF}/\tau})$

All the equations are first order and the current waveforms will therefore be exponential in form. For the series machine when regenerating, the exponential of the transient term is positive since the self-excited generator is basically unstable and only restrained by the onset of saturation.

Acceleration and Deceleration between Current Limits

With a suitable current detector and control scheme, acceleration and deceleration can be conducted at some constant "mean" current varying between two specified limits I_A and I_B say. The ON period stops when I_A is reached and starts again when the current falls to I_B. The chopping frequency is not fixed but is determined by the system response to this control and is typically in the range 50–500 Hz, for a vehicle drive. So long as there is scope for further adjustment of the duty-cycle ratio, the current will continue to pulsate between these limits so that the mean torque is then "constant" and the rate of change of speed will be constant. Thereafter the current will fall until steady-state speed is reached. Figure 7.1c shows the initial part of such a current/time, speed/time schedule.

EXAMPLE 7.1

An electrically-driven automobile is powered by a d.c. series motor rated at 72 V, 200 A. The motor resistance and inductance are respectively 0.04 Ω and 6 milli-henrys. Power is supplied via an ON/OFF controller having a fixed frequency of 100 Hz. When the machine is running at 2500 rev/min the generated-e.m.f. per field-ampere, k_{fs}, is 0.32 V which may be taken as a mean "constant" value over the operating range of current. Determine the maximum and minimum currents, the mean torque and the mean power produced by the motor, when operating at this particular speed and with a duty-cycle ratio δ of 3:5. Mechanical, battery and semi-conductor losses may be neglected when considering the relevant diagrams of Fig. 7.1a.

Chopping period = 1/100 = 10 msec and for δ = 3/5; ON + OFF = 6 + 4 msec.

The equations are:

for ON period: $V = k_{fs}i + Ri + Lpi$—from eqn (7.2a).

Substituting: $72 = 0.32i + 0.04i + 0.006 \, di/dt$.

For OFF period: $0 = 0.32i + 0.04i + 0.006 \, di/dt$—from eqn (7.2b).

Rearranging:

ON $0.0167 \, di/dt + i = 200 = I_{max}$.

OFF $0.0167 \, di/dt + i = 0 = I_{min}$.

Current oscillates between a "low" of i_1 and a "high" of i_2, with $\tau = 0.0167$ second

ON $i_2 = i_1 + (200 - i_1)(1 - e^{-0.006/0.0167})$,

$i_2 = 200 - (200 - i_1) \, e^{-0.36} = \underline{60.46 + 0.698i_1}$.

OFF $i_1 = i_2 + (0 - i_2)(1 - e^{-0.004/0.0167})$

$i_1 = i_2 \, e^{-0.24} = \underline{0.787 \, i_2}$.

Hence, by substituting: $i_2 = 60.46 + 0.698 \times 0.787 \, i_2$,

213

from which $i_2 = 134.1$ A and $i_1 = 105.6$ A.

Torque $= k_\phi i = \dfrac{k_{fs}i}{\omega_m} \times i = \dfrac{k_{fs}}{\omega_m}i^2$.

Mean torque $= \dfrac{0.32}{2500 \times 2\pi/60}\left(\dfrac{134.1^2 + 105.6^2}{2}\right) = \underline{17.8 \text{ Nm}}$.

Mean power $= \omega_m T_e = \dfrac{2\pi}{60} \times 2500 \times 17.8 = \underline{4.66 \text{ kW}} = \underline{6.25 \text{ hp}}$.

EXAMPLE 7.2

The chopper-controlled motor of the last question is to be separately excited at flux corresponding to its full rating. During acceleration, the current pulsation is to be maintained as long as possible between 170 and 220 A. During deceleration the figures are to be 150 and 200 A. The total mechanical load referred to the motor shaft corresponds to an armature current of 100 A and rated flux. The total inertia referred to the motor shaft is 1.2 kg m². The battery resistance is 0.06 Ω and the semiconductor losses may be neglected. Determine the ON and OFF periods for both motoring and regenerating conditions and hence the chopping frequency when the speed is 1000 rev/min.

Calculate the accelerating and decelerating rates in rev/min per second and assuming these rates are maintained, determine the time to accelerate from zero to 1000 rev/min and to decelerate to zero from 1000 rev/min. Reference to all the diagrams of Fig. 7.1 will be helpful.

Rated flux at rated speed of 2500 rev/min corresponds to an e.m.f.:

$$E = V - RI_a = 72 - 0.04 \times 200 = 64 \text{ V}$$

At a speed of 1000 rev/min, therefore, full flux corresponds to $64 \times 1000/2500 = 25.6$ V

Acceleration   Total resistance $= R_a + R_B = 0.04 + 0.06 = 0.1 \ \Omega$

For ON period $E_B = E + Ri_a + Lpi_a$,

$$72 = 25.6 + 0.1i_a + 0.006pi_a.$$

Rearranging: $0.06 \, di_a/dt + i_a = 464 = I_{max}$.

Solution is: $i_2 = i_1 + (I_{max} - i_1)(1 - e^{-t_{ON}/\tau})$

and since i_1 and i_2 are known: $220 = 170 + (464 - 170)(1 - e^{-t_{ON}/0.06})$.

$$\frac{220 - 170}{464 - 170} = 1 - e^{-t_{ON}/0.06}$$

from which: $\underline{t_{ON} = 0.01118}$.

For OFF period $0 = 25.6 + 0.04i_a + 0.006pi_a$ (note resis. $= R_a$).

Rearranging: $0.15 \, di_a/dt + i_a = -640 = I_{min}$.

Solution is: $i_1 = i_2 + (I_{min} - i_2)(1 - e^{-t_{OFF}/\tau})$.

Substituting i_1 and i_2: $170 = 220 + (-640 - 220)(1 - e^{-t_{OFF}/0.15})$,

214

$$\frac{170 - 220}{-640 - 220} = 1 - e^{-t_{OFF}/0.15},$$

from which: $\quad t_{OFF} = 0.008985 \quad t_{ON} + t_{OFF} = 0.02017$ second.

Duty cycle $\delta = 0.01118/0.02017 = \underline{0.554}$. Chopping frequency $= 1/0.02017 = \underline{49.58\,\text{Hz}}$.

Deceleration

Thyristor ON
$$0 = E - R_a i_a - Lpi_a.$$

Substituting:
$$= 25.6 - 0.04 i_a - 0.006 p i_a.$$

Rearranging:
$$0.15\, di_a/dt + i_a = 640.$$

Solution is:
$$i_3 = i_4 + (I_{max} - i_4)(1 - e^{-t_{ON}/\tau}).$$

Substituting:
$$200 = 150 + (640 - 150)(1 - e^{-t_{ON}/0.15}),$$

$$\frac{200 - 150}{640 - 150} = 1 - e^{-t_{ON}/0.15},$$

from which: $\quad t_{ON} = 0.01614.$

Thyristor OFF
$$E_B = E - R i_a - L p i_a,$$
$$72 = 25.6 - 0.1 i_a - 0.006 L p i_a.$$

Rearranging:
$$0.06\, di_a/dt + i_a = -464.$$

Solution is:
$$i_4 = i_3 + (I_{min} - i_3)(1 - e^{-t_{OFF}/\tau}).$$

Substituting:
$$150 = 200 + (-464 - 200)(1 - e^{-t_{OFF}/0.06}),$$

$$\frac{150 - 200}{-464 - 200} = 1 - e^{-t_{OFF}/0.06}$$

from which $\quad t_{OFF} = 0.004697 \quad t_{ON} + t_{OFF} = 0.02084$ second.

Duty cycle $\delta = 0.01614/0.02084 = \underline{0.774}$. Chopping frequency $= 1/0.02084 = \underline{47.98\,\text{Hz}}$.

Accelerating time

Load torque $= k_\phi I_a = \dfrac{E}{\omega_m} I_a = \dfrac{64}{2500 \times 2\pi/60} \times 100 = 24.45\,\text{Nm}.$

During acceleration $= k_\phi I_{mean} = \dfrac{64}{2500 \times 2\pi/60} \times \dfrac{220 + 170}{2} = 0.2445 \times 195 = 47.67\,\text{Nm}.$

Constant $d\omega_m/dt = \dfrac{T_e - T_m}{J} = \dfrac{47.67 - 24.45}{1.2} = 19.35\,\text{rad/s per second}$

$$= 19.35 \times \frac{60}{2\pi} = \underline{184.8\,\text{rev/min per sec.}}$$

Accelerating time to 1000 rev/min $= \dfrac{1000}{84.8} = \underline{5.41\,\text{seconds.}}$

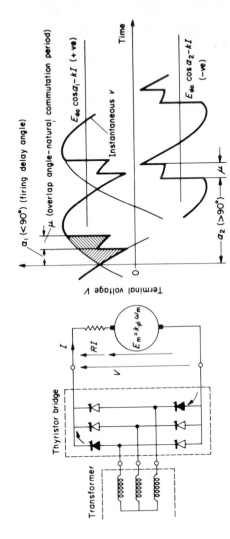

FIG. 7.2. Thyristor converter/d.c. machine system.

216

Decelerating time

During deceleration $= k_\phi I_{mean} = 0.2445(-200 - 150)/2 = -42.8\,\text{Nm}$.

Note that this electromagnetic torque is now in the same sense as T_m, opposing rotation.

The mechanical equation is: $\qquad T_e = T_m + J\,d\omega_m/dt,$

$$-42.8 = 24.45 + 1.2\,d\omega_m/dt.$$

from which:

$$\frac{d\omega_m}{dt} = \frac{-67.25}{1.2} = -56.04\,\text{rad/s per second} = \underline{-535.1\,\text{rev/min per second}}.$$

Time to stop from 1000 rev/min with this torque maintained $= 1000/535.1$ $= \underline{1.87\,\text{seconds.}}$

7.2 THYRISTOR CONVERTER/D.C. MACHINE DRIVE

This is the most common variable-speed drive for general use. The circuit diagram for the 3-phase bridge configuration and the terminal-voltage waveforms are shown on Fig. 7.2. The average "Thevenin" e.m.f. behind the bridge circuit can be expressed as $E_{do} \cos \alpha$. E_{do} is the mean value of the bridge output voltage on zero current. Firing of the thyristors can be delayed by angle α from the point in the a.c. cycle where the circuit conditions are first suitable for the thyristor to conduct. From α between 0° and 180°, switching over of the thyristors is simply accomplished by natural commutation, since circuit voltages arise naturally, in the correct direction to switch off the conducting thyristor at the right time. With this range of firing-angle control, the voltage on no-load would vary between $+E_{do}$ and $-E_{do}$, though in practice the reverse voltage is not as high as this from considerations of commutation failure at large values of α. It is possible to linearise the transfer characteristic by suitable control in the firing circuits. The effect of supply and transformer-leakage inductance on the delay of current transfer' (commutation)' from thyristor to thyristor is to cause a voltage drop which is proportional to current, so that the d.c. terminal voltage can be expressed finally as $V = E_{do} \cos \alpha - kI$.

The same terminal voltage appears across the machine, for which it can be expressed as $V = E_m + RI$. Both of these expressions neglect the harmonics, assume that the d.c. circuit inductance is high and that the current is continuous. They enable the steady-state behaviour to be calculated and can be represented graphically by straight lines on the two right-hand quadrants of a V/I, 4-quadrant diagram[1].

The current in the circuit is unilateral, but the polarity of either element can be reversed and hence cause reverse power flow. For the power-electronic circuit this means making α greater than 90°, when the rectifying action is changed to inverting action, from d.c. to a.c. For the machine, the polarity can be reversed by changeover of armature connections; by reversal of field current, which is rather slower, or by reversing rotation which is of course much slower and not usually a practicable proposition. The operational modes can be determined from the power expressions:

Machine motoring: $E_m I_a$ +ve; $(E_{do} \cos \alpha)I_a$ +ve; P.E. circuit rectifying.

Machine generating: $E_m I_a$ −ve; $(E_{do} \cos \alpha)I_a$ −ve; P.E. circuit inverting.

Machine plugging: $E_m I_a$ −ve; $(E_{do} \cos \alpha)I_a$ +ve; P.E. circuit rectifying.

To cover the usual four quadrants of machine operation without a switching changeover, duplication of power-electronic equipment is used, with one bridge for one direction of motor current and the other bridge in inverse parallel for the opposite direction of current. The bridge controls are interlocked so that they cannot operate as short circuits on one another. Full "Ward–Leonard" control now becomes available. The circuit is shown on Fig. 7.3 together with an indication of how a speed reversal takes place. Converter 1 is changed to Converter 2, an operation for which in practice about 20–50 msec is allowed. Typically, reversal

218

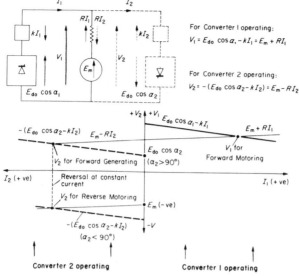

For Converter I operating:

$$V_1 = E_{do} \cos \alpha_1 - kI_1 = E_m + RI_1$$

For Converter 2 operating:

$$V_2 = -(E_{do} \cos \alpha_2 - kI_2) = E_m - RI_2$$

FIG. 7.3. Dual converter.

is carried out with the control maintaining constant "mean" current, to give uniform deceleration and acceleration.

On the circuit, positive voltages are shown by the arrowheads, though in the equations, these voltages may have negative values. The equations are:

Converter 1 operating: $\quad V_1 = E_{do} \cos \alpha_1 - kI_1 \quad = E_m + RI_1 \quad$ (7.4)

Converter 2 operating: $\quad V_2 = -(E_{do} \cos \alpha_2 - kI_2) = E_m - RI_2 \quad$ (7.5)

These equations are shown as straight lines on the figure, the intersection of the machine and converter characteristics giving the operating points.

EXAMPLE 7.3

Determine, for the following conditions, the appropriate firing angles and d.c. machine e.m.f.s for a d.c. machine/thyristor-bridge system for which $E_{do} = 300$ V, the bridge circuits absorb 15 V at rated motor current and the machine has a *per-unit* resistance of 0.05 based on its rated voltage of 250 V.

(a) Machine motoring at rated load current and with its terminal voltage at 250 V.

(b) Machine generating at rated load current and with its terminal voltage at 250 V.

(c) Machine plugging at rated load current and with its terminal voltage at 250 V.

(d) For condition (a), what would be the torque and speed if:
    (i) flux is at rated value?
    (ii) speed is 1.5 *per unit*?

(e) If the motor load for condition (a) is such that the torque is proportional to (speed)^2, what firing angle would be necessary to have the motor running at half speed with rated flux?

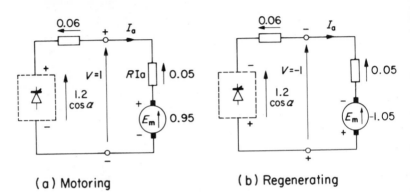

(a) Motoring   (b) Regenerating

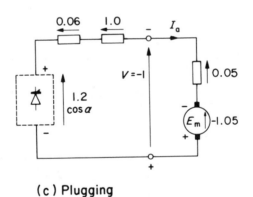

(c) Plugging

FIG. E.7.3.

Conditions (a), (b) and (c) are shown on the figure. The question will be worked out in *per unit* for convenience, but can be worked out in actual values and checked against the answers. (Take rated current as 100 A say, and let this be 1 *per-unit* current.) The overall equations are:

$$E_{do} \cos \alpha - kI_a = V = E_m + RI_a = k_\phi \omega_m + RT_e/k_\phi. \tag{7.6}$$

$$E_{do} = 300/250 = 1.2 \ per \ unit \quad k = 15/250 = 0.06 \ per \ unit.$$

1 *per-unit* speed $= V_R/k_{\phi R} = 1/1$ say 1000 rev/min.

$\therefore$ rated speed $= E_R/k_{\phi R} = 0.95/1 = 950$ rev/min.

(a) $V = 1 = 1.2 \cos \alpha - 0.06 \times 1.$ $\therefore \cos \alpha = 1.06/1.2; \quad \alpha = 27°96.$

(b) $V = -1 = 1.2 \cos \alpha - 0.06 \times 1.$ $\therefore \cos \alpha = -0.94/1.2; \quad \alpha = 141°6.$

(c) $V = -1 = 1.2 \cos \alpha - 0.06 \times 1 + 1 \times 1; \cos \alpha = 0.06/1.2; \quad \alpha = 87°1.$

Condition (c) requires a resistor to absorb 1 *per-unit* V, specified at the machine terminals. Plugging is not a normal steady-state mode for this circuit.

(d) $V = 1 = E_m + RI_a = k_\phi \cdot \omega_m + 0.05 \times 1$, so $k_\phi \omega_m = 0.95$.
   (i) For rated flux (1 *per unit*), $\omega_m = 0.95$ which is rated speed and T_e is also 1 p.u.
   (ii) For 1.5 *per unit* speed, $k_\phi = E/\omega_m = 0.95/1.5 = 0.633$ which is also T_e.

(e) With rated flux, current will be $(\frac{1}{2})^2$ since T_e is proportional to $\omega_m^2 \therefore I_a = 0.25$. Substitute in equation: $1.2 \cos \alpha - (0.06 + 0.05)0.25 + 0.95 \times 0.5$ from which $\cos \alpha = 0.5025/1.2 = 0.4188 \ \underline{\alpha = 65°2}.$

7.3 POWER-ELECTRONIC CONTROL OF A.C. MACHINES

The power-electronic circuit arrangements for a.c. machines are in general, more complex than for d.c. machines where only a 2-line supply to the armature is necessary. A.C. schemes in which semi-conductor devices switch the power ON and OFF cyclically, either at double line-frequency or at lower rates, cause a variation of mean a.c. voltage, though with a proliferation of harmonics. Such a simple voltage-control can be used on single-phase supplies and is especially suitable for the universal a.c./d.c. commutator motor. Good speed control is available because of the machine characteristics. The performance can be calculated with reasonable accuracy by neglecting the harmonics and assuming that the change of mean (r.m.s.) voltage is the only consideration. This method was used when discussing the similarly controlled, but rectified thyristor-bridge/d.c. machine circuit. Neglecting harmonics means neglecting the extra machine losses, commutation problems and the development of torque pulsations, rather than resulting in significant errors in speed/mean-torque calculations.

Consequently, many of the examples already dealt with earlier in the text may be considered as if the control was exerted through power-electronic circuits. As an illustration, voltage control of a 3-phase induction machine was covered in Examples 4.6, 4.8 and 4.9. The effects on the characteristics were explored without reference to the source of the variable voltage, which could have been a variable-ratio transformer or variable-voltage generator. But bilateral semi-conductor power switches in the supply lines could achieve a more economic arrangement, though with the penalty of extra machine losses and harmonic generation.

Similarly the effects of variable frequency and/or voltage were considered in Examples 4.6, 4.10, 4.11 and 4.14 without specifying the power supply which would most likely be from a static frequency converter. The later constant-current schemes, Examples 4.11–4.16, and slip-power recovery drives, Examples 4.19 and 4.21, could all use power-electronic circuits for their implementation and microelectronics for their control and supervision.

For synchronous machines, field excitation supplied through power semi-conductors is well-established practice. Speed-control schemes, however, which require variable frequency, are still undergoing developments. Earlier problems have, in an introductory manner, covered both possibilities in the electrical-drives area. The controlled excitation required in Example 5.12 showed the changes brought about in load-angle variation. Example 5.13 and Section 5.5 introduced the novelty of supplying constant current instead of constant voltage and Examples 5.14 and 5.15 showed the effect of variable frequency and voltage.

Although calculation of performance neglecting harmonics as just described is suitable for many purposes, it is not a satisfactory situation for the drives specialist who may need to analyse it in greater detail. Here, there is only limited space to indicate how the general problem may be approached.

Figure 7.4 shows the most common arrangement for mains-supplied frequency conversion. From the supply, a d.c. output is first produced to give the "d.c. link"—which could of course come from a battery in appropriate applications. The other end of the d.c. link has a similar 3-phase bridge which is so switched that current is routed through the machine in a sequence like that from a 3-phase supply, and at a variable switching speed to change the frequency. Transfer of current between the semi-conductor switches may require additional "forced commutation" circuits, or they may be commutated naturally as for the thyristor-bridge/d.c. machine circuit. The output waveform for one of the simplest schemes is as shown. The zero occurs when, as indicated, two thyristors conduct in parallel and bring the associated machine line-terminals to zero potential difference. Fourier analysis of this particular waveform gives the instantaneous voltage as:

$$v = \frac{4V}{\pi}\left[\cos \pi/6 \sin \omega t + \frac{\cos 5\pi/6 \sin 5\omega t}{5} + \frac{\cos 7\pi/6 \sin 7\omega t}{7} \cdots\right]$$

$$= \frac{2\sqrt{3}V}{\pi}\left[\sin \omega t \quad + \frac{\sin 5\omega t}{5} \quad - \frac{\sin 7\omega t}{7} \cdots\right].$$

On the assumption that superposition is valid, each harmonic can be considered as producing its own rotating field at n times the

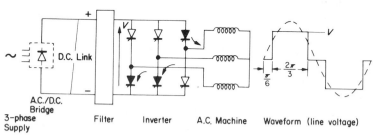

FIG. 7.4. Inverter drive (quasi-square wave).

fundamental synchronous speed. If the voltages for the other two phases are considered, with the angle ωt changed to $(\omega t - 2\pi/3)$ and $(\omega t - 4\pi/3)$ respectively, it will be found that the phase sequence for the 5th harmonic is reversed from both the fundamental and the 7th harmonic. The induction torques of the 5th and 7th-harmonic currents therefore tend to cancel, with only a small resultant braking torque from the 5th-harmonic component. The torque due to the fundamental voltage can be calculated from its r.m.s. value which, from the above, $= (2\sqrt{3}V)/(\pi\sqrt{2}) = 0.78V$, and the methods of Chapters 4 and 5 can be applied.

The smoothing filter in the d.c. link is sometimes capacitive, giving a constant-voltage system with a flat-topped voltage wave, or inductive, giving a constant d.c.-link current and a flat-topped current wave. In the latter case, the waveform of Fig. 7.4 would be that of current. As far as the machine is concerned, the harmonic-current components are little different from the voltage-fed machine, because although the reactance is higher at the higher harmonic frequencies, the slip for the harmonic rotating field speeds is very large and so the impedance is about the "low" short-circuit value. These effects tend to cancel so that the nth harmonic current is about $1/n$ times the fundamental value as for the current-fed machine.

In spite of the above remarks which suggest that there is a tendency for harmonic effects to cancel, there is an important feature which cannot be neglected. The harmonics do produce a torque pulsation and it is important to be able to calculate this. The most straightforward way of analysing the overall problem is to transform all the variables to d–q axes[2]; the m.m.f. of the three phases being produced by a current i_D on the direct axis (usually the A-phase axis or the field-winding axis in the case of a synchronous machine) and a current i_Q on an axis in "electrical" quadrature. Similarly for the rotor currents, we would have i_d and i_q on the same two axes. The voltages too must be transformed to d–q axes, including the harmonic components of interest, and the impedance matrices must be expressed in d–q terms—one for each harmonic if all frequency effects are included. After solving for d–q currents, or transforming to these for a current-fed machine, the instantaneous-torque expression is fairly simple and will of course give all the torque components. For the synchronous machine, without dampers and neglecting resistance it is:

$$T_e = -[i_d i_q(X_d - X_q) + i_q i_f X_{fd}]/\omega_s; \text{ or in terms of inductances:}$$
$$= -[i_d i_q(L_d - L_q) + i_q i_f L_{fd}] \times \text{pole pairs.} \qquad (7.7)$$

For the induction machine it is:

$$T_e = X_m(i_d i_Q - i_q i_D)/\omega_s; \text{ or in terms of inductances:}$$
$$= M(i_d i_Q - i_q i_D) \times \text{pole pairs.} \qquad (7.8)$$

As an alternative, after working through the transformations[1], the last equation can be written as eqn (5.16) but for present purposes,

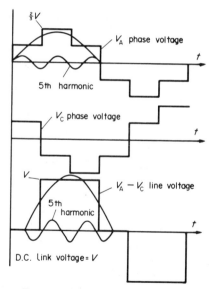

FIG. 7.5. Quasi-square wave inverter
waveforms.

225

another derivative, eqn (5.15), is more convenient, viz.:

$$T_e = 3MI_m I_2' \sin(\varphi_m - \varphi_2) \times \text{pole pairs.} \qquad (7.\text{?}$$

We can now make an engineering estimate of the torque pu
sation for such inverter-fed induction motors. If the machin
windings are connected in star as shown, the phase-voltage wave
forms are quite different from the line voltage, as indicated on Fig. 7.
for phases A and C. These are subtracted to give v_{AC}, which is th
quasi-square line-voltage waveform of Fig. 7.4. For all waveform
3rd and triplen harmonics are not present, but the other harmonic
combine to give the usual 30° shift between phase and line wave
When this is allowed for, on the harmonic scale, the expression f
the phase voltage waveform can be deduced as:

$$\frac{1}{\sqrt{3}} \times \frac{2\sqrt{3}}{\pi} \times \quad V\left(\sin \omega t + \frac{\sin 5\omega t}{5} + \frac{\sin 7\omega t}{7} \cdots\right)$$

$$= \sqrt{2}\, V_1\left(\sin \omega t + \frac{\sin 5\omega t}{5} + \frac{\sin 7\omega t}{7} \cdots\right),$$

where $V_1 = \sqrt{2}\, V/\pi$ is the r.m.s. value of the fundamental com
ponent of the phase voltage. The 5th harmonic waveform is sket
ched in on Fig. 7.5 to show why the harmonic signs have change
from the line-voltage expression.

Considering each voltage harmonic separately, applied to its ow
equivalent circuit with appropriate correction for frequency-in
creased reactances, and voltages reduced to V_1/n, we could cal
culate the harmonic currents and sum them to get the primary
secondary and magnetising-current waveforms. Each roto
(secondary) harmonic current will react with its own harmoni
magnetising-current to produce a steady-component of torque. I
will react with all the other harmonic magnetising currents t
produce a component of the pulsating torque. In fact, only th
interaction of the 5th and 7th harmonic rotor currents, I_5' and I
say, with the fundamental magnetising current I_{m1} will be of grea
significance. As stated earlier, the steady-torque component
produced by 5th and 7th harmonics tend to cancel. These ap

226

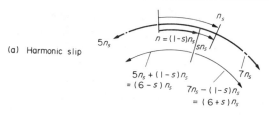

(a) Harmonic slip

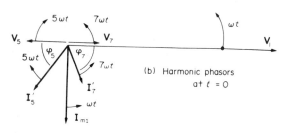

(b) Harmonic phasors
at $t = 0$

FIG. 7.6. Pulsating-torque calculations.

proximations will be justified later. At this stage we will make one further approximation, viz.: that the fundamental harmonic magnetising current I_{m1} is given by $(V_1/X_m)\underline{/-90°}$, from the approximate circuit, though the exact calculation of I_m is not very much more difficult.

For the rotor currents, we require the slip, and if this is s for the fundamental, it will be $6 - s$ for the 5th harmonic producing a backwards rotating field at $5\omega_s$, and $6 + s$ for the 7th harmonic producing a forwards rotating field at speed $7\omega_s$ (see Fig. 7.6a). Hence, taking V_1 as reference: and using the approximate circuits:

$$I_5' = \frac{V_1}{5} \frac{1}{(R_1 + R_2'/(6 - s) + j5(x_1 + x_2')} \text{ and } i_5' = \sqrt{2} I_5' \sin(5\omega t - \varphi_5),$$

$$I_7' = \frac{V_1}{7} \frac{1}{(R_1 + R_2'/(6 + s) + j7(x_1 + x_2')} \text{ and } i_7' = \sqrt{2} I_7' \sin(7\omega t - \varphi_7).$$

Consider the instant of time, $\omega t = 0$, when the fundamental and

227

harmonic voltages are momentarily zero and initially are all increasing positively as t increases. Note this means that the 5th harmonic, of reverse phase-sequence, must be shown in antiphase with V_1 and V_7 as on Fig. 7.6b, which is the phasor diagram for this instant. Now when the fundamental rotor-current I_2' reacts with its own magnetising current I_{m1}, its phasor leads the I_{m1} phasor if producing forwards motoring-torque. Hence, I_7' reacting with I_{m1} at the instant shown is producing a positive torque and the angle between these phasors, taking $\omega t = 0$ as reference is:

$$(-\varphi_7 + 7\omega t) - (-90 + \omega t) = 6\omega t + (90 - \varphi_7).$$

The angle of I_5' (lagging V_5 of reverse phase-sequence) leads I_{m1} by:

$$(180 + \varphi_5 - 5\omega t) - (-90 + \omega t) = 270 + \varphi_5 - 6\omega t = -[6\omega t + (90 - \varphi_5)].$$

Thus, the total torque due to 5th and 7th harmonic rotor-currents reacting with the fundamental magnetising current is, from eqn (7.9):

$$3M\frac{V_1}{X_{m1}}[-I_5' \sin(6\omega t + 90 - \varphi_5) + I_7' \sin(6\omega t + 90 - \varphi_7)] \times \text{pole pairs.}$$

$$(7.10)$$

The expression shows that 5th and 7th harmonics combine to give a pulsating torque at 6 times fundamental frequency. In Section 7.5, as an illustration of a.c. machine simulation, the computed results from an "exact" solution, including all the harmonics, show that this 6th harmonic pulsation is almost completely dominant (Fig. 7.10, see also T7.4). If the motor had been current fed, the division of 5th and 7th harmonic currents into magnetising and rotor currents would have had to invoke the standard parallel-circuit relationships, as in Section 4.3, Examples 4.11–4.15.

Variable-frequency supplies can also be used to power synchronous machines and the various equations used in Chapter 5 have shown how the performance can be calculated. As for the induction machine, voltage and frequency must be adjusted together if the flux per pole (approximately proportional to V/f) is to be maintained constant. Some control of the characteristic can be exercised from the supply system but eqn (5.13) shows that if the load angle δ can be controlled, the performance can be optimised. Load angle is related to the position of the shaft and if a suitable position detector is fitted, it can be used to trigger the power semiconductors in the inverter at a preferred instant in the cycle. With forced-commutated inverters, good control can be exerted since the switchover of current (commutation) can be presumed to occur almost instantaneously. If natural commutation is used, to simplify the power-electronic circuits and make a more economically viable proposition, then there are restrictions on the firing-angle range. In addition the motor must always be overexcited to ensure the leading power-factor necessary to this naturally-commutated mode. Analysis becomes more complicated since the commutation time is now much longer and cannot be neglected. A computer simulation of the system becomes almost essential for reasonable calculations of performance.

Synchronous motors with position control are in fact similar in principle to the d.c. motor for which the armature coils are also switched—by the "forcing" action of the mechanical commutator and brushes. This ensures that under any particular polarity of the field, the armature conductors always carry current in the same direction to give maximum torque production. This occurs if the brush axis is set perpendicular (electrically) to the field axis so that the torque angle is 90 electrical degrees. Commutators usually have many segments reflecting the large number of coil subdivisions, so that the torque pulsations due to switching are negligibly small. The quasi-square wave inverter only has six commutations per cycle which is a relatively coarse switching rate. This can be improved by employing pulse-width modulation schemes. However, the maximum ratings and speeds of a.c. machines are higher than for d.c. machines, quite apart from their lower maintenance requirements and these are important factors in choosing a drive. Brushless d.c. machines are also made and the armature coils can now be on the stator since the static switching-circuits have replaced the mechanical commutator[1]. They ensure that the armature-conductor currents reverse in step with the rotation of the poles. Fundamentally there is no real difference between such motors and synchronous motors with position control activating the switching arrangements. In either case, the armature-coil frequency changes automatically to match the rotational speed, so operation is stable over the speed range. Control of d.c. link voltage and current has a similar effect to the control of d.c. machine armature voltage or current.

A rather different form of variable-frequency supply is sometimes used which employs the cycloconverter principle. It is similar in concept to Fig. 7.3 in that the positive half cycle is supplied by one bridge and the negative half cycle by the other bridge. It has some advantages at the lower end of the frequency range, being able to regenerate with natural commutation. The waveform is made up of selected parts of the supply-voltage waveforms and is rich in harmonics.

7.4 COMPARISON OF D.C., INDUCTION AND SYNCHRONOUS MACHINE-DRIVES WITH POWER-ELECTRONIC CONTROL

The choice of machine type for a particular electrical drive involves many factors which cannot be discussed here in detail. Most drives are adequate with a nominally constant speed for which induction machines are usually suitable. But there is a large and increasing number of systems requiring, or would benefit from variable-speed facilities. Rapid speed response is often necessary, so it is appropriate to consider this one aspect, since modern control methods permit schemes for comparison which would not otherwise have been possible.

D.C. Machines

From a control viewpoint and for ready understanding, this is the simplest variable-speed machine. Because the torque angle is fixed the torque is proportional to the product of flux and armature current. The effect of saturation is to increase the (relatively small) field power but not to interfere significantly with maximum-torque capability over the working speed-range. This is the factor which determines the speed response of a drive and the most useful method of comparison is to draw the maximum-torque envelope over this speed range. Figure 7.7a shows this, and there are two well-defined, lower regions which are explained adequately on the figure. A typical maximum current of 2 *per unit* at a flux of 1 *per unit* defines the bottom constant-torque region, though values of $I_a = 2.5$ are not uncommon for large d.c. machines. When full voltage is reached, further speed increase demands field weakening and loss of maximum torque, the power being approximately constant in the middle region. The third, upper region is less well defined, speed increase being limited by commutation and stability—quite apart from mechanical limitations. For constant reactance voltage, the (speed $\times I_a$) product should be constant, so reduction of current and its unstabilising effects with weak field would with this product be a suitable though somewhat approximate criterion. Actually, field-weakening ranges of more than 4/1, at constant power are often demanded for certain d.c. metal- and paper-mill drives.

Induction Machines

Figure 7.7b is the corresponding diagram for the induction machine. Its shape is based on the work done in Examples 4.11–4.15 in Section 4.3. To make a reasonable comparison, a maximum torque of 2 per unit is shown. This would require a current nearer to 170 A than the rated 103 A in the above examples. The bottom

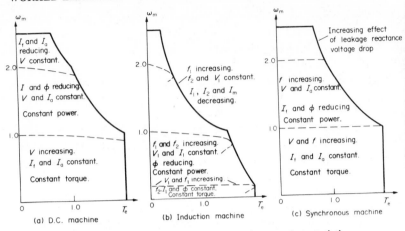

FIG. 7.7. Comparison of maximum speed/torque characteristics.

region, for constant torque, is very small and depends on the value of this current. Even with the smaller, rated current the speed limit for this region was less than 0.2 *per unit*. The slip frequency is maintained constant at the relatively low value of $R_2' \times f_{base}/(x_2' + X_m)$ [see development of eqn (4.17)] in order to maintain the constant value of I_2', I_m and flux for this particular I_1 setting.

The second, constant-power region extends to rated frequency (f_{base}) at which the equivalent-circuit parameters x_1, x_2' and X_m have been specified. Since V is at its maximum in this range, only the frequency f_1 can be controlled, in such a manner relative to speed that I_1 remains constant. To get some idea of the control, we can use the approximate circuit neglecting stator resistance and look at the expression for input impedance which has to be constant; i.e.

$$Z = \frac{R_2'}{f_2/f_1} + j(x_1 + x_2')\frac{f_1}{f_{base}}$$

$$= \frac{f_1}{f_{base}}\left[\frac{R_2'}{f_2/f_{base}} + j(x_1 + x_2')\right] \text{ must be constant.}$$

So as f_1 increases, f_2 must increase, to the value at f_{base} which gives

232

he maximum torque from the constant-voltage circuit; eqn (4.12),
.e.

$$\frac{R_2'}{f_2/f_1} = (x_1 + x_2')\frac{f_1}{f_{base}}$$

or: $\dfrac{R_2'}{f_2/f_{base}} = x_1 + x_2'$ giving: $f_2 = \dfrac{R_2'}{(x_1 + x_2')} \times f_{base}.$ (7.11)

The flux falls in this region as the m.m.f. diagram changes shape
rom that of Fig. 4.2b to Fig. 4.2a with corresponding torque
·eduction (see Section 4.3). This constant-power region finishes
where that of the d.c. machine starts.

Further frequency increase, with f_2 monitored at the eqn (7.11)
setting and no longer compensating for the reactance increase, will
:ause I_1 to fall in the third upper region. The maximum torque for a
·articular I_1 will still be obtained but since I_2' and I_m depend directly
on I_1, all sides of the m.m.f. diagram of Fig. 4.2a will be falling so that
here is a square-law decrease of maximum torque. Note that in the
constant-voltage region, any particular slip will give a reducing torque
as f_1 increases, see eqn (4.5) and this is reflected in a steeper
speed-regulation curve as indicated by the broken lines.

Synchronous Machine

Open-loop control of a synchronous machine with variable
requency requires a restraint on the rate of frequency increase, to
avoid the load angle falling too far back, beyond 90°, as the rotor
attempts to accelerate and keep up with the rotating field. A margin
would have to be provided to prevent stalling and therefore maximum torque over the speed range would not be available since this
demands certain angles between the m.m.f. space vectors. Some
closed-loop system would be necessary to ensure stable operation,
and position-detector control has already been mentioned in Sec-
ion 7.4. This would permit the current-controlled mode discussed
n Section 5.5 in which particular currents at particular phase
angles can be provided. In this case, the machine is nearer to the

d.c. machine. Various control strategies have been explained. Referring to Fig. 5.2a, suppose that φ_{ma} is held at 90°, which would mean that I_a would be at unity power factor, neglecting leakage impedance. If I_m is at the rated value, 1 *per unit*, and I_a is controlled at 2 per unit, the torque will then be 2 *per unit* in the lower region of Fig. 7.7c up to rated voltage, as for the d.c. machine. The field m.m.f. would have to be $\sqrt{5}$ *per unit*, to close the m.m.f. triangle. Beyond this speed, increase of frequency will bring about a reduction of I_m and flux ($\phi \propto E/f \simeq V/f$). If I_a is maintained, there will be a second, constant-power region comparable with that of Fig. 7.7a. In fact this region could continue beyond 2 *per-unit* speed but the frequency increase of leakage-reactance voltage drop could no longer be ignored. The consequent reduction of air-gap e.m.f. E would result in a more severe fall of flux than that due to frequency increase alone, so the speed/torque envelope would be rather less than shown. In these upper regions too, there would have to be reductions of field current if the angle φ_{ma} is to be maintained at 90°.

A different control strategy, taking the flux into saturation as described in Section 5.5, could give improved performance over a limited speed range where the excess flux would not lead to unacceptable iron losses. Supposing I_m was 1.5, giving a flux of about 1.25, allowing for saturation as in Example 5.15(j). Equal currents $I_a = I_f'$ of about 1.75 would give 2 per-unit torque with a better torque per ampere than just described; i.e. 2/3.5 as against $2/(2 + \sqrt{5}) = 2/4.2$, though not quite as good as the d.c. machine at $2/(2 + 1) = 2/3$.

In summary, it can be seen that the d.c. machine gives the best acceleration performance and simplest characteristic control and the induction machine the poorest. This reflects the physical complexity of the one with respect to the other. The cage-rotor motor is much cheaper and relatively maintenance free. Offsetting this to some extent is the greater complexity and expense of the power-electronic circuitry for the a.c. machines though the synchronous machine can match, and in some respects give slight improvements on the d.c. machine characteristic, with sufficient sophistication in the control system. Most systems require additional equipment to obtain full 4-quadrant operation; e.g. a dual converter or a cyclo-converter. This kind of drive for d.c. machines is well established and at the time of writing it still holds the field in certain important applications, for best control and reliability, per unit cost; e.g. lift and certain mill drives. Indeed, it is not unknown for a line of inverter drives to need replacement by d.c. machines because of premature drive-system changes. But development continues, and power tran-sistors are replacing thyristors with some success so that certain advantages on costs may eventually be achieved and justify changes in machine type. At the same time it must be remembered that such improvements may be passed over to d.c. machine systems too. For example, a high-frequency power-transistor chopper controlling a simple rectified supply to a d.c. machine would remove one of the disadvantages of naturally-commutated thyristor systems, in that voltage (and speed) control is obtained here by phase delay and corresponding power-factor deterioration.

7.5 MATHEMATICAL AND COMPUTER SIMULATION OF MACHINE SYSTEMS

If the machine equations are expressed in such a manner as to allow for switching operations and other non-linearities like saturation, the possibility of a general analytical solution is usually lost. However, a step-by-step numerical solution can be used and as this proceeds, any change in the system condition or configura-tion can be included. Again, only a limited treatment is given here, to illustrate the method with some simple examples covering forced- and natural-commutation schemes.

Figure 7.8 shows a flow diagram for a section of a computer program calculating the electromechanical performance following some system change, e.g. acceleration from zero speed; or a

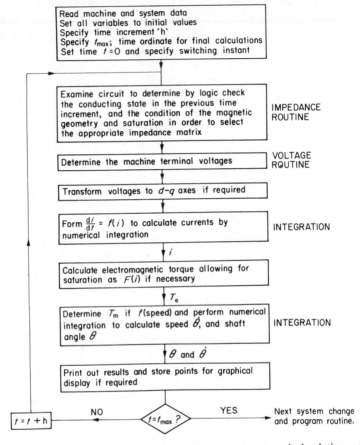

FIG. 7.8. General flow diagram for digital-computer numerical solutions of electromechanical performance.

transient following a load change or a voltage/frequency change. Following the specification of the data, the time limits of the calculation and the system change being investigated, the machine and circuits are scanned to determine the appropriate equations. If

236

power semi-conductors are involved, then this will require a logic check, at each time increment, to find the conducting state of every circuit branch including such switching devices. For a fairly simple representation:

A diode will conduct if the forward voltage drop across it is equal to or greater than 1 V (say).

For a power transistor, a firing pulse must be present for conduction, AND the forward voltage drop must be greater than 1 V.

For a thyristor in a naturally-commutated system, conduction will continue if it was conducting in the previous time increment, with a current greater than the holding value—say 100 mA; OR it will conduct if the forward voltage drop is greater than 1 V, AND a firing pulse is present.

For a thyristor in a forced-commutated system, the thyristor switch-off time can be specified.

If a no-conduction condition is detected, it may be necessary to calculate the voltage across such an element arising from the rest of the circuit and apply this to the element in the simulation, so that its current will calculate zero. It may be possible, with certain types of simulation, to set this semi-conductor impedance to several thousand ohms say, and solve the circuit without mathematical instabilities.

With the conducting paths known, the equations can now be set up, making allowance for the semi-conductor voltage drops if these are of relative significance. The machine terminal voltages and the impedance matrices may be affected by the nature of the conducting paths so these must now be determined. If a d–q simulation is being used, transformation of these voltages to d–q axes must be performed. For a current-fed system, the determination of any unknown currents is usually fairly simple. In any case an expression for di/dt is required in terms of the circuit parameters. From the circuit equation:

$$v = Ri_1 + L_{11}\, di_1/dt + L_{12}\, di_2/dt \cdots + f(\text{speed, currents})$$

the general form:

$$\frac{di_1}{dt} = \frac{v - Ri_1 - f(\text{speed, currents}) - \sum_{1}^{n} L_{1_n} di_n/dt}{L_{11}}$$

is obtained. Numerical integration methods predict the change of i during the time increment, from the initial value and the rate of change. This is done for all the conducting paths, using matrix techniques if there are several of these. The electromagnetic torque can then be calculated.

The next step is to calculate the speed $\dot{\theta}$ and the shaft angle θ if this is required, e.g. to allow for change of inductances with shaft orientation. θ will normally be in electrical degrees. Referring to the earlier equations for the mechanical system:

$$\frac{d\omega_m}{dt} = \frac{T_e - T_m}{J}$$

and hence:

$$\frac{d\dot{\theta}}{dt} = \frac{T_e - T_m}{J} \times \text{pole pairs} \qquad \text{(in electrical rad/s)}$$

and:

$$\frac{d\theta}{dt} = \dot{\theta}$$

are the two relevant first-order equations required for numerical solution.

If the mechanical load is a function of speed, it can be continually updated throughout the solution at each incremental step. In a similar manner, inductances can be changed if there is a variation with position or with current value.

The time increment is now added, the new circuit conduction condition checked and the new driving function (voltage or current) at this new time is inserted to repeat the calculation procedure, until t_{max} is reached.

EXAMPLE 7.4

Show in outline how the battery-supplied, chopper-controlled, d.c. series motor could be simulated for a computer solution. What differences would be necessary to deal with the separately-excited d.c. motor with regenerative operation included?

The equations for the chopper-controlled d.c. machine were derived in Section 7.1 and the expressions for di/dt required for numerical solution follow as below.

	Thyristor ON	Thyristor OFF
Series motor	$\dfrac{E_B - 1 - Ri_a - k_\phi\omega_m}{L}$	$\dfrac{-1 - R_a i_a - k_\phi\omega_m}{L}$
Separately excited. Motoring	$\dfrac{E_B - 1 - Ri_a - k_\phi\omega_m}{L}$	$\dfrac{-1 - R_a i_a - k_\phi\omega_m}{L}$
Separately excited. Regenerating	$\dfrac{-1 - R_a i_a + k_\phi\omega_m}{L}$	$\dfrac{-E_B - 1 - Ri_a + k_\phi\omega_m}{L}$

This is a forced-commutated circuit and δ, the duty cycle, which is the ratio $t_{ON}/(t_{ON} + t_{OFF})$, is controllable as required, either from speed demand, current limit or manually. No logic check on thyristor conduction is required, the circuit becomes conducting almost instantaneously in the controlled ON period and non-conducting in the controlled OFF period. The duty cycle shown on the figure starts from $t' = 0$, t' being set to zero at the beginning of each cycle. The ON period lasts until t' is greater than t_{ON}.

The flow diagram will be generally similar to Fig. 7.8, the appropriate value of di/dt being used from the above expressions. For the series motor, the $k_\phi = f(i_a)$ curve would have to be available and for the separately-excited motor k_ϕ would have to be specified. The mechanical equation is standard and after the speed is found, it only remains to check the time and whether t' must be set to zero before repeating the calculation with the time incremented.

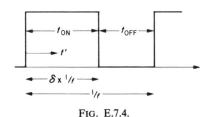

Fig. E.7.4.

239

The above example is instructive as an introduction but it is unlikely that such a program would be used. The reason is that the analytical solutions described in Section 7.1 are usually adequate. The time-constant of the electrical circuit is very short by comparison with the mechanical system and the electrical transients can therefore be solved as if the speed was constant. Example 7.2 is an indication of how the mechanical transient could be dealt with, though once the duty cycle reaches unity, no further current limit control is available and the chopper is usually shorted out to save energy. Subsequent speed changes can be brought about by field weakening and this can readily be incorporated in a different computer program if studies of the complete accelerating period are required. If studies of the chopper circuit itself are to be undertaken then a program recording all the events within a duty cycle would be necessary. The time-constants of the forced-commutated circuits and the protective circuits for the thyristors are now very much shorter than those of the main power circuit. A nodal-type simulation would then be appropriate to deal with all the parallel branches in the power-electronic detail circuitry.

EXAMPLE 7.5

Set up the equations for the single-phase thyristor bridge/d.c. motor circuit and explain how the conducting conditions can be determined and a computer simulation implemented. Allow for all circuit resistances and inductances.

The first figure shows the circuit; currents and voltages being indicated. The transformer is represented by its secondary e.m.f. e_{ac} behind the leakage and supply impedances referred to the secondary, $r + l\text{p}$, where p represents d/dt. This is a naturally-commutated circuit since the a.c. voltage developed across the thyristors v_f reverses every half cycle and reduces the thyristor current to zero naturally. There is a period of "overlap", however, when the incoming thyristors share the total load current until the outgoing thyristors have their currents eventually reduced to zero. For the single-phase bridge, this means that the d.c. terminals are short circuited through the thyristors so that the terminal voltage is zero during overlap. If the equations are set up for this case when all thyristors are conducting, it is merely a question of setting the appropriate terms to zero, if a current falls to zero.

Consider a path through thyristors 1 and 3, when all thyristors are conducting:

$$e_{ac} = r(i_1 - i_2) + l\text{p}(i_1 - i_2) + 1 \text{ V} + L_L\text{p}i_a + R_L i_a + e_m + 1 \text{ V}.$$

240

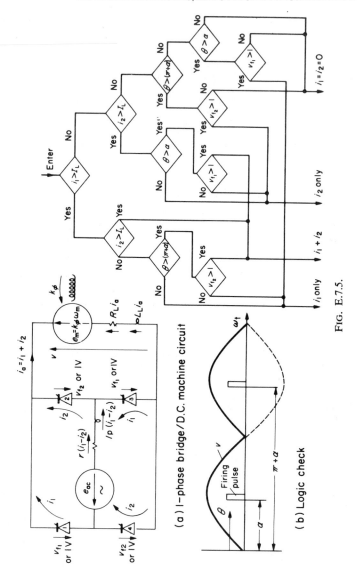

(a) 1—phase bridge/D.C. machine circuit

(b) Logic check

FIG. E.7.5.

241

from which:

$$pi_1 = \frac{e_{ac} - Ri_1 - Ri_2 - e_m - 2\,\text{V}}{L} - \frac{L'}{L} pi_2$$

where $R = R_L + r$; $R' = R_L - r$; $L = L_L + l$; $L' = L_L - l$ and $i_a = i_1 + i_2$.

For a path through thyristors 2 and 4 for the same condition:

$$-e_{ac} = 1\,\text{V} + L_L pi_a + R_L i_a + e_m + 1\,\text{V} - lp(i_1 - i_2) + r(i_1 - i_2)$$

from which:

$$pi_2 = \frac{-e_{ac} - R'i_2 - R'i_1 - e_m - 2\,\text{V}}{L} - \frac{L'}{L} pi_1;$$

pi is thus available for each current, to perform the numerical integration a$\blacksquare$ required.

To determine the conducting condition, the voltages developed by the circui$\blacksquare$ across each thyristor must be monitored whilst it is switched off, since when th$\blacksquare$ gate firing pulse is applied, conduction will not start unless v_f is greater than th$\blacksquare$ normal forward volt drop, taken to be 1 V. It is assumed that v_{f1} is the same fo$\blacksquare$ thyristors 1 and 3 and v_{f2} is the same for thyristors 2 and 4.

For a path through thyristors 1 and 3 when they are not conducting:

$$v_{f1} = -e_m - R_L i_2 - L_L pi_2 - v_{f1} + lpi_2 + ri_2 + e_{ac}$$

from which:

$$2v_{f1} = -e_m + e_{ac} - R'i_2 - L'pi_2.$$

Similarly:

$$2v_{f2} = -e_m - e_{ac} + Ri_1 + Lpi_1.$$

The phase delay angle α (or $\pi + \alpha$ for thyristors 2 and 4) and the value of flux $\blacksquare$ must be specified in the data. i_1 and i_2, ω_m and e_m, will be known from the previou$\blacksquare$ time increment and solution and e_{ac} will be known from its time-function expres$\blacksquare$ sion. The pattern of logical checks is shown, by means of which, working throug$\blacksquare$ the various questions, each thyristor is checked for previous conduction ($i > I_L$, th$\blacksquare$ *latching* or *holding* value) and the possibility of starting conduction.

The normal condition is for i_1 or i_2 to be conducting so these questions are aske$\blacksquare$ first since if the answer is YES the remaining questions are unnecessary. If th$\blacksquare$ answer is NO, for either or both currents, then the phase delay of the firing pulses i$\blacksquare$ checked against the progression of angle $\theta = \omega t$, measured from the beginning of th$\blacksquare$ cycle, to see if a firing pulse is present. If not, then that thyristor will be non$\blacksquare$ conducting in the next increment. If the answer is YES, the forward voltage acros$\blacksquare$ that thyristor must be checked to see if it is greater than 1 V (say). There are fou$\blacksquare$ possible answers to the overall question pattern. Either circuit can be conductin$\blacksquare$ both can be conducting (overlap), or both currents can be zero (a discontinuou$\blacksquare$ current condition). With these conditions known, the appropriate equations can b$\blacksquare$ formed and i_1 and/or i_2 can be determined by numerical integration. The solutio$\blacksquare$ thereafter follows the pattern of the general flow diagram of Fig. 7.8.

Again the time-constants of the electrical system are usually very much shorter than for the mechanical system and it may be sufficient to study the circuit for a particular speed, flux and constant e.m.f. Natural commutation may take more than millisecond and full-scale simulations may be necessary, however, to check that his aspect of circuit operation is working correctly; it is liable to break down under ertain conditions.

Simulations for 3-phase A.C. Machines

These simulations are usually more complex than for d.c. machines. For steady-state (constant-speed) calculations, equivalent-circuit methods can be used, of course, as already demonstrated. The equivalent-circuit model is based on a viewpoint which notes that for a uniform air-gap machine, or along a salient-pole axis, the magnetic permeance does not change with flux-wave position, so inductances are not time dependent. The nduced voltages on the circuit take account of the flux-wave movement but are usually expressed in terms of the winding carrying line-frequency currents. But inductance variation is the source of the motional e.m.f. $(i \cdot dL/dt)$. It is the particular choice of viewpoint which has removed this time dependence. A formal transformation to d–q axes, which may be stationary with respect o the flux wave as for the salient-pole machine, but are not necessarily so as for the uniform air-gap machine, permits much greater flexibility in analytical solution of both steady and transient states. Time dependence of inductances must be and can be removed providing certain conditions are fulfilled[2]; e.g. sinusoidal distribution of d-axis and q-axis flux and any winding imbalance confined to one side of the air gap. Analytical solutions at a particular speed for one variable, current say, are then possible. For an electromechanical transient, including speed as a variable, a numerical solution would be necessary. Even then the d–q simulation permits the greatest economy in computation time because the equations are so concise and the inductances are constant. However, if the necessary conditions are not fulfilled, the transformation will not lead to time-independent inductances; numerical solutions become necessary and it may then be convenient to use a real-(phase-)axis simulation, (A–B–C, a–b–c). In the present in stance, no extensive additional knowledge is required to follow the procedure of setting out these equations and it will be a suitable conclusion to the text. They are necessarily in matrix form since this is the way they are manipulated in the computer program. For the purposes of illustration, a uniform air-gap machine will be considered, having three stator phases, A, B and C, and three rotor phases, a, b and c, with axes as shown on Fig. 7.9. Taking the A-phase axis as the reference position, the rotor a-phase will be at some electrical angle θ to the stator A-phase and θ varies with rotation and time.

When parameter tests are conducted, they yield an equivalent circuit stator inductance $L_s = (x_1 + X_m)/\omega$ which is 50% higher than the stator-phase self-inductance, L_{AA} say[1]. This is because the other two phases are excited and contribute this extra flux. So $L_{AA} = L_{BB} = L_{CC} = L_s \times 2/3$. The mutual inductance between stator phases is half of this because they are displaced by 120° and $\cos 120° = -\frac{1}{2}$. A similar situation exists for the rotor phases, which in referred terms often have the same inductance, i.e. $L_{aa} = L_{AA}$ For the coupling between stator and rotor phases, if M is the magnetising inductance of the equivalent circuit ($= X_m/\omega$), then when A-phase and a-phase are in alignment physically and additive magnetically, the maximum value of mutual inductance occurs, of value $+M \times 2/3$. For any angle θ, $L_{Aa} = (2/3)M \cos \theta$. The other stator/rotor mutual inductances vary similarly but with a phase displacement, in accordance with the matrix below. This should be checked from Fig. 7.9 by considering when a particular pair of stator and rotor phases are in alignment and give maximum mutual inductance.

Consider the voltage equation for the A-phase:

$$v_A = R_A i_A + p(L_{AA} i_A) + p(L_{AB} i_B) + p(L_{AC} i_C) + p(L_{Aa} i_a) + p(L_{Ab} i_b) + p(L_{Ac} i_c). \quad (7.12)$$

This can be put in a general form as a matrix equation for all

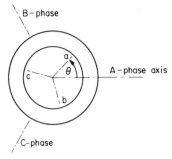

FIG. 7.9. Real-axis simulation of 3-phase machine.

phases as:

$$v = Ri + p(Li)$$

where each term is a matrix.

For the whole system:

$$
v = \begin{array}{|c|}
\hline
\mathbf{v}_{\text{stator}} \\
\hline
\mathbf{v}_{\text{rotor}} \\
\hline
\end{array}
=
\begin{array}{|c|c|}
\hline
\mathbf{R}_s + p\mathbf{L}_{ss} & p\mathbf{L}_{sr} \\
\hline
p\mathbf{L}_{rs} & \mathbf{R}_r + p\mathbf{L}_{rr} \\
\hline
\end{array}
\times
\begin{array}{|c|}
\hline
\mathbf{i}_{\text{stator}} \\
\hline
\mathbf{i}_{\text{rotor}} \\
\hline
\end{array}
$$

where:

$$
\mathbf{L}_{ss} = \frac{2}{3} \times
\begin{array}{c|ccc}
 & A & B & C \\
\hline
A & L_s & -L_s/2 & -L_s/2 \\
B & -L_s/2 & L_s & -L_s/2 \\
C & -L_s/2 & -L_s/2 & L_s \\
\end{array}
= \mathbf{L}_{rr} \text{ (say).}
$$

245

		a	b	c
	A	$M \cos \theta$	$M \cos (\theta - 2\pi/3)$	$M \cos (\theta - 4\pi/3)$
$\mathbf{L}_{sr} = \mathbf{L}_{rs}(\text{transposed}) = \frac{2}{3} \times$	B	$M \cos (\theta - 2\pi/3)$	$M \cos (\theta - 4\pi/3)$	$M \cos \theta$
	C	$M \cos (\theta - 4\pi/3)$	$M \cos \theta$	$M \cos (\theta - 2\pi/3)$

The form of the $\mathbf{L}_{sr}$ and $\mathbf{L}_{rs}$ matrices, which are identical, follow from the choice of axes recommended in reference 2, where it is explained that several advantages arise in the manipulation of the equations and the application to different machine types.

In solving the equations for currents, given the voltages, the impedance matrix has to be inverted; $\mathbf{i} = \mathbf{Z}^{-1}\mathbf{v}$, and since in real axes, this matrix has 6×6 elements, much computer time would be absorbed in the process. However, this would ignore the fact that for a 3-line, 3-phase circuit, the sum of the three currents is zero and hence one current can be expressed in terms of the other two. By substituting this condition in the above equations, or alternatively by a formal mathematical transformation expressing this relationship, the matrix can be reformulated with 4×4 elements. The transformed voltages applied are then reduced to two line-values instead of the three phase-values: $[v_A = \hat{V} \sin \omega t, \ v_B = \hat{V} \sin (\omega t - 120°)$ and $v_C = \hat{V} \sin (\omega t + 120°)]$, for the stator. For the rotor, if short circuited, the phase and line voltages at the rotor terminals are zero.

The matrix voltage equation is expressed in terms of the motional and transformer components:

$$\mathbf{v} = \mathbf{Ri} + \mathbf{i} \, d\mathbf{L}/dt + \mathbf{L} \, d\mathbf{i}/dt$$

$$\mathbf{Ri} + \mathbf{i} \frac{d\mathbf{L}}{d\theta} \frac{d\theta}{dt} + \mathbf{L} \, d\mathbf{i}/dt$$

from which:

$$\frac{d\mathbf{i}}{dt} = \left[\mathbf{v} - \left(\mathbf{R} + \frac{d\mathbf{L}}{d\theta} \dot{\theta} \right)\mathbf{i} \right] \Big/ \mathbf{L}.$$

This is the expression required for numerical integration for this real-axis simulation. It will be noticed that the speed $\dot\theta$, in electrical radians per second, comes into the motional-voltage term and also the variation of inductance with angle must be known in order to obtain $dL/d\theta$. Since in this particular case L_{ss} and L_{rr} are constants because of the uniform air gap, the matrix to be differentiated is just:

$$
\begin{array}{|c|c|}
\hline
 & \mathbf{L}_{sr} \\
\hline
\mathbf{L}_{rs} & \\
\hline
\end{array}
$$

a fairly simple operation because of the sinusoidal assumptions for the round-rotor machine.

The electromagnetic torque is obtained from the matrix expression[2]:

$$T_e = \frac{1}{2}\mathbf{i}_t\frac{d\mathbf{L}}{d\theta}\mathbf{i} \times \text{pole pairs}$$

$$= \frac{1}{2}\begin{array}{|c c|}\hline \mathbf{i}_{\text{stator}} & \mathbf{i}_{\text{rotor}}\\\hline\end{array} \times \frac{d}{d\theta}\begin{array}{|c|c|}\hline & \mathbf{L}_{sr}\\\hline \mathbf{L}_{rs} & \\\hline\end{array} \times \begin{array}{|c|}\hline \mathbf{i}_{\text{stator}}\\\hline \mathbf{i}_{\text{rotor}}\\\hline\end{array} \times \text{pole pairs.}$$

The above equations, though referring specifically to the 3-phase, uniform air-gap machine, can be applied to any polyphase machine with appropriate modifications. The only significant difficulty is in defining the inductance/angle function from which $dL/d\theta$ is deduced. This is a matter for either design calculations or actual measurements. But the method is universal, not restricted by winding unbalance or asymmetry, nor by the magnetic geometry such as the presence of saliency on both sides of the air gap, nor even allowance for the often-neglected fact of rotor and stator teeth and slots. It is not an analytical method but must use numerical solutions implemented through a computer as indicated on the general flow-diagram of Fig. 7.8. For a simple uniform air-gap machine one can compare the computer time required to achieve comparable accuracy. Based on the time for a d–q simulation, the real-axis simulation would require two to ten times this, depending on the waveform. Such a difference, though becoming less important as computers continue to improve, would not be justified. But if the situation is such that the d–q transformation does not yield constant inductances, then a lengthy computation time is endemic in the problem and a real-axis simulation may be the most convenient. For single-phase machines, unlike the model for analytical solutions, the real-axis equations are simpler than for 3-phase machines because there are fewer of them.

The final figures use the simulation just described to illustrate some instructive electromechanical transients. Figure 7.10 is for an inverter-fed induction motor, accelerated from zero speed up to the

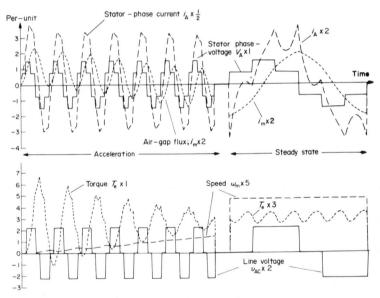

FIG. 7.10. Acceleration and steady-state waveforms of inverter-fed induction motor.

248

steady-state speed where the slip is about 6 per cent, full-load mechanical torque being coupled throughout. The bottom figures show the quasi-square-wave line-voltage which is applied at full value and frequency. In practice, such a source would be applied at reduced voltage and frequency, but is computed as shown to illustrate the nature of current and torque transients for direct-on-line start. A sine-wave supply would have given similar peak values but without the 6-pulse ripple. The torque peaks reach nearly 7 *per unit* and the first seven cycles are shown. The computer graph plot is then stopped until the steady-state is reached and then the expanded waveforms for one cycle are plotted. The speed is then constant but the torque pulsations are considerable at about ±0.33 *per unit*. The dominant frequency is 6th harmonic as deduced from Fig. 7.6b and eqn (7.10). But the waveform shows a slight even-harmonic asymmetry, and this will be due to the small effect of 11th and 13th rotor harmonic currents giving a 12th-harmonic component of torque. The top diagrams show the phase-voltage waveform, deduced from the calculated currents and the sum of the impedance drops in accordance with eqn (7.12). It is the same shape as already found in Fig. 7.5. The stator-phase current reaches starting peaks of over 7 *per unit* and on steady state is rich in 5th and 7th harmonic components. The peak currents reached on steady state are somewhat higher than those occurring with a sinusoidal-voltage supply which would give a current sine-wave running through the distorted wave shown here. The remaining waveform is for the flux, neglecting saturation and deduced by combining the stator A-phase current with the referred and transformed a-phase rotor current; viz. the waveform of I_m. Because of the parameters of this particular machine, 1 *per unit* I_m corresponds to about normal peak flux and the diagram shows that the peak flux on steady state is a few per cent higher than the normal value for a sine-wave supply. More interesting is that in spite of the violent i_A fluctuations, the induced rotor-current acts to damp these out as shown by the nearly sinusoidal flux-waveform. The rotor current in fact has a pronounced 6th harmonic component superimposed on its slip-frequency sine-wave variation. This ripple, which is only to be expected since there are six switching changes per cycle, is similar to the torque pulsation. This is also to be expected since it is the reaction between the nearly sinusoidal flux wave and the rotor current which produces the torque. On observing the flux transient, it is seen that this dies out from a high peak in a few cycles, the value then being about half the normal rated value for a short time, due to the high voltage drop across the primary impedance during starting. It is also seen that the flux wave is approximately 90° lagging on the phase-voltage wave.

Figure 7.11 is for the same machine, this time running at rated torque as an induction motor from a 50-Hz sinusoidal-voltage supply. The top diagram shows that the phase current lags the voltage by about 45° and the rotor current can be seen oscillating at the very much lower slip frequency of about 3 Hz. At time 0.14 sec

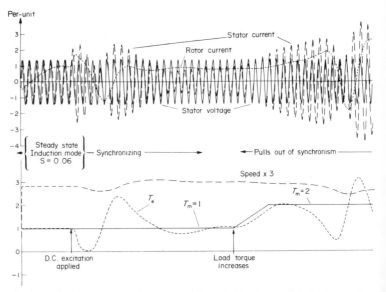

Fig. 7.11. 3-phase wound-rotor a.c. machine. First loaded as an induction motor, then synchronised, then overloaded to pull-out.

250

from the beginning of the plot, the rotor is supplied with a d.c. voltage, sufficient to cause it to pull into step as a synchronous motor. This takes about 0.5 sec, during which time the stator and rotor currents exceed their rated values quite considerably. When synchronisation is successfully achieved, at time 0.6 sec from the beginning of the plot, the mechanical torque T_m is increased linearly up to 2 *per unit*. It is appropriate now to look at the bottom diagram and see the electromagnetic torque T_e initially in balance with T_m, the speed being about 0.94 times the synchronous value. The electromagnetic-torque-transient is quite violent during synchronising and the speed dips, then overshoots and at 0.6 second, it is virtually synchronous, with T_e again almost in balance with T_m. The increase of T_m is then slowly followed by T_e as the load angle increases and speed falls. However, the load angle must have increased well beyond 90° and the torque commences another violent oscillation which is sufficient to pull the machine out of synchronism. The armature current and rotor current again rise to excessive values, but the combination of induction torque produced by the induced rotor-currents reacting with the stator currents, and the pulsating torque produced by the reaction of the d.c. component of rotor current reacting with the stator currents, is still sufficient to hold the load torque though with an appreciable speed oscillation. Actually, the pull-out torque in the induction mode is 3.2 *per-unit*, see Tutorial Example T7.4, and in the mode shown, T_m would have to approach nearly 3 *per unit* to completely stall the machine. To restore synchronism (apart from reducing the load to about 1.5 *per unit*), it would be necessary to increase the excitation by about 50%.

APPENDIX

TUTORIAL EXAMPLES WITH ANSWERS

THE following examples are provided so that there is opportunity to check understanding of the various problems encountered in the main text. Most of them are at
least slightly different from these, but the necessary background has been covered for
all. Chapter 1 on basic theory should be thoroughly understood and the recommendation to incorporate the question data on a simple diagram should be followed.
This is especially important when dealing with 3-phase circuits so that mistakes of
interpretation are avoided when extracting phase voltages, currents and impedances
from the data given. Note that the "rating" refers to the total power or VA, the line
voltage and the line current. Chapter 2 on Transformers revises all these points and
the practice of declaring the no-load voltage ratio is followed, so that this is also the
turns ratio when reduced to phase values. Answers, and some part answers, are
given to all numerical problems, together with an indication in some cases of
theoretical points which are raised. Accuracy is generally to three figures, though
sometimes more, where appropriate. Although much care has been taken, there may
be a few errors and the author would be very grateful to be informed about any
which are discovered.

CHAPTER 1. INTRODUCTION

No examples are set for this revisory chapter but two convention problems were
raised therein. On p. 7 the motor convention equation always has a positive sign
and on p. 8 the generator convention equation always has a negative sign.
    Referring to the question concerning Fig. 1.5 for the generator phasor diagrams
on p. 11. With a motor convention, the current phasor in Figs. 1.5a and 1.5b would be
in the lower half of the diagrams. E would still be $V - jXI - RI$, but because of the
lower position of the current phasor, E would now lead V in both cases. For a
generator convention, the I phasor would be reversed, together with the sign in the
above equation but the phasor diagrams would be otherwise unchanged in shape,
the new current phasor being in the upper half of the diagram, with the power-factor
angle less than 90°.

CHAPTER 2. TRANSFORMERS

    In the following examples, the approximate equivalent-circuit can be used and in
some cases, the magnetising impedance may be omitted altogether. For deter-

mination of turns ratio and for 3-winding transformers, all impedances of the transformer are neglected.

T2.1. A 3-phase, 50-Hz, 6600/400-V star/zigzag transformer has a core cross-sectional area of 0.04 m². Calculate the number of turns required for each coil of primary- and secondary-winding sections, if the maximum flux density is not to exceed 1.1T. Note, each secondary phase is made up of two equal sections, taken from neighbouring phases and connected in opposition so that the phase voltage is the phasor difference of the two sections; i.e. phase voltage = √3 × secondary-section voltage.

T2.2. A 3-phase, 3-winding, 1000-kVA, 50-Hz transformer is required to meet the following specification:

Primary 66 kV (line) star connected.
Secondary 6.6 kV (line) delta connected.
Tertiary 440 V (line) star connected.

The maximum flux is not to exceed 0.1 Wb.

(a) Determine the required number of turns per phase on each winding.

(b) Taking the magnetising current as 5% of the rated current and the iron loss as 10 kW total, determine the input current, power factor, kVA and kW when the secondary is loaded at 600 kVA, 0.9 pf lagging and the tertiary is loaded at 400 kVA, 0.8 pf lagging.

T2.3. In a certain transformer, the winding leakage reactances are six times the winding resistances. Estimate the power factor at which the voltage regulation is zero. If the leakage reactance is 10%, what is the maximum regulation in *per unit* for a current of 1 *per-unit*?

T2.4. A single-phase, 50-Hz, 500-kVA, 33 000/3300-V transformer has the following parameters: $R_1 = 8.6\,\Omega$, $R_2 = 0.08\,\Omega$, $x_1 = 52\,\Omega$, $x_2 = 0.46\,\Omega$.
On no load, the h.v. current at 33 kV is 0.3 A and the power input is 3.5 kW. Calculate:

(a) The regulation at rated current and power factors of: 0.866 lag, 0.866 lead and u.p.f.

(b) The efficiencies at the same load current and power factors (neglect regulation).

(c) The maximum efficiency.

(d) The in-phase and quadrature components of the no-load current.

(e) The primary current and power factor and the secondary current when the secondary power-factor is 0.8 lagging and the efficiency is at its maximum for this power factor.

T2.5. A 3-phase, 50-Hz, 300-kVA, 11 000/660-V, star/delta transformer gave the following line-input readings during light-load tests:

Open circuit   660 V,   8 A, 2.4 kW
Short circuit   500 V, 15 A, 4.1 kW

Calculate and show on a per-phase equivalent circuit, the parameters deduced from these tests, referred to the h.v. side. Also show all currents, input power factor and secondary terminal voltage when the secondary is supplying rated current at 0.8 p.f. lagging. Allow for the voltage regulation.

T2.6. An 800-kVA transformer at normal voltage and frequency requires an input of 8 kW on open circuit. The input on short circuit at rated current is 15 kW. The transformer has to operate on the following duty cycle:

6 h at 450 kW, 0.8 p.f.
4 h at 650 kW, 0.9 p.f.
5 h at 250 kW, 0.95 p.f.
Remainder of 24-h day on no load.

Calculate the all-day efficiency defined as: output in kWh/(output in kWh + losses in kWh). What is the efficiency at a constant load of 800 kVA at 0.8 p.f.?

T2.7. Two single-phase transformers A and B operate in parallel. $E_A = 200$ V and $E_B = 203$ V, $Z_A = Z_B = 0.01 + j0.1$ Ω, all data referred to the secondary side. Calculate I_A in terms of I_B (magnitude and phase), when the load impedance has the following values:

(a) $Z = 10 + j1$ Ω.

(b) $Z = 0.1 + j1$ Ω.

What is the function of transformer A in case (a)? Phasor diagrams would be informative.

T2.8. The following data refer to two 3-phase, delta/star connected transformers:

Transformer	kVA rating	Line voltage	Short-circuit test at rated current
A	600	2300/398	160 V, 4.2 kW
B	900	2300/390	100 V, 5.1 kW

Calculate the total current supplied by the two transformers connected in parallel to a star-connected load of 0.132 Ω per phase and of power factor 0.8 lagging.
If the load is disconnected, what will be the secondary circulating current and the change in secondary terminal-voltage from the loaded condition?

T2.9. A single-phase transformer supplies a full-load secondary current of 300 A at 0.8 p.f. lagging when the load voltage is 600 V. The transformer is rated at 6600/600 V on no load and is provided with tappings on the h.v. side to reduce this ratio. It is supplied from a feeder for which the sending-end voltage is maintained at

6.6 kV. The impedances are as follows:

Feeder (total)	$= 1 + j4 \ \Omega$
Transformer primary	$= 1.4 + j5.2 \ \Omega$
Transformer secondary	$= 0.012 + j0.047 \ \Omega$

To what value must the turns ratio be adjusted if the secondary terminal voltage is to be 600 V under the full-load condition? Neglect the magnetising current and the effect of the changed turns-ratio on the referred impedance.

CHAPTER 3.   D.C. MACHINES

In the following questions, the brush voltage-drop, the magnetising effects of armature reaction and the mechanical losses may be neglected unless specifically stated otherwise.

T3.1. A 25 hp, 500-rev/min d.c. shunt-wound motor operates from a constant supply voltage of 500 V. The full-load armature current is 42 A. The field resistance is 500 Ω and the armature resistance is 0.6 Ω. The magnetisation characteristic was taken at 400 rev/min as follows:

Field current	0.4	0.6	0.8	1.0	1.2 A
Generated e.m.f.	236	300	356	400	432 A

Calculate the mechanical loss torque using the full-load data (1 hp = 746 W), and assume it is constant in the following calculations:

(a) Calculate the field current and the external field resistance for operation at rated load and speed.

(b) What is the speed when the load is removed, leaving just the loss torque?

(c) With the excitation of part (a), at what speed must the machine be driven to regenerate at rated current?

(d) What extra field-circuit resistance is necessary to cause the machine to run on no load at 600 rev/min?

(e) What extra armature-circuit resistance is needed to cause the machine to develop half its rated electromagnetic torque at a speed of 300 rev/min with field current as in (a)? What would be the output power at the coupling?

T3.2. A 500-V, d.c. separately excited generator at its normal rating gives an output of 50 kW at 1000 rev/min. The armature-circuit resistance is 0.4 Ω.

The machine is to be run as a motor, but with the voltage reduced to 200 V. At what speed will it run if set at rated flux and taking rated armature current?

What reduction of flux will be necessary to run at 1000 rev/min with the same armature current and how will the electromagnetic torque differ from that developed as a generator at normal rating?

T3.3. A 500-V d.c. shunt motor has a rated output at the coupling of 40 kW when

255

running at 500 rev/min, the efficiency then being 90%. The armature- and field-circuit resistances are 0.23 Ω and 400 Ω respectively. The following magnetisation curve was taken when running as an open-circuited generator at 600 rev/min:

Field current	0.25	0.5	0.75	1.0	1.25	1.5 A
Generated e.m.f.	170	330	460	531	572	595 V

Determine, at the rated condition:

(a) the armature current;

(b) the electromagnetic torque;

(c) the loss torque.

Find also the additional field-circuit resistance necessary to give a speed of 1200 rev/min, the armature current and loss torque being assumed constant and rated voltage being applied. What will be the output power at this condition?

T3.4. Derive the speed/torque expression for a d.c. machine. Hence explain the various methods of controlling the speed of such a motor, commenting on their advantageous and disadvantageous features.

A d.c. generator at its normal rating gives an output of 100 kW at 500 V when driven at 500 rev/min. It is to be run as a motor from a 500-V supply at a speed of 750 rev/min, the additional cooling at this speed permitting an armature-current increase of 10% above the rated value. Calculate the electromagnetic torque the motor will develop under this condition. What value of flux is necessary and what total mechanical power will the motor produce? Express this flux, torque and power as fractions of rated flux, torque and power. The armature resistance is 0.15 Ω.

T3.5. A d.c. motor has a full-load armature rating of 7.5 kW, 220 V, 45 A at 800 rev/min. The armature resistance is 1 Ω. Determine the mechanical loss torque and assume this is constant, independent of speed. The mechanical load torque has a characteristic such that beyond 800 rev/min, it falls off inversely as speed; i.e., a constant-power law. Determine the percentage of rated flux required to increase the speed to 2400 rev/min, and the corresponding value of armature current.

T3.6. Derive expressions for armature current and flux for operation of a d.c. motor at any specified voltage, speed, electromagnetic torque and armature-circuit resistance.

A 500-V, d.c. motor at rated load runs at 1500 rev/min and takes an armature current of 50 A. The armature resistance is 0.5 Ω and the shunt-field resistance is 200 Ω. The mechanical loss torque is 5 Nm. Determine:

(a) The electromagnetic torque, the mechanical output and the efficiency.

(b) The electromagnetic torque when the flux is weakened to give a speed of 2000 rev/min with armature current allowed to increase by 25%.

(c) The armature current and *per-unit* flux ($k_\phi/k_{\phi(\text{rated})}$) required to sustain operation at 1000 rev/min with terminal voltage halved and armature-circuit resistance doubled. Assume the total mechanical torque is proportional to (speed)^2.

T3.7. A d.c. generator has $R_a = 1\,\Omega$ and $R_f = 480\,\Omega$. Its o.c. characteristic is as follows:

Field current	0.1	0.2	0.4	0.6 A
Generated e.m.f.	85	160	233	264 V

The machine is to be run as a motor from 230 V with an armature current of 30 A. Find:

(a) The additional resistance in the field circuit to give a speed of 750 rev/min.

(b) The additional resistance in the armature circuit to give a speed of 300 rev/min when the field winding is connected directly across the 230-V supply.

(c) The resistance in parallel with the armature terminals, but otherwise as in condition (b), to give a speed of 200 rev/min. What will then be the supply current?

T3.8. A d.c. series motor was run at constant speed of 1500 rev/min, with varying voltage and load to give the following points:

Terminal voltage	61	71	81	93	102.5	110 V
Current	1.39	1.68	1.98	2.42	2.87	3.22 A

If the motor is supplied at 110 V, calculate the speed/torque curve:

(a) with the natural armature-circuit resistance of 7.4 Ω;

(b) with an additional series resistor of value 30 Ω.

What is the torque at 1500 rev/min in each case and what is the operating mode when the speed goes negative in case (b)?

T3.9. A d.c. series motor was run at 500 rev/min when the following magnetisation characteristic was taken:

Field current	5	10	15	20	25	30 A
Generated e.m.f.	192	276	322	356	384	406 V

The armature and field resistances are each 1 Ω. The motor is connected in series with a resistor of 20 Ω across a 420-V d.c. supply. Across the armature terminals is a further, diverter resistor of 21 Ω. Calculate the speed/torque curve with this connection and show the currents and voltages at the various points in the circuit when the field current is 20 A. For what purpose would this characteristic be useful?

T3.10. A d.c. series motor of resistance 0.12 Ω has a magnetisation curve at 750 rev/min as follows:

Field current	50	100	150	200	250	300 A
Generated e.m.f.	110	220	300	360	400	420 V

The motor is controlling a hoist in the dynamic-braking connection. Determine the resistance to be connected across the machine terminals so that when the overhauling torque is 1017 Nm, the speed is limited to 500 rev/min. How much extra resistance will be required to maintain this speed when the total torque falls to 271 Nm?

If the drive is now changed to hoisting with this last resistor in circuit and a supply voltage of 400 V, what will be the operating speed for a motoring torque of 271 Nm?

T3.11. The d.c. series motor of T3.8 is to be braked from the full-load motoring condition (110 V, 1500 rev/min). If the initial braking current is to be limited to twice the full-load value of 3.22 A, what resistor would have to be inserted in series with the armature:

(a) for rheostatic (dynamic) braking;

(b) for plugging (reverse-current) braking?

At what speed, in each case, would the braking torque be equal to the full-load value?

T3.12. Illustrate on a 4-quadrant diagram, the various methods of electrical braking using the following data for a separately-excited d.c. machine:

Rating: 500 V, 50 A, 500 rev/min
Armature resistance 0.5 Ω
Rated flux maintained throughout.

Calculate the speed/torque equations for:

(a) regenerative braking into rated voltage supply;

(b) reverse-current braking with the same supply and an additional 10 Ω limiting resistor;

(c) rheostatic braking with a 5-Ω external limiting resistor.

At what speed in each case will full-load torque be developed? Comment on the special features of each mode, pointing out the advantages and limitations. See also the second part of Tutorial Example T6.5.

T3.13. A 500-V, separately-excited d.c. motor takes an armature current of 100 A when driving its mechanical load at rated speed of 600 rev/min. The total mechanical torque as a function of speed is given by the following expression:

$$T_m = k[1 + (\omega_m/20\pi) + (\omega_m/20\pi)^2] \text{ Nm},$$

where ω_m is the speed in rad/s. The armature-circuit resistance is 0.4 Ω. Calculate the torque at rated speed and the value of k.

If the speed is increased to 700 rev/min by field weakening, what percentage change of flux and of armature current would be required? Comment on the suitability of this method of speed control for this particular load.

T3.14. A d.c. separately excited motor has a *per-unit* resistance of 0.05 based on rated armature voltage and current. For the 3rd base quantity in the *per-unit* system, take rated flux, which gives rated torque at rated armature current. In the following, *per-unit* quantities are being referred to throughout.

At rated flux and rated torque, what is the rated speed, i.e. when rated voltage is applied?

The motor drives a load which requires a torque of 0.3 at starting and thereafter increases linearly with speed reaching 1.0 at rated speed. What is the expression for this mechanical torque as a function of speed?

Assuming the magnetisation characteristic can be expressed by the following relationship:

$$I_f = \frac{0.6\phi}{1 - 0.4\phi}$$

where ϕ is the flux, calculate flux, field current and armature current for the following conditions:

(a) Voltage = 0.5, speed = 0.5.

(b) Voltage = 1.0, speed = 1.2.

(c) Voltage = 0.5, speed = 0.4 and total armature-circuit resistance = 0.15.

T3.15. A separately excited d.c. motor is permanently coupled to a mechanical load with a total characteristic given by $T_m = 0.24 + 0.8\omega_m$ *per unit*. T_m is unity at rated speed where rated flux and armature current are required to produce the corresponding T_e at rated voltage. Per-unit R_a based on the rated terminal voltage and armature current is 0.05. *Per-unit* speeds are based on the speed at rated voltage and flux with zero torque. The required portion of the magnetisation curve of *per-unit* flux against *per-unit* field current may be taken as a straight line passing through $\phi = 0.6$, $I_f = 0$ and $\phi = 1.0$, $I_f = 1.0$. Calculate the *per-unit* field and armature currents to sustain operation at:

(a) half rated voltage and speed;

(b) rated voltage and speed of:
 (i) 0.74 *per-unit*;
 (ii) 1.25 *per-unit*.

(If *per-unit* ideas are insecure, take rated V as 100 V, rated I_a as 100 A (i.e. $R_a = 0.05\,\Omega$), rated speed as 100 rad/s (955 rev/min) and hence $k_{\phi(\text{rated})} = (100 - 100 \times 0.05)/100 = 0.95$ Nm/A.)

CHAPTER 4. INDUCTION MACHINES

For this chapter, the approximate equivalent circuit will normally be used unless specifically stated otherwise. If no data given for the magnetising branch they may be discounted. Also, mechanical loss will be neglected unless the data include this.

T4.1. The primary leakage-impedance per phase of a 3-phase, 440-V, 50-Hz, 4-pole, star-connected induction machine is identical with the referred secondary impedance and is equivalent to a 1-Ω resistor in series with a 10 mH inductor. The magnetising impedance may be considered as connected across the primary terminals and consists of a 300-Ω resistor in parallel with a 200 mH inductor. Calculate, for a slip of 0.05:

   (a) the input current and power factor;

   (b) the electromagnetic torque;

   (c) the mechanical output-power if the mechanical loss-torque is 1 Nm;

   (d) the efficiency.

If the mechanical load-torque were to be increased from this figure, at what speed would the motor begin to stall?

T4.2. A 3-phase, 440-V, 50-Hz, 4-pole, star-connected induction machine gave the following line-input readings during parameter tests:

Locked rotor (short circuit)	120 V	25 A	2.0 kW
No-load (running uncoupled)	440 V	8 V	1.5 kW

Separate tests determined the friction and windage loss as 600 W.

Using the approximation that the magnetising branch is connected across the terminals, deduce the value of the equivalent-circuit parameters, dividing the leakage impedance equally to give identical stator and (referred) rotor values. Note that the mechanical loss must be deducted from the no-load input before calculating R_m and X_m.

   (a) At the full-load slip of 4% determine the input current and power factor, the rotor (referred) current, electromagnetic torque, output power and efficiency.

   (b) What is the starting torque at full voltage and the ratio of starting to full-load current?

T4.3. Using the data for the machine of the last question, calculate at a speed of 1560 rev/min:

   (a) the stator current and power factor;

   (b) the rotor current;

   (c) the electromagnetic torque;

   (d) the mechanical coupling-power;

   (e) the efficiency.

Repeat the calculations using the same parameters in the "exact" circuit and draw a power-flow diagram similar to that of Example 4.7 to illustrate this operating mode.

From the "exact" circuit calculate the self-inductance of the stator and rotor and the mutual inductance, all referred to the stator winding, for the condition with all three phases excited with balanced currents.

T4.4. A 50-Hz, 6-pole, wound-rotor induction motor has a star-connected stator and a delta-connected rotor. The effective stator/rotor turns ratio per phase is 2/1. The rotor leakage impedance at standstill is $0.36 + j1.5 \ \Omega$, the corresponding figure for the stator being $1.4 + j7 \ \Omega$ per phase.

If the impressed stator voltage is 220 V/phase, calculate:

(a) the actual rotor current at starting;

(b) the actual rotor current when running at 960 rev/min;

(c) the initial rotor current when, from condition (b), the stator supply sequence, (and hence the rotating field) is suddenly reversed;

(d) the electrical input power for condition (c) and the mode of operation;

(e) the required resistance in series with the slip rings, to give maximum torque at starting.

Note: for convenience, refer all quantities to the rotor winding.

T4.5. Determine the value of the starting torque and the maximum torque (in terms of the full-load torque) for an induction motor with a full-load slip of 4%. The primary and secondary leakage reactances are identical when referred to the same winding and the leakage reactance is five times the resistance. Note: use $I_2^2 R_2/s$ ratios so that any constants will cancel.

T4.6. In a certain 3-phase induction motor, the stator and referred-rotor impedances are identical, the leakage reactance being four times the resistance. Determine the effect on the starting torque, the speed at which maximum torque occurs and the maximum torque itself of doubling:

(a) the rotor resistance;

(b) the stator resistance.

Hence sketch the shape of the three speed/torque curves corresponding to normal operation, condition (a) and condition (b). Note: let $R_1 = R_2' = R$ and $x_1 = x_2' = 4R$, then use ratios of the appropriate expressions.

T4.7. On locked-rotor test, an induction motor takes three times full-load current (3 *per-unit*), at half rated-voltage. The motor has a full-load slip of 4% and is to be started against a load requiring 1/3 of full-load torque. An auto-transformer is used to reduce the motor terminal voltage at starting so that it is just sufficient to meet this requirement. What percentage tapping will be necessary and what will then be the supply current expressed in *per unit*?

Note: if the ratio of starting torque at full voltage to rated torque is expressed in terms of the appropriate $I_2^2 R_2/s$ ratios, the value of the *per-unit* starting torque will be given in terms of *per-unit* current and full-load slip. Hence the required starting current in *per-unit* for the reduced starting torque and the transformer tapping will follow.

T4.8. The speed/electromagnetic-torque curve for a 50-Hz, 4-pole induction motor at rated voltage is given by the following points:

Speed	1470	1440	1410	1300	1100	900	750	350	0 rev/min
Torque	6	12	18	26	30	26	22	14	10 Nm

261

The mechanical load it drives requires a torque of 14 Nm and the mechanical loss torque can be taken as 1 Nm. What is the speed at normal voltage?

It is required to reduce the speed to 1200 rev/min. Assuming that the load and loss torques do not change with speed:

(a) What voltage reduction would be required?

(b) What percentage increase in rotor resistance would be required if the voltage was left unchanged?

Comment on these two methods of achieving this speed reduction.

T4.9. A 3-phase, 440-V, 50-Hz, 6-pole, delta-connected induction motor drives a fan at 920 rev/min when supplied at rated voltage. The motor has a high-resistance speed/torque characteristic and the following equivalent-circuit parameters:

$$R_1 = 8\,\Omega, \quad R_2' = 16\,\Omega, \quad x_1 = x_2' = 12\,\Omega.$$

Assuming the total mechanical torque varies in proportion to the square of the speed, what supply voltage would be required to run the fan at 460 rev/min and what will then be the rotor current and copper loss?

As an alternative, calculate the required extra rotor-resistance to get half speed with full voltage. Calculate the rotor current and copper loss to compare with the previous method. Refer also to T4.20.

T4.10. A certain 3-phase induction motor on locked-rotor test takes full-load current at a power factor of 0.4 lagging from a normal-frequency supply. If the motor is operated with a 30% reduction in both voltage and frequency, estimate the new starting torque and maximum torque in terms of normal values. Sketch the two speed/torque curves for comparison. Assume the impedance is divided equally between stator and (referred) rotor.

Note: take $R_1 + R_2' = 0.4$ and $x_1 + x_2'$ as $\sin(\cos^{-1} 0.4)$ and use ratios from appropriate expressions.

T4.11. A 3-phase, 440-V, 50-Hz, 6-pole, star-connected induction motor has the following equivalent-circuit parameters at normal supply frequency:

$$R_1 = 0.2\,\Omega, \quad R_2' = 0.18\,\Omega, \quad x_1 = x_2' = 0.58\,\Omega \text{ per phase.}$$

The machine is run up and controlled from a variable-frequency supply, the voltage of which is directly proportional to the frequency up to 440 V at 50 Hz. Find the supply frequency which gives maximum torque and compare the value of this torque with the starting torque at rated voltage and frequency.

Note: set voltage, synchronous speed and reactances at kV, $k\omega_s$ and kx respectively in the approximate-circuit expressions, then differentiate with respect to k.

T4.12. For a certain 3-phase induction motor, $R_2 + jx_1 = R_2' + jx_2'$ and $x_1/R_1 = 3$ at normal frequency. Calculate speed/torque coordinates at zero torque, maximum motoring torque and at zero speed for the following conditions:

(a) rated voltage V and rated frequency f;

(b) rated voltage $V/3$ and rated frequency $f/3$;

(c) $V/3$ and f;

(d) V and $1.5f$.

Express speeds as fractions of rated synchronous speed and torques as fractions of the maximum torque at rated voltage and frequency.

Note: use equations (4.5), (4.12) and (4.13) with $R_1 = R'_2 = R$ and $x_1 = x'_2 = 3R$ at normal frequency. Using torque ratios will permit common terms to cancel. $\hat{s}$ values will be with respect to the *actual* supply frequency.

T4.13. Sketch the speed/torque characteristics for an induction motor drive supplied from a variable-frequency source, explaining why it is desirable to maintain a particular relationship between supply voltage and frequency.

A 3-phase, 400-V, 50-Hz, 6-pole, star-connected induction motor has leakage impedances $z_1 = z'_2 = 0.15 + j0.75 \, \Omega$ per phase at rated frequency. Calculate the torque at rated voltage and frequency for the rated slip of 3%.

If the same torque is required at starting and also at 750 rev/min, to what values must the supply frequency and voltage be adjusted if the machine flux-per-pole is to be the same as at the rated condition?

T.14. A 3-phase, 50-Hz, 4-pole induction motor at rated voltage and frequency has the speed/torque characteristic given in Example 4.9. The motor is controlled to maintain the flux-per-pole-constant at any particular torque. Estimate the frequency required to produce:

(a) maximum torque at starting;

(b) a speed of 750 rev/min with a torque of 9 Nm.

T4.15. Show that if rotor leakage reactance is neglected, maximum torque for a constant-current induction motor drive occurs when the rotor current and magnetising current are equal in value at $I_1/\sqrt{2}$. Show also that for maximum torque during a constant-current acceleration, the rotor frequency must be constant.

Using the data from T4.1, but neglecting the magnetising resistance, calculate the maximum torque:

(a) with rated voltage and frequency applied—use the approximate circuit;

(b) with a constant-current drive at a (referred) rotor current corresponding to that of condition (a), including x'_2 and:
   (i) neglecting saturation of X_m;
   (ii) assuming saturation reduces X_m to $(62.8)/3 \, \Omega$ per phase.

T4.16. A 3-phase, 660-V, 50-Hz, 4-pole, delta-connected induction motor has $z_1 = z'_2 = 0.15 + j0.75 \, \Omega$ per phase at standstill. The full-load slip is 3%. Compare the torque developed at full load with that developed immediately after making the following alternative changes from the full-load condition:

(a) reversal of two primary-supply leads;

263

(b) disconnection of a.c. supply from primary and replacement by a d.c. voltage across two lines, previously adjusted so that the same air-gap flux will exist as before the changeover.

What is the initial *per-unit* current in each case, based on full-load current?

T4.17. A 3-phase, 1100-V, 50-Hz, 6-pole, star-connected induction machine when operating at full load as a motor running at 980 rev/min takes a total current of $113.5 - j76.3$ A per phase. The current through the magnetising branch $-3.8 - j59.3$ A per phase, with the terminal voltage as the reference phasor. The primary and (referred) secondary impedances are of equal value at standstill at $0.1 + j0.4 \, \Omega$ per phase.

Derive the equivalent circuit for the d.c. dynamic braking condition and add an extra rotor (referred) resistance of $3.5 \, \Omega$ per phase. What is then the electromagnetic torque when changed over from motoring, assuming the air-gap flux is unchanged?

To maintain this air-gap flux what is the required stator current: (a) in a.c. terms and (b) in d.c. terms; two of the phases being connected in series for d.c. excitation purposes? What excitation voltage would be required?

Calculate also the speed at which maximum torque occurs when dynamic braking and the ratio of this torque to that which occurs immediately after changing over the connections from rated motoring load.

T4.18. A 3-phase, 400-V, 50-Hz, 4-pole, star-connected, double-cage induction motor has the following equivalent circuit parameters per phase at standstill:

Primary	$0.0625 + j0.25$	*per-unit*, $0.5 + j2 \, \Omega$;
Outer cage	$0.25 + j0.075$	*per-unit*, $2 \; + j0.6 \, \Omega$;
Inner cage	$0.0375 + j0.3125$	*per-unit*, $0.3 + j2.5 \, \Omega$.

The *per-unit* impedances are based on rated voltage and any convenient output, say 20 kW, for which the ohmic impedances are shown (base impedance = $8 \, \Omega$). Calculate the *per-unit* starting torque and also the mechanical power when the speed is 1410 rev/min. Use *per-unit* values in the calculation but check the answers using real values.

T4.19. Solve the single-phase induction-motor problem of Example 4.18 for a slip of 0.03, using the exact equivalent circuit though neglecting the very small effect of R_m; i.e. $X_m/2 = 20 \, \Omega$, $R'_2/2 = 0.1 \, \Omega$, $x'_2/2 = 0.5 \, \Omega$.

Note: combine the primary, forward-circuit and backwards-circuit impedances in series to determine the total current. Hence follow the e.m.f.s E_f and E_b and the currents I_f, I_b, I_{mf} and I_{mb}. Compare answers with those from the approximate circuit in Example 4.18. The calculation of the torque pulsation will be deferred to Tutorial Example T7.6, which could be referred to with advantage.

T4.20. Consideration is to be given to controlling the fan-motor drive of Tutorial Example T4.9 by means of a slip-power recovery scheme to compare the performance. The rotor power-factor at 460 rev/min is to be unchanged but the impedance drop of the equivalent circuit, which previously was supplied entirely by the stator voltage (121.8 V), will now be provided by rated voltage V_1 $(440 + j0) - V_3'/s$; eqn (4.19). V_3' will have to be in phase with V_1 if there is to be no change of power factor. The value of the current will be less however because the torque expression is different, eqn (4.20). Determine V_3' and this new current, the VA, the corresponding rotor copper-loss and the slip power recovered, $3(V_3'I_2' \cos \varphi_3)$. Also determine the maximum VA rating of the injected-power source to give speed control over the whole range to zero speed. Compare, on a phasor diagram, the three methods of speed reduction.

T4.21. Show that the linear speed of a rotating field at frequency f, number of pole pairs p, pole pitch $\tau = \pi d/2p$ m is $v = 2\tau f$ m/s. Hence determine the pole pitch of a linear induction motor required to have a speed of 200 miles per hour with a slip of 0.5, from a 50-Hz supply.

CHAPTER 5. SYNCHRONOUS MACHINES

Unless specifically stated otherwise, the following problems will assume that the air gap is uniform, and that resistance and mechanical losses are neglected.

T5.1. A 3-phase, 3.3-kV, 50-Hz, 6-pole, star-connected synchronous motor gave the following test points when run at synchronous speed as a generator, on open circuit and then on short circuit:

Open-circuit test	Line voltage	2080	3100	3730	4060	4310 V
	Field current	25	40	55	70	90 A
Short-circuit test	Armature current 100 A with field current = 40 A.					

The armature leakage impedance and all power losses may be neglected.

Calculate the excitation current required at rated voltage and frequency when operating with a mechanical output of 500 kW and an input power factor of 0.8 leading. Allow for the saturation of the magnetising reactance $X_{mu}(= X_{su}$ since $x_{al} = 0$).

What overload torque, gradually applied, would pull the machine out of synchronism with this calculated field-current maintained? What then is the permissible overload in *per unit* based on full-load torque? (Overload = Max./Rated.)

T5.2. Recalculate the answers for Examples 5.5 and 5.6 where appropriate but neglecting the resistance to check the errors in the approximation.

T5.3. A 3-phase, 500-kVA, 6600-V, 50-Hz, 6-pole, star-connected synchronous motor has a synchronous impedance per-phase which can be taken as $j70\,\Omega$. At its normal rating, the motor is excited to give unity power-factor at the input terminals. Find:

(a) the rated current;

(b) the e.m.f. behind synchronous impedance (E_t);

(c) the rated electromagnetic torque;

(d) the pull-out torque with excitation as in (b);

(e) the required increase in excitation (E_f) which will just permit an overload margin of 100% before pulling out of synchronism;

(f) the load angle, armature current and power factor if this excitation is maintained at rated load.

T5.4. A 3-phase, 6600-V, star-connected synchronous motor has a synchronous impedance of $(0 + j30)\,\Omega$ per phase. When driving its normal load, the input current is 100 A at a power factor of 0.9 lagging.

The excitation is now increased by 50% above the value required to sustain the above condition, the mechanical load being unaltered. What changes in machine behaviour will take place?

With the new excitation, to what value and power factor will the armature current settle down if the mechanical load is removed altogether?

T5.5. A 3-phase, 11-kV, 50-Hz, 6-pole, star-connected synchronous motor is rated at 1 MVA and power factor 0.9 leading. It has a synchronous impedance which may be taken as entirely inductive of value $j120\,\Omega$ per phase. Calculate the rated current, the e.m.f. behind synchronous impedance, the electromagnetic torque and the output hp.

Calculate the new values of armature current and excitation required to give operation at rated power but at 0.8 p.f. lagging. Express these values as fractions of rated values.

With the same excitation and armature current, at what power and power factor would the machine operate if running as a generator?

Note: use the cosine rule on the voltage triangle.

T5.6. Make a concise comparison of synchronous- and induction-machine performance features.

A 3-phase, 1000-kVA, 6.6-kV synchronous motor operates at unity power-factor when at its rated load condition. Its synchronous impedance can be taken as $j40\,\Omega$ per phase. Determine the e.m.f. behind synchronous impedance.

For a 50% change of this excitation voltage (both increased and decreased values), what changes would take place in the motor performance?

T5.7. A 3-phase, 440-V, 50-Hz, 6-pole, star-connected synchronous motor has a synchronous impedance of $(0 + j10)\,\Omega$ per phase. At its normal rating, the armature current is 20 A and the power factor is 0.9 leading. The load torque is slowly increased from this condition to 300 Nm. By what percentage must the excitation be increased to avoid pulling out of step with this load torque?

T5.8. A round rotor machine has 3-phase windings on stator and rotor, the stator being connected to the 3-phase mains. Explain briefly why the machine will work in the induction mode at all speeds other than one particular value, with the rotor short circuited, whereas, in the synchronous mode, this speed is the only value at which it *will* operate when the rotor is d.c. supplied.

A 3-phase, 6.6-kV, star-connected synchronous motor has a synchronous impedance of $(0 + j48)\,\Omega$ per phase, and is running at its rated output of 650 kW. What will be the input current and power factor when the excitation is so adjusted that the e.m.f. behind synchronous impedance is 1.5 times the applied voltage?

If the supply voltage was to suffer a fall of 50%, would you expect the machine to continue supplying the load at synchronous speed? Would the reaction to this voltage fall have been generally similar if the machine had instead been motoring in the induction mode? Give reasons for your answers.

T5.9. Solve the numerical examples of T5.2 to T5.8 using the phasor loci and operating charts as in the solution of Example 5.16. Note that the Examples 5.5 to 5.7, for which the resistance was included, can also be solved by this method but with $V/(R_a + jX_s)$ defining the circle centre, the excitation term drawn from this being $E_f/(R_a + jX_s)$.

T5.10. A 3-phase, 3.3-kV industrial plant has the following induction-motor drives:

	IM 1	IM 2	IM 3
Rated output	50	100	150 kW
Full-load efficiency	93%	94%	94.5%
Full-load power factor	0.89	0.91	0.93

A star-connected synchronous motor rated at 150 kVA is to be installed and is to be overexcited to improve the overall plant power factor to unity when all machines are operating at their full ratings.

What is the required excitation in terms of the e.m.f. (E_f) if $Z_s = 0 + j50\,\Omega$ per phase? What power output will the synchronous motor be delivering if its efficiency is 95%?

T5.11. A 3.3-kV, 3-phase industrial installation has an overall power factor of 0.88 lagging. A 200-kVA synchronous motor is added to the system and is run at zero power factor and slightly reduced rating to provide power-factor correction only. The total load is then 350 kVA at unity power factor.

If it was decided to run the synchronous machine at its rated kVA and use it as a source of mechanical power, what gross mechanical power would it produce with the overall power factor of the installation at:

(a) unity;

(b) reduced to 0.96 lagging?

Note: I_{PS} and I_{QS} are both unknowns but are the quadrature components of the rated synchronous machine current I_S.

T5.12. Convert eqn (5.12) to an expression giving the total torque in *per-unit* for any frequency, k times the base frequency at which E_f and X_s are specified. It will be the same form as eqn (5.20) except for a factor $-\sin(\delta - \alpha)$ multiplying the first term and with the factor k as a divisor.

Refer to the above equation and the preamble before Example 5.15, using the same values of R_a and X_s as in this example, to determine the required excitation (E_f) in *per unit* when operating at rated frequency, rated voltage and current and a power factor of 0.8 leading. If the load is increased slowly, what maximum value of electromagnetic torque with the corresponding current will be reached before pulling out of synchronism?

What value of terminal voltage would be required, with the excitation maintained, to sustain this maximum torque when (a) k = 0.3, and (b) k = 0.1?

T5.13. Solve Tutorial Examples T5.3 to T5.8 using the current-source equivalent circuit of Fig. 5.3c and the sine or cosine rules, where appropriate.

T5.14. A salient-pole synchronous motor has $V = 1$ *per unit*, $X_d = 0.9$ *per unit* and $X_q = 0.6$ *per unit*. Neglect R_a. The current is 1 *per unit* at power factor 0.8 leading. Calculate the required excitation, power and torque in *per unit* and also the components I_d and I_q. What is the maximum torque?
Note: refer to the equations in Example 5.21, the phasor diagram of Fig. 5.4a and the relationships $I_q = I_a \cos(\varphi - \delta)$ and $I_d = I_a \sin(\varphi - \delta)$, δ being negative for motoring.

T5.15. The same synchronous motor as in the previous question has its e.m.f. E_f reduced to 1 per unit, the power remaining the same. What will now be the load angle, power factor, I_a, I_d and I_q? What will be the maximum torque and its reduction from the previous maximum value with the higher excitation?
Note: with the data given, for a specified power of 0.8, an explicit solution is not possible but using eqn (5.19) a simple iteration will quickly produce the value of δ. Eqns (5.16) and (5.17) then solve for the currents.

T5.16. Use eqn (5.15), (5.16) or (5.17) as appropriate to check any, or all, of the various torque calculations for uniform air-gap induction and synchronous machines.

CHAPTER 6. TRANSIENT BEHAVIOUR

T6.1. Consider an idealised thermal system and a small change of temperature rise $\Delta\theta$ taking place in time Δt. It has a heat source of P watts, a heat storage capacity of $M.S$ joules per °C, where M = mass in kg and S = specific heat in joules per kg per °C change, and radiates heat at the rate of $K.\theta$ watts per second, where K has the units of watts/°C and θ is the temperature rise above the surroundings. Balance the heat generated in time Δt against the heat stored and radiated and hence show that the temperature rises exponentially in accordance with eqn (6.2).

Assuming that an electrical machine can be so represented, calculate the maximum and minimum temperature rises occurring eventually when it has been subjected repeatedly to the following duty cycle for an appropriate period:

(a) full-load ON for a time equal to the thermal time constant, τ;

(b) load reduced to zero for a time equal to one half of the thermal time constant.

Express the temperature rises in terms of the final temperature rise θ_m which would occur if the full load were to be left on indefinitely.

Starting from cold, what would be the temperature rises at times τ, 1.5τ and 2.5τ? What is the r.m.s. value of the duty cycle in terms of the full-load power P?

T6.2. A 230-V, 50-hp, 935-rev/min, separately-excited d.c. motor has a rated armature current of 176 A. The armature-circuit resistance is 0.065 Ω. If a starting resistance of 0.75 Ω is connected in series, what will be the initial starting current and torque exerted with rated field current maintained?

With a Coulomb-friction load of 271.3 Nm and a total coupled inertia of 3.58 kg m², what will be the final balancing speed and the time taken to reach 98% of this speed?

If the motor were to be supplied from a constant-current source instead, set at a value corresponding to the initial starting current above, what would then be the time to full speed from rest? Explain fully the difference between the two time periods calculated.

T6.3. Using the data of Example 6.3, consider the next step of the starting period when it can be assumed that on current falling to 60 A, the circuit resistance is reduced so that the current again increases to 80 A. What will be the value of the total circuit resistance required for this?

Set up the new transient speed equation and find:

(a) the new electromechanical time constant;

(b) the next balancing speed if the resistance is left in circuit.

Neglect the circuit inductance.

T6.4. A 250-V, 500-rev/min d.c. separately-excited motor has an armature resistance of 0.13 Ω and takes an armature current of 60 A when delivering full-load power at rated flux, which is maintained constant throughout. Calculate the speed at which a braking torque equal to the full-load torque will be developed when:

(a) regeneratively braking at normal terminal voltage;

(b) plugging braking but with an extra resistor to limit the initial torque on changeover to 3 per-unit;

(c) dynamically braking with an extra resistor to limit the peak current to 2 per-unit.

For cases (b) and (c), write down the torque balance-equation and hence find the maximum total inertia in each case which could be reduced to zero speed in 2 sec, the full-load, friction torque being coupled throughout.

For case (b), what is the total time to reverse to 95% of the final balancing speed with the extra resistance in circuit? Note the reversal of friction torque with rotation reversal.

T6.5. For a 3-phase induction motor, express the rotor copper loss as a function of electromagnetic torque and slip. Noting that $T_e = J \, d\omega_m/dt = -J\omega_s \, ds/dt$ (see Example 6.10), integrate the expression for copper loss over a range of slip and show that the energy dissipated in rotor heat $= \frac{1}{2}J\omega_s^2(s_1^2 - s_2^2)$. Hence show that for acceleration from zero to synchronous speed with zero load and for deceleration from synchronous speed to zero under dynamic braking conditions, the energy loss in rotor heating is equal to the stored mechanical energy in the rotating mass at synchronous speed. Show also that when plugging from synchronous speed to zero speed, the rotor heat energy is equal to three times this kinetic energy at synchronous speed.

Now consider the d.c. separately excited machine under similar conditions. ω_s is replaced by the no-load speed $\omega_0 = V/k_\phi$, and $\omega_m = \omega_0(1 - s)$ where $s = I_aR/(k_\phi\omega_0)$. Noting also that I_a = armature copper loss/I_aR where $I_aR = V - k_\phi\omega_m$, use the d.c. machine equations where appropriate to show that the rotor energy loss is the same in terms of the kinetic energy, as for the induction machine for the same transient conditions.

T6.6. A 300-V, d.c. series motor driven at 500 rev/min as a separately excited generator, with the armature loaded to give the same current as in the field winding, gave the following characteristic:

Terminal voltage	142	224	273	305	318 V
Field current	15	25	35	45	55 A

The field and armature resistances are each 0.15 Ω.

The motor is to be braked from normal motoring speed where it is developing an electromagnetic torque of 300 Nm when supplied from 300 V. An external resistor is to be inserted to limit the initial current to 55 A. It can be assumed that on changeover, the response of flux following the increase of current is completed before the speed changes significantly so that the e.m.f. rises also.

(a) Determine the speed when motoring at 300 Nm, from 300 V, and the corresponding values of current and flux (k_ϕ).

(b) Calculate the required resistor values for plugging and for dynamic braking.

(c) Estimate the times in (b) for the speed to fall to such a level that the braking torque is equal in magnitude to the full-load torque, the load torque being uncoupled, leaving the inertia as 10 kg m^2.

Note: the motor curves must be calculated in order to solve part (a) but on braking, only two specific points are required and the average braking torque can be used. Nevertheless, it may be a good idea to sketch the braking curves to clarify the method.

T6.7. Using the data of Example 4.9 and the associated figure, calculate the time to accelerate from zero speed to 1400 rev/min at full voltage and with the natural rotor resistance. Take the total drive inertia as 0.05 kg m^2 as in Example 6.6 and take points on the curves at speed intervals of 200 rev/min.

T6.8. A 10-pole, 50-Hz induction motor drives a d.c. pulse generator through a flywheel coupled between the two machines. The pulse requires a motor output torque of 2713 Nm for 4 sec and the combined inertia of machines and flywheel is 1686 kg m^2. The no-load speed of the motor is 597 rev/min and the speed at rated torque of 977 Nm is 576 rev/min. Assuming the fall of speed with torque is linear, what is the peak motor-torque at the end of the load pulse?

T6.9. A mine winder requires the following duty cycle for its d.c. motor:

Time period	Condition	Torque required
0–20 sec	Constant acceleration up to 45 rev/min	2.712×10^5 Nm
20–50 sec	Constant speed of 45 rev/min	1.356×10^5 Nm
50–70 sec	Regenerating with constant torque	-0.678×10^5 Nm
70–90 sec	Rest period	

Plot the torque and power duty-cycles, find the average power throughout the cycle and draw a line at the appropriate height representing this average power. The area above (and below) this line represents the magnitude of the energy pulsation in watt-seconds. If this is provided by the stored energy of the flywheel and inertia of the motor-generator set supplying the winder motor, then the m.g. set motor will be shielded from the peak. The m.g. set speed will have to fall, under control, from ω_1 to ω_2 to release this energy of magnitude $\frac{1}{2}J\omega_1^2 - \frac{1}{2}J\omega_2^2$ watt-seconds. By equating, the value of J follows. Determine this inertia if the m.g. set motor speed falls from 740 to 650 rev/min.

What is the peak power when motoring and when regenerating? Neglect machine losses.

CHAPTER 7. POWER-ELECTRONIC/ELECTRICAL MACHINE DRIVES

T7.1. A d.c. separately excited motor is supplied from a 50-V source through a fixed-frequency chopper circuit. At normal motor rating the armature current is 30 A and the speed is 1000 rev/min. The armature resistance is 0.2 Ω. If the current pulsations can be taken as relatively small so that the mean current can be used in calculations, what is the required duty-cycle ratio of the chopper if the motor is to operate at a mean torque corresponding to the full rating and at a speed of 400 rev/min?

T7.2. A battery-driven vehicle is powered by a d.c. series motor. The time-constant of armature and field together is 0.2 sec, the resistance being 0.1 Ω. At a speed of 1000 rev/min, the mean generated volts/field A over the operating range of current is 0.9. A fixed frequency, 200-Hz chopper is used to control the speed and when this is 1000 rev/min, the mark:space ratio is 3:2. The battery voltage is 200 V. Find the maximum and minimum values of the current pulsation and hence determine the mean torque and power output if the mechanical losses are 1000 W.

T7.3. On a thyristor converter/d.c. machine system, the converter mean voltage falls from 500 V on no load to 460 V when delivering 100 A, there being no gate firing delay. The d.c. motor has an armature resistance of 0.3 Ω. Determine the required firing-delay angle α under the following conditions:

271

(a) As a motor taking 50 A and excited to produce an e.m.f. $E_m = 400$ V.

(b) As a motor at normal rating, 460 V, 100 A, 1000 rev/min. Calculate $k_{\phi R}$.

(c) Regenerating at rated terminal-voltage and current.

(d) Motoring at half-speed, the total torque being proportional to (speed)^2 and the flux being set at rated value.

If speed increase is required by field weakening, what permissible torque can the motor deliver at 1250 rev/min without exceeding rated current and what would then be the flux in *per unit*? The firing-delay angle is $0°$.

T7.4. Referring to Figs. 7.10 and 7.11, the induction machine equivalent circuit parameters at 50 Hz are as follows:

$$R_1 = 6.7\,\Omega, \quad R_2' = 7.7\,\Omega, \quad L_{11} = L_{22}' = 0.436\,\text{H}, \quad M' = 0.41\,\text{H},$$
$$x_1 = x_2' = \omega(L_{11} - M') = 8.168\,\Omega.$$

Values are per phase, with all phases excited. The motor is 4-pole, 50-Hz and star-connected, the rated line voltage being 220 V.

For reference purposes and to relate the normal values to Figs. 7.10 and 7.11, first use the exact equivalent circuit to work out the rated input current, power factor, rotor current and electromagnetic torque at a slip of 0.06. Also estimate the maximum torque from the approximate circuit and express this in *per-unit* based on the rated torque. This will help to explain the behaviour on Fig. 7.11 when the motor pulls out of synchronism.

The motor is now to be supplied from a quasi-square-wave, voltage-source inverter as shown on Fig. 7.4, with a d.c. link voltage so adjusted that the r.m.s. value of the fundamental of phase-voltage waveform is the same as its rated sinusoidal voltage. Determine the d.c. link voltage required.

Using the method described in Section 7.3 culminating in eqn (7.10), estimate the value of the 6th-harmonic torque pulsation as a function of time. Compare this with the value measured from Fig. 7.10 which is based on 1 per-unit torque = 1.9 Nm and 1 per-unit current = 1.3 A. (The computed peak value of pulsation is ±0.327 Nm.)

T7.5. The cylindrical-rotor synchronous machine of Example 5.15 (and Tutorial Example T5.12) is provided with load-angle (δ) control through a position detector. By differentiating the torque expression of eqn (5.13) determine the angle at which δ must be set to produce maximum torque:

(a) at rated voltage and frequency;

(b) at $0.3 \times$ rated frequency;

(c) at $0.1 \times$ rated frequency.

Use eqn (5.13) modified to *per-unit* terms and expressed for any frequency, $k \times$ the base frequency at which E_f and X_s are specified.

Check the value of $\alpha = \tan^{-1} R_a/kX_s$ at each frequency and show that $\delta - \alpha$ is $-90°$ at maximum torque for parts (a), (b) and (c).

Check also, using the answers to T5.12 for V and E_f, that the maximum torque for (b) and (c) is the same as for (a) if the excitation is maintained at the part (a) setting.

T7.6. For this problem, reference back will be necessary to Example 4.18, Tutorial Example T4.19, eqn (7.9) in Section 7.3 and the general approach of Tutorial Example T7.4. Use the answers obtained in Tutorial Example T4.19 shown on Fig. T7.6 below, to calculate the average torque and the plusating torque for the single-phase induction-motor operation. The average torque is due to the reaction of I_f with I_{mf}, minus the reaction of I_b and I_{mb}. The pulsating torque is due to the reaction of I_f with I_{mb} plus the reaction of I_b with I_{mf}. Compare the average-torque answer with that obtained in T4.19 and express the pulsating torque as a fraction of the average torque.

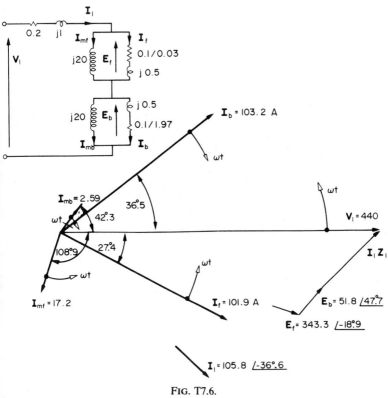

FIG. T7.6.

T7.7. A single-phase a.c. load is connected through a bilateral thyristor-type semi-conductor switch. It conducts if the voltage across it is 1 V or more, in either direction, and the time angle ($\theta = \omega t$) of the sine-wave supply voltage $e = E \sin \omega t$,

273

is greater than the firing-delay angle α measured from voltage zero for the positive halfwave, and greater than $(\pi + \alpha)$ for the negative half wave. Draw up a logic-check diagram, similar to that of Example 7.5, which will check the conduction condition.

Consider how this could be applied to a star-connected 3-phase source supplying a 3-phase star-connected induction motor which is voltage controlled for speed variation.

ANSWERS TO TUTORIAL EXAMPLES

T2.1. Primary 400 turns; Secondary 14 turns per section.

T2.2. (a) $N_1 = 1800$, $N_2 = 312$, $N_3 = 12$. (b) $I_1 = 9$ A, $\cos \varphi = 0.845$, 1030 kVA, 870 kW.

T2.3. $\cos \varphi = 0.986$ lead; 0.101 *per-unit* at 80°5 lag.

T2.4. (a) 96 V, 25.1 V, −52.5 V. (b) 98.2% and 98.559% at u.p.f. (c) 98.56%. (d) $I_0 = 0.106 - j0.28$ A. (e) 14.78 A at 0.79 p.f., $I_2 = 145.2$ A.

T2.5. Answers are on attached figure.

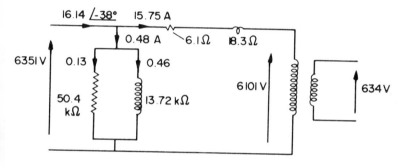

FIG. T2.5.

T2.6. 95.71%; 96.53%.

T2.7. (a) $I_A = I_B \times 0.827 / 112°7$, transformer A is working with reverse power flow. (b) $I_A = I_B \times 0.7 / 0°$.

T2.8. $I_{total} = 1670 / -38°5$; circulating current = $179.4 / -83°7$, terminal voltage increased from 381.8 line V to 392.3 line V.

T2.9. 95.3%.

T3.1. $k_{\phi R} = 9.068$ Nm/A, $T_{loss} = 24.7$ Nm. (a) $I_f = 0.9$, 55.6 Ω. (b) 525 rev/min. (c) 553 rev/min. (d) ≃ 160 Ω. (e) 9.64 Ω, 5.2 kW (7 hp).

T3.2. 296 rev/min; flux and torque reduced to 29.6% of rated value.

T3.3. (a) 87.64 A. (b) 802.4 Nm. (c) 38.5 Nm. ≃990 Ω. 37.1 kW.

T3.4. 1308 Nm, 5.946 Nm/A, 102.7 kW; or 0.588, 0.646, and 0.973 *per-unit*.

275

T3.5.   4.5 Nm; 32%; 51.1 A.
T3.6.   (a) 151.2 Nm, 23 kW, 87.5%.   (b) 2.238 Nm/A.   (c) 32.35 A, 0.687 *per-unit.*
T3.7.   (a) $\simeq 670\,\Omega$.   (b) 2.52 Ω.   (c) 6.85 Ω, 46.5 A.
T3.8.   (a) 1.77 Nm.   (b) 0.53 Nm, mode is plugging.
T3.9. ω_m (rad/s)/T_e (Nm) points $-88.5/-36.6$, $-32.3/309$. Remaining answers on
attached figure. Mode gives limited speed on zero load and has some
regenerative capability; see Fig. E.3.17(c).

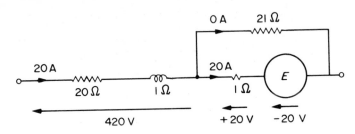

FIG. T3.9.

T3.10.   1.04 Ω; extra 0.35 Ω; 865 rev/min. Note: 1017 Nm requires 214 A; 271 Nm
needs 97 A.
T3.11.   (a) 6 Ω, 750 rev/min.   (b) 23 Ω, 207 rev/min.
T3.12.   (a) $\omega_m = 55.12 - T_e/164.6$,   553 rev/min.   (b) $\omega_m = -55.12 - T_e/7.838$,
26 rev/min.   (c) $\omega_m = -T_e/14.96$, 290 rev/min.
T3.13.   732 Nm, k = 244. Flux reduced by 17.5%, armature current increased by
42.5%. Excessive armature current required beyond base speed and excessive flux required if lower speeds are attempted by strengthening the flux
(see also T3.15).
T3.14.   0.95 per unit; $T_m = 0.3 + 0.737\omega_m$.   (a) 0.928, 0.885, 0.72.   (b) 0.769, 0.666,
1.54.   (c) 1.034, 1.058, 0.575.
T3.15.   (a) 0.965, 0.628.   (b) (i) 1.725, 0.65.   (b) (ii) 0.33, 1.694.

T4.1.   (a)   14 A   at   0.85 p.f.   lag.   (b)   51.5 Nm.   (c)   7.54 kW.   (d)   82.6%.
1265 rev/min.
T4.2. $R_1 = R_2' = 0.53\,\Omega$; $x_1 = x_2' = 1.28\,\Omega$; $R_m = 215\,\Omega$; $X_m = 32.1\,\Omega$.
(a) 22 A at 0.86 p.f. lag, 18.1 A, 84.5 Nm, 12.1 kW, 84%.
(b) 85.1 Nm, 4.5/1.
T4.3.   (a) 21.5 A at 0.837 p.f. lead ("exact" = 19.9 A at 0.821 p.f. lead).   (b) 19.6 A
(18.7 A).   (c)   96.9 Nm   (88.9 Nm).   (d)   16.4 kW   (15.1 kW).   (e) 83.5%
(82.4%). $L_{11} = L_{22}' = 106$ mH, $M' = 102$ mH. See flow diagram on Fig. T4.3.
Actual directions shown, values in kW.

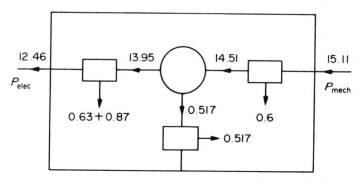

FIG. T4.3.

T4.4.   (a) 33 A.   (b) 11.1 A.   (c) 33.4 A.   (d) 1.79 kW; plugging mode.   (e) 0.97 Ω.
T4.5. $T_{start} = 0.298\, T_{fl}$; $T_{max} = 1.405\, T_{fl}$.
T4.6.   Answers on Fig. T4.6. Torques are expressed in terms of normal peak torque.

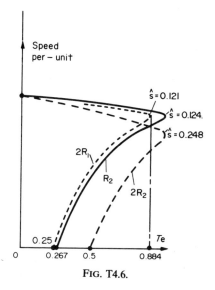

FIG. T4.6.

277

T4.7. $T_s = I^2 \times s_{fl} \times T_{fl}$ (all in *per unit*). Tapping at 0.481. Motor current = 2.89 p.u. and transformer input current = 1.39 p.u.

T4.8. (a) 71.7% voltage reduction (can be estimated by drawing curves). (b) Extra $2.75R_2$. (See also T4.9 and T4.20.)

T4.9. 6.32 Nm at 460 rev/min requires 121.8 V and 2.73 A giving 357 W rotor copper loss; or, extra 465 Ω (referred) and 0.51 A giving same rotor loss.

T4.10. Answers on Fig. T4.10. Torques are expressed in terms of normal peak torque.

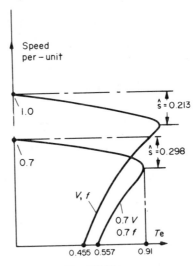

FIG. T4.10.

T4.11. k = 0.328 giving V = 144 V and f = 16.4 Hz. Torque = 377 Nm compared with 223 Nm.

T4.12. Answers on Fig. T4.12.

T4.13. 266 Nm; 1.5 Hz, 22.6 line V; 39 Hz, 314 line V.

T4.14. (a) 13.3 Hz. (b) 28 Hz ($f_2 = 3$ Hz).

T4.15. (a) $I_2' = 26.24$ A, $T_{max} = 83.7$ Nm. (b)(i) 393 Nm; (b)(ii) 118 Nm.

T4.16. Rated torque = 1446 Nm; rated current = 123 A. (a) $T_e = 0.19$ p.u. $I_2' = 3.54$ p.u. (b) $T_e = 1.34$ p.u. $I_2' = 6.6$ p.u.

T4.17. $X_m = 10$ Ω, $T_e = 2722$ Nm, $I_2' = 161$ A. (a) $I_1 = 177$ A. (b) $I_{dc} = 217$ A, $V_{dc} = 43.5$ V. Max. torque = 4340 Nm (1.59×) at 346 rev/min.

T4.18. $T_s = 0.802$ p.u. or 102 Nm. Power = 0.842 p.u. or 16.9 kW for $T_e = 0.896$ p.u.

T4.19. $Z_f = 3.091 + j0.9903$, $Z_b = 0.048 + j0.488$, $Z_{input} = 3.339 + j2.478 = 4.16/36.6$. Remaining answers shown on Fig. T7.6 for Tutorial Example T7.6.

278

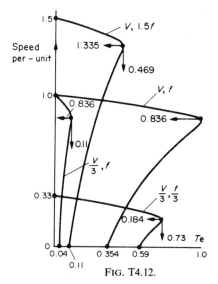

FIG. T4.12.

T4.20. $V_3' = 171.8$ V, $I_2' = 0.758$ A, 390 VA, Rotor loss = 27.6 W, Slip-power recovered = 329.4 W. VA rating from rated I_2' (2.1 A) and max. $V_3' = 440$ V is 2770 VA. Phasor diagrams for comparison on Fig. T4.20.

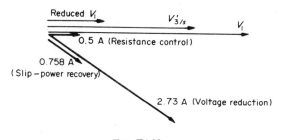

FIG. T4.20.

T4.21. $\tau = 1.789$ m.

T5.1. $X_{su} = 19.1\ \Omega$. $k_{fs} = 76.6$ line V/A, $I_f = 77.4$ A. Max. $T_e = 10\,620$ Nm = 2.22 p.u.

T5.2. $-18°7$, 31 830 Nm, 229 A at 0.95 lead, 6910 line V, 2010 kW. (6) 3750 line V, 95.7 A at 0.998 lead.

T5.3. (a) $I_{aR} = 43.74$ A. (b) $E_f = 4888\underline{/-38°9}$ (phase V). (c) 4775 Nm. (d)

279

7620 Nm. (e) For 9550 Nm, $E_f = 10.61$ kV (line). (f) $\delta = -30°$, $I_a = 48.65$ A at 0.898 lead.

T5.4. $-\delta$ reduced to $29°3$ from $47°7$. I_a reduced to 96 A and power factor to 0.937 lead. On no load the current becomes 57 A at zero leading-power-factor (sync. capacitor).

T5.5. 52.49 A, 10.72 kV/phase, 8594 Nm, 900 kW. I_a becomes 59.1 A and E_f 6.05 kV. (1.125 p.u. and $0.56 \times E_{f(rated)}$.) 900 kW at 0.8 p.f. lead.

T5.6. $E_f = 5173\underline{/-42°6}$, $I_{aR} = 87.48$ A. $1.5E_f$ gives $\delta = -26°8$ and $I_a = 117.1$ A at 0.747 p.f. lead. $0.5 E_f$ requires $-\sin\delta > 1$ to sustain load, so pulls out of step.

T5.7. Normal pull-out torque = 280.8 Nm so E_f must be increased by 6.8%.

T5.8. 61.5 A at 0.91 p.f. lead $-\sin\delta = 0.4775$ so would still be < 1 if V (or E_f) was halved. For induction motor $T \propto V^2$ so much more sensitive to V reduction.

T5.10. $I_{QS} = 24.3$ A, $I_{PS} = 9.88$ A, Power = 53.65 kW, $E_f = 1.66$ p.u. (3160 V/phase).

T5.11. At zero load, kVAr = 188.6. (a) 66.7 kW. (b) $I_{QS} = 5.05$ A, $I_{PS} = 34.63$ A. Power = 198 kW.

T5.12. $E_f = 1.766\underline{/-28°}$; and at $T_{max'} = 1.61$, $\delta = -87°13$, and $I_a = 1.985\underline{/-24°47}$ A. (a) 0.363. (b) 0.18.

T5.14. $E_f = 1.692$, Power = Torque in *per unit* = 0.8. $I_d = 0.555$, $I_q = 0.832$. $T_{max} = 1.955$ p.u. $= 2.44 \times T_{fl}$ at $\delta = -75°2$.

T5.15. $\delta = -30°1797$, $I_a = 0.851$ A at 0.94 p.f. lag, $I_d = 0.1506$, $I_q = 0.8379$. $T_{max} = 1.223$ p.u., reduction of 37.5%; at $\delta = -68°5$.

T6.1. $P\Delta t = MS\Delta\theta + K\theta\Delta t$, $\tau = MS/K$, $\theta_m = P/K$. 0.813 θ_m, 0.493 θ_m, 0.632 θ_m, 0.773 θ_m. $\sqrt{2/3}.P$.

T6.2. 561 rev/min, 2.35 sec. 0.98 sec to full speed—constant torque maintained till maximum speed reached, so acceleration constant at maximum.

T6.3. 2.063 Ω. (a) 1.418 sec. (b) 296 rev/min.

T6.4. (a) 531.7 rev/min. (b) 2.6 Ω extra, -177.3 rev/min, $J = 34$ kg m², 15 sec total. (c) 1.89 Ω extra, 249.7 rev/min, $J = 19.3$ kg m².

T6.6. (a) 445 rev/min, $I_a = 49.5$ A, $k_\phi = 6.1$ Nm/A. (b) 10.45 Ω and 5 Ω extra. (c) 0.27 sec and 0.11 sec, to speeds of 363 rev/min and 411 rev/min.

T6.7. 2.58 sec.

T6.8. 1680 Nm.

T6.9. Average power = 319.6 kW. Energy area = 16 770 kW sec, $J = 24450$ kg m². 1278 kW, -318.5 kW.

T7.1. $\delta = 0.472$.

T7.2. 125.9 A to 113.9 A. Mean torque = 123.9 Nm and power output = 11.97 kW.

T7.3. (a) $29°5$. (b) $0°$, $k_{\phi R} = 4.106$. (c) $147°$. (d) $62°3$. 328 Nm at $k_\phi = 0.8$ p.u.

T7.4. $I_1 = 1.286$ A, at $47°2$ lag; $I_2' = 0.882$ A; $T_e = 1.907$ Nm. Max. $T_e = 6.09$ Nm = 3.2 p.u. D.C. link voltage = 282.2 V. $I_s' = 0.3095$ A, $I_7' = 0.158$ A, $\varphi_s = 84°4$, $\varphi_7 = 86°$. Torque pulsation $= -0.368 \sin(6\omega t + 7°3)$. Note: approximate circuit overestimates I_{m1}, mostly explaining discrepancy from computed pulsation of 0.327 Nm.

T7.5. (a) $\delta = -87°13$. (b) $\delta = -80°53$. (c) $\delta = -63°41$.

T7.6. Average torque = $440.96 - 6.88 = 434.1$. Pulsation = $439.9 \sin(2\omega t + 26°)$.
Ratio = 1.013, so pulsation slightly bigger than average value.

T7.7. Answer on Fig. T7.7. For 3-phase motor, each phase would have to be checked in this way, making appropriate corrections for time-phase shift of waveforms. At least two thyristor-units must be free to conduct for current to flow at all. Voltage equations must then be set up in accordance with the overall conducting pattern.

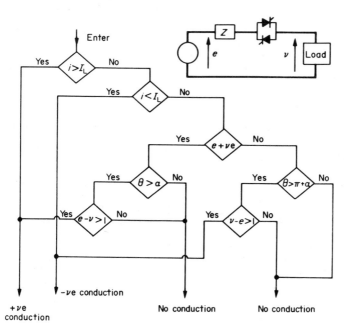

FIG. T7.7.

REFERENCES

1. HINDMARSH, JOHN, *Electrical Machines and Their Applications*, 3rd edition, Pergamon Press, 1981.
2. HANCOCK, N. N., *Matrix Analysis of Electrical Machinery*, 2nd edition, Pergamon Press, 1974.
3. HANCOCK, N. N., *Electric Power Utilisation*, Pitman, 1967.
4. ALLEN, T. P. and STEVEN, R. E., *Selected Calculations in Electric Power*, Hodder & Stoughton, 1979.
5. CHALMERS, B. J. and ÖNBILGIN, G., Analysis of highly saturated synchronous motor with cylindrical excited rotor, *International Journal of Electrical Engineering Education*, Vol. 16, No. 1, 1979.